The Prose Works

of

Sir Philip Sidney

In Four Volumes

Volume IV

SIR PHILIP SIDNEY

THE COUNTESS OF PEMBROKE'S

ARCADIA

BEING THE ORIGINAL VERSION

EDITED BY

ALBERT FEUILLERAT

CAMBRIDGE
AT THE UNIVERSITY PRESS
1967

PUBLISHED BY
THE SYNDICS OF THE CAMBRIDGE UNIVERSITY PRESS

Bentley House, 200 Euston Road, London, N.W.1
American Branch: 32 East 57th Street, New York, N.Y. 10022

First printed 1912
Reprinted 1962
1963
1967

First printed in Great Britain at the University Press, Cambridge
Reprinted by offset-lithography by
Lowe & Brydone (Printers), Ltd., London, N.W.10

PUBLISHER'S NOTE

FEUILLERAT'S edition of the complete works of Sir Philip Sidney has long been out of print, but has continued to be in demand by scholars. Bibliographical research has shown that Feuillerat did not work from the best copy-texts, and that many of his readings are corrupt. Further, three more manuscripts of Sidney have been discovered since Feuillerat's edition was printed. It may, however, be many years before a new and definitive edition is published, and it has therefore been decided to reissue with minor corrections the complete prose works in Feuillerat's edition. The publisher gratefully acknowledges the advice of Professor R. W. Zandvoort and Mrs Jean Bromley in connection with this reprint.

The prose works are divided among the four volumes as follows: vol. I, *Arcadia*, 1590; vol. II, *Arcadia*, 1593 and *The Lady of May*; vol. III, *The Defence of Poesie*, Political Discourses, Correspondence and Translation; vol. IV, *Arcadia* (original version). These volumes combine with Professor Ringler's newly edited *Complete Poems* to make all Sidney's works available again.

The parts of Feuillerat's prefatory notes which are not relevant to this reprint have been removed; the remaining parts are set out below.

*   *   *

This first form of Sidney's celebrated romance is certainly inferior in literary value to the revised form published in 1590. Though it has the advantage of presenting a simpler and, in a way, more coherent story, it fully deserves the criticism which Sidney himself passed upon it when he wrote to his sister: "Here now have

PREFATORY NOTE

you (most deare, and most worthy to be most deare Lady) this idle work of mine...being but a trifle, and that triflinglie handled. Your deare selfe can best witnes the maner, being done in loose sheetes of paper, most of it in your presence, the rest, by sheetes, sent unto you, as fast as they were done. In summe, a young head, not so well stayed as I would it were...[1]." It is at best the immature work of a young man of great promise who is trying his hand at romance writing. But for that very reason it is of first-rate importance if we want to form a clear idea of Sidney's precocity of mind. A comparison between the two forms shows with what marvellous rapidity Sidney, in the space of some five years, gained not only in literary skill but also in richness and ripeness of thought. Sir Philip's progress as a story-teller has already, and on the whole satisfactorily, been studied by Dr Samuel Lee Wolff in his book entitled *The Greek Romances in Elizabethan Prose Fiction*; the study of Sir Philip as a thinker is an entirely unexplored field and will fully reward those who undertake it[2].

So far as is known, five manuscripts of the "old Arcadia" have escaped the ravages of time. Two are in Oxford, the one in the Bodleian Library (MS è Mus. 37), the other in the Library of Queen's College (R. 38/301). Another MS, from the Phillips Collection, bought by the late Miss Mary E. Davies, of Wedderburn House, Hampstead, is now in the British Museum. The two remaining MSS are in the United States: the Asburnham MS, in the Henry E. Huntington Library at San Marino, California; the Clifford MS, in the collection of Mr W. A. White, of New York.

---

[1] This letter was printed as a preface to the revised form; but it certainly applies to the older form (cf. prefatory note to the last part of the edition of 1613, vol. II, 350)..

[2] It may be thought surprising that no attempt has been made here to give the chief results of such a comparison. Indeed I had at first contemplated to offer in this prefatory note at least an outline of the question. But I have since heard that Mr R. W. Zandvoort, of Nimeguen, has long been desirous to treat the same subject. So, in order not to forestall him I gave up the idea. I print, however, at the end of this volume a Table showing the relation of the "old Arcadia" to the 1590—93 Arcadia. This table does not pretend to be exhaustive or to go into minute details; but it will, I hope, facilitate the work of comparison.

PREFATORY NOTE

The text of the present edition is set up from the Clifford MS. This is a large quarto, carefully written in a sixteenth century English hand. It is in a beautiful state of preservation. This, and the fact that it is practically inaccessible to European scholars, were my chief reasons for choosing it in preference to the others.

In its present state the manuscript consists of 226 folios. This reckoning does not include two preliminary leaves and another leaf at the end, which are unnumbered. The first folio (which is also unnumbered) is blank. The text begins on folio 2 and ends on folio 216 r. The Clifford MS contains in addition "Divers and Sondry Sonnetts" covering folios 216 v–226 v. All these poems (with the exception of one which was never printed) are to be found in the 1598 edition.

The recto of each of the preliminary leaves is scribbled over with several names, apparently those of the successive owners of the MS: "Davide Morgan" (twice), "Hughe," "John Lloid" (three times), "Arthur Throgmorton," "Alexander Clifforde." In the same way, on the verso of the last leaf are found: "Alex. Clifforde" (twice), "Willm Clyforde is my name," "Mountgomrey." It is somewhat startling to come across this conjunction of Mountgomrey with Clyforde. For it should be remembered that Anne Clifford, daughter of George Clifford, third Earl of Cumberland, married in 1630, as her second husband, Philip Herbert, fourth Earl of Pembroke and Montgomery and Sir Philip Sidney's nephew. But it would be dangerous to speculate too much on this coincidence.

My aim has been to reproduce the original as accurately as possible. The spelling and the punctuation have been carefully preserved. I have, however, corrected obvious mistakes and filled half a dozen blanks. All these emendations have been supplied from the 1590 and 1593 texts, and will be found indicated in a list at the end of the volume.

I am aware that a collation of the other MSS of the *Arcadia* would have been welcome. The dispersion of the MSS, and several other reasons which one can easily guess, have rendered this impossible. I have, however, ascertained that the list of

PREFATORY NOTE

variants which could have been gathered would not have been worth the trouble and cost involved[1].

[1] The title of the Phillips MS is interesting. It runs as follows:"A treatis made by Sir Phillip Sydney, Knyght, of certeyn accidents in Arcadia, made in the yeer 1580 and emparted to some few of his frends in his lyfe tyme and to more sence his unfortunat deceasse."

CONTENTS

The First Booke or Acte of the Countess of PEMBROOKES ARCADIA

ARCADIA amonge all the Provinces of *Grece* was ever had in singuler reputation, partly for the sweetnes of yᵉ Aire and other naturall benefittes: But, principally, for the moderate & well tempered myndes of the people, who, (fynding howe true a Contentation ys gotten by following the Course of Nature, And howe the shyning Title of glory somuche affected by other Nacions, dothe in deede help litle to the happines of lyfe) were the onely people, wᶜʰ as by theire Justice and providence, gave neyther Cause nor hope to theyre Neighboures to annoy them, so were they not stirred with false prayse, to truble others quyett. Thinckinge yt a smalle Rewarde for yᵉ wasting of theire owne lyves in ravening, that their posterity shoulde longe after saye, they had done so: Eeven the *Muses* seemed to approove theire good determinacõn, by chosing that Contrie as theire cheefest reparing place, and by bestowing theire perfections so largely there, that the very *Shepeardes* them selves had theire fancyes opened to so highe Conceiptes (as the moste learned of other nations have bene longe tyme since content) bothe to borrow theyre names, and imitate theire Conning. In this place some tyme there dwelte a mighty Duke named *Basilius*, a Prince of sufficient skill, to governe so quyett a Contrie, where the good myndes of the former Princes had sett downe good Lawes, and the well bringing up of the People did serve as a moste sure Bonde to keepe them: Hee marryed *Gynecia*, the Daughter of the Kinge of *Cyprus*, a Lady worthy enoughe to have had her Name in continuall Remembrance, yf her later tyme had not blotted her well governed youthe: Allthoughe the wounde fell more to her owne Conscyence, then to the knouledg of the worlde, fortune somethinge supplying her wante of vertue. Of her the Duke had twoo faire Daughters, the elder *Pamela*, the younger *Philoclea*, bothe

1

COUNTESS OF PEMBROOKES

so excellent in all those giftes wch are allotted to reasonable
Creatures, as they seemed to bee borne for a sufficient proof that,
Nature ys [no] Steppmother to that Sexe: Howmuche soever
the Rugged disposicõn of some men sharp witted onely in evill
speaking, have soughte to disgrace them. And thus grewe they
on, in eche good increase, till, *Pamela*, a yeare older then
Philoclea came to the poynte of Seaventeene yeares of age: At
wch tyme, the Duke *Basilius*, not so muche stirred wth the Care
for his Contrie and Children, as with the vanity wch possesseth
many who (making a perpetuall mansion of this pore baiting
place of mans lyfe) are desyerus to knowe the Certeinty of
thinges to come, wherein there ys no thinge so certeyne as oure
Continuall uncerteinty. *Basilius*, I say, wolde needes undertake
a Jorney to *Delphos*, there, by the Oracle to enforme him self,
whither the rest of his lyfe shoulde bee continewed in like tenor
of happynes, as thitherunto yt had bene accompanyed wth the
wellbeeyng of his wyfe and Children: Whereuppon hee had
placed greatest parte of his owne felicity, neyther did hee longe
stay; But the woman appoynted to that Impiety (furiusly
inspired) gave him in verse, this Answer.

> *Thy Elder care shall from thy carefull face*
> *By Princely meane bee stolne, and yet not lost;*
> *Thy Younger shall with Natures bliss embrace*
> *An uncouth Love, whiche Nature hateth moste:*
> *Thow with thy Wyffe adultery shalt committ,*
> *And in thy Throne, a forreyn State shall sitt,*
> *All this on thee this fatall yeare shall hitt.*

Whiche as in parte yt was more obscure, then hee coulde
understand, so did the whole beare suche manifest threatninges,
that his amasement was greater then his fore Curiosity: Bothe
passions proceeding oute of one weykenes, in vayne, to desyer to
knowe that, of whiche in vayne thow shalt bee sory after thow
haste knowne yt. But thus the Duke answered, though (not
satisfyed) hee returned into his Contrie wth a Countenance well
witnessing the dismayednes of his hart, whiche, notwithstanding
uppon good Consideracõns hee thought not good to disclose,
but onely to one chosen frende of his named *Philanax*; whome
hee had ever founde a frende, not onely in affection but judgment, and no less of the Duke, then Dukedome: A rare temper

2

ARCADIA

whilest moste men eyther servilly yeelde to all appetites, or wth an obstinate austerity, looking to that they fancy good, wholly neglect ye Princes person. But suche was this man, and in suche a man had *Basilius* bene happy, yf his mynde (corrupted wth a Princes fortune) had not resolved to use a frendes secretsie, rather for Confirmacõn of fancyes, then correcting of errors, wch in this mighty matter hee well shewed: For having with many wordes discovered unto him bothe the Cause and success of his *Delphos* Jorney, in the ende hee tolde him that to prevent all these inconvenyences, of the losse of his Crowne and Children: For, as for the poynte of his wyfe, hee coulde no way understand yt. Hee was resolved for this fatall yeare to reteyre him self with his wyfe and Daughters into a Solitary place: Where beeyng twoo Lodges buylte of purpose, hee wolde in the one of them recomend his Daughter *Pamela* to his Principall Hearde-man, A place (in that worlde not so farr goñ into paynted vanityes) of some credit by name *Dametas*. In whose blunt truthe hee had greate Confidence, thincking y^t a Contrary salve ageanst the Destinie threatning her myshapp by a *Prince*, to place her wth a Shepeard: In the other lodge hee and his wyfe woulde keepe theyre younger Jewell *Philoclea*. And (bycause the Oracle tuched some straunge love of hers) have the more Care of her in especiall keeping away her nearest Kinsemen, whome, hee deemed cheefly understood; and therewithall, all other likely to moove any suche humor. And so for him self, beeyng so crewelly menassed by fortune hee wolde drawe him self oute of her way by this Lonelynes, whiche hee thought was the surest meane to avoyde her blowes: where for his pleasure, hee woulde bee recreated wth all those sportes and Eglogues, wherein ye Shepeardes of that Contry did muche excell. As for the governement of the Contrie, & in especiall manning of his Frontiers, for, that onely way, hee thoughte a foreyne Prince mighte endanger his Crowne, hee wolde leave the Charge to certeyne selected persons: The Superintendance of all wch hee woulde committ to *Philanax*, and so ended his speeche for fashions sake, askinge him his Counseyll. But *Philanax* having forthewth taken into ye depth of his Consideracõn, bothe what the Duke saide, and wth what mynde hee spake yt, with a true harte and humble Countenance, in this sorte answerede. Moste Redoubted and beloved Prince, yf aswell yt had pleased yo^w at

3

yor goyng to *Delphos*, as nowe to have used my humble service, bothe I shoulde in better season and to better purpose have spoken, and yo^w perhaps at this tyme shoulde have bene, as no way more in daunger, so, undoubtedly muche more in quyetnes. I woulde then have saide unto yo^w that wisdome and vertue bee the onely destinyes appointed to man to followe, wherein one oughte to place all his knowledge; synce they bee suche guydes as can not fayle, whiche besydes theyre Inwarde Comforte, do make a man see so direct a way of proceeding, as prosperity must necessarily ensewe: And allthoughe the wickednes of the worlde shoulde oppress yt, yet, coulde y^t not bee sayde, that evell happened to him, who should falle accompanyed wth vertue. So that eyther standing or falling with vertue, a man ys never in evell Case: I woulde then have sayde, the heavenly powers to bee reverenced and not searched into, and theyre mercy rather by prayers to bee soughte, then theyre hidden Counsells, by Curiosity; These kyndes of sowthesaying Sorcerers (since the heavens have lefte us in oure selves sufficient) to bee nothinge but fancyes wherein there must eyther bee vanity or infalliblenes, and so eyther not to bee respected, or not to bee prevented: But, since yt ys weykenes to muche to remember what shoulde have bene done, and that youre Commaundem^t stretcheth what shall bee done, I doo (moste deare Lorde) wth humble boldenes say that the maner of youre Determeynacõn dothe in no sorte better please mee, then the Cause of your goynge. These thirty yeares past have yow so governed this Realme, that, neither youre Subjectes have wanted Justice in yo^w, nor yow obeydience in them, and youre Neighboures have founde yow so hurtlesly stronge, that they thought yt better to rest in youre frendship then make nowe tryall of youre enmity: Yf this then have proceeded oute of the good Constitution of youre State, and oute of a wyse providence generally to prevent all those thinges, wch mighte encomber youre happynes, why shoulde yow now seeke newe Courses, since youre owne example comfortes yo^w to continew on? and that yt ys moste certeyne, no Destiny nor influence, whatsoever can bringe manns witt to a higher poynte then wisdome and goodnes. Why shoulde yo^w deprive youre self of governing youre Dukedome, for feare of loosing youre Dukedome, like one that should kill him self for feare of deathe? Nay rather, yf this Oracle bee to bee accoumpted of, arme up

4

youre corage the more ageanste yt, for who will sticke to him
that ab[and]ones him self: Let youre Subjectes have yo^w in
theyre eyes, Let them see the benefit of youre Justice daily more
and more, and so must they needes rather like of present suretyes,
then uncerteyne Chaunges, Lastly, whether youre tyme calle
yo^w to live or dye, doo bothe like a Prince. And even ye same
mynde holde I as tuching my Ladies youre Daughters, in whome
Nature promyseth nothing but goodnes, and theyre education
by youre fatherly Care hathe bene hetherto suche, as hathe bene
moste fitt to restreyne all evell giving theire myndes to all
vertuous delightes, and not greeving them for want of well
ruled Liberty, now to falle to a sodeyn Streytening them:
What can yt doo, but argue suspicõn, the moste venemoust
galle to vertue: Leave womens myndes, the most untamed that
way, of any, See, whither any Cage can please a Byrde, or
whether a Dogg growe not fiercer wth tyinge: what doth
Jelosy else but stirr up ye mynde to thincke what yt ys, from
whiche they are restreyned? For they are Treasures or thinges
of great delighte, wch men use to hyde, for the aptnes they have
to catche mens fancyes, and the thoughtes once awaked to that,
harder sure yt ys to keepe those thoughtes from accomplishment,
then yt had bene before to have kept the mynde (whiche
beeyng the cheef parte by this meanes ys defyled) from thincking.
Now further, recõmending so principall a Charge of her (whose
mynde goeth beyonde the governing of many hundreds of suche),
to suche a person, as *Dametas* ys, besydes that, ye thinge in yt
self ys straunge, yt comes of a very yll grounde, that ignorance
shoulde bee ye mother of faythfullnes. O, no, hee can not bee
good, that knowes not whye hee ys good, but standes so farr
good, as his fortune may keepe him unassayed, but, coming to
y^t his rude simplicity ys eyther easily chaunged, or easily
deceyved: And so growes that to bee the last excuse of his
faulte, wch seemed might have beene the first foundacõn of his
faythe. Thus farr hathe youre Comaundemẽt and my zeale
drawne mee to speake, whiche I like a man in a valley may
discerne hilles, or like a pore passinger may espy a Rock, so
humbly submitt to youre gracyous Consideracõn: Beseeching
yo^w to stand wholly uppon youre owne vertue, as the surest
way, to meynteyne yow in that yo^w are and to avoyde any
evell wch may bee imagined. Whilest *Philanax* used these

wordes, a man mighte see in the Dukes face, that as hee was
wholy wedded to his owne opinion, so, was hee greeved to have
any man saye that, wch hee had not seene: yet did the good
will hee bare to *Philanax* so farr prevail wth him, that hee
passed into no further Choler, but, with shorte maner asked him:
And woulde yow then (saide hee) that, in chaunge of fortune
I shoulde not chaunge my Determinacõn, as wee doo oure
apparell according to the ayer, and as the Shipp dothe her
course wth the wynde? Truely sir (answered hee) neither doo I
as yet see any chaunge, and thoughe I did, yet woulde I thincke
a constant vertue well settled litle Subject unto yt: And as in
greate necessity I wolde allowe a well proportioned chaunge,
so in the sighte of an Enimy to arme him self the lighter, or at
every puffe of wynde to stryke saile, ys suche a Chaunge, as
eyther will breade yll Success, or no success. To give place to
blowes (sayde the Duke) ys thoughte no smalle wisedome:
That ys true saide *Philanax*, but to give place before they come,
taketh away the occasion when they come to give place. Yet,
the Reedes stand with yeelding, saythe the Duke, and so are
they but Reedes: Moste worthy Prince sayde *Philanax*, but
the Rockes stand still and are Rockes. But, the Duke having
used thus muche Dukely sophistry to deceyve him self and
making his will, wisdome, tolde him resolutely, hee stoode upon
his owne determeynacõn, and therefore willed him with certeyne
other hee named, to take the governement of the State, and
specially to keepe narrowe watche of the Frontiers. *Philanax*
acknoulledging him self muche honored by so great trust, went,
with asmuche care to performe his Comaundement, as before
hee had wth faythe yeelded his Counsell: whiche in the later
short disputacyons hee had rather proportioned to *Basilius*
wordes, then to any soundnes of argument. And *Basilius*,
according to his determeynacion retyered him self into the
solitary place of the twoo Lodges, where hee was daily delighted
with the Eglogues and pastymes of Shepeheardes: In the one
of whiche Lodges hee him self remayned wth his wyfe, and y^e
beauty of the worlde *Philoclea*, in the other neare unto him hee
placed his Daughter *Pamela* with *Dametas*, whose wyfe was
Miso, and Daughter *Mopsa*, unfitt Company for so excellent a
Creature, but to exercyse her patience and to serve for a foyle to
her perfections. Nowe, newely after that the Duke had begone

6

this solitary lyfe there came (followyng the trayne theyre vertues ledd them) into this Contry, twoo young Princes: The younger, but cheefer, named *Pyrocles* onely sonne to *Evarchus* kinge of *Macedon*, the other his Cosyn germayne, *Musidorus* Duke of *Thessalia*, bothe like in vertues, nere in yeares, nere in blood, but nearest of all in frendshipp: And bycause this matterr ronnes principally of them, a fewe wordes, howe they came hether, will not bee superfluous. *Evarchus* kinge of *Macedon*, a Prince of suche Justice, that hee never thought him self privill-ledged by beeyng a Prince, nor did measure greatenes by any thinge but by goodnes, as hee did thereby roote an Awfull love in his subjectes towardes him, so yet coulde hee not avoyde the assaultes of Envy ye enimy and yet the honor of vertue: For, the Kinges of *Thrace*, *Pannonia* and *Epyrus* not beeyng able to attayne to his perfections, thoughte in theyre base wickednes best to take away so odious a Comparison, least his vertues joyned to the fame and force of the *Macedonians*, might in tyme bothe conquer the bodyes, and winne the myndes of theyre Subjectes. And thus Conspiring together, they did three sondry wayes enter into his kingdome at one tyme: whiche sodeyne, and daungerus Invasions, allthough they did no thing astonish *Evarchus*, who carryed a hart prepared for all extremityes, (as a man that knewe bothe whatt yll mighte happen to a Man never so prosperus, and with all, what the uttermoste of that yll was) yet were they Cause, that *Evarchus* did sende away his youngest sonne *Pyrocles* (at that tyme but sixe yeares olde) to his Sister the *Dowager* & Regent of *Thessalia*, there to bee brought up wth her sonne *Musidorus*: whiche thoughe yt proceeded of necessity, yet, was not ye Counsell in yt self unwyse. The sweete Emulation that grewe, beeyng an excel-lent Nurse of the good partes in these twoo Princes in deede borne to the exercyse of vertue: For, they accoumpting thincrease of theyre yeares wth thincrease of all good Inward and owteward qualityes, and taking very tymely into theyre myndes, that the Devine parte of man was not inclosed in this body for nothinge, gave them selves wholy over to those knoul-ledges, wch mighte in the Course of theyre lyfe bee Ministers to theyre well dooyng. And so grewe they on till *Pyrocles* came to bee xvii^{teene} and *Musidorus* xviii^{teen} yeares of age: At whiche tyme *Evarchus*, after tenne yeares warr having conquered the Kingdome of *Thrace,* and brought the other twoo to bee his Tributaryes, lived in the principall City of *Thrace* called at that tyme *Bisantium.* Whether hee sent for his sonne and Nevew to delighte his aged eyes in them, and to make them to enjoy the fruites of his victoryes: But so pleased yt God, who reserved them to greater traverses bothe of good and evell fortune, that the sea (to whiche they committed them selves) stirred to terrible tempest, forced them to falle farr from theyre Course, uppon the Coaste of *Lydia.* Where, what befell unto them, what valyant actes they did, passing, (in one yeares space) throughe the lesser *Asia, Syria* and *Egipt,* how many Ladyes they defended from wronges, and disinherited persons restored to theyre Righte, yt ys a worcke for a higher style then myne: This onely shall suffyce, that, theyre fame returned to fast before them into *Grece,* that the Kinge of *Macedon* receyved that, as the Comfort of theyre absence allthoughe accompanyed wth somuche more longing, as hee founde ye manifestacyon of theyre worthynes greater. But they desyerus, more and more to excercyse theyre vertues, and increase theyre experience, tooke theyre Jorney from *Egipt* towardes *Grece:* whiche they did, they twoo alone, because that (beeyng theire native Contry) they mighte have the more perfect knowledg of yt, wherein, they that holde the Countenaunces of Princes, have theyre eyes moste daseled: And so taking *Arcadia* in theyre way, for the fame of the Contry, they came thether newly after that this straunge solitarynes had possessed *Basilius.* Now so fell yt unto them, that they lodged in the howse of *Kerxenus* a principall gentleman in *Mantinea* (so was the City called) nereto the sollitary dwelling of the Duke: yt was *Pyrocles* eyther evell or good fortune, walking with his hoste in a fayre gallery, that hee perceyved a picture newly made by an excellent Artificer, wch conteyned the Duke and Duches, with theyre younger Daughter *Philoclea* with suche Countenaunce and fashion as the maner of theyre lyfe held them in. Bothe the Parentes eyes cast with a loving Care upon theyre beutyfull Chylde, shee drawne aswell as yt was possible Arte shoulde counterfeict so perfect a worckmanship of Nature: For therein, besydes the shewe of her beutyes a man might judge eeven the nature of her Countenaunce, full of bashfullnes love and reverence, and all by the Cast of her eye, mixt with a sweete greef

8

to fynde her vertue suspected. This moved *Pyrocles* to falle into questions of her, wherein beeyng answered of the gentleman so muche as hee understoode, wch was of her straunge kynde of Captivity neyther was yt knowne, how Longe yt should last, and there was an opinion growne, the Duke wolde graunte his Daughters in mariage to nobody: As the moste noble harte ys moste subject unto yt, from questyons grewe to pitty, and when with pitty once his harte was made kinder according to the aptnes of the humor, yt receyved streight a crewell impression of that wonderfull passion, wch to bee defined ys impossible, by reason no wordes reache neare to the straunge nature of yt, they onely knowe yt whiche Inwardly feele yt, yt ys called Love. Yet did not the pore youthe at first knowe his Diseaze, thinck-ing yt onely suche a kynde of desyer, as hee was wonte to have to see suche unwonted sightes and his pitty to bee no other but the fruites of his gentle Nature: But even this arguyng with him self, came to a further thoughte, and the more hee argued, the more his thoughte increased. Desyerus hee was to see the place where shee remayned as thoughe the Architecture of the Lodges woulde have beene muche for his learning: But more desyerus to see her self to bee Judge forsoothe of the paynters Conning, for thus at the first did hee flatter him self, as thoughe ye wounde had bene no deeper. But when within short tyme hee came to the Degree of uncerteyn wisshes and that those wissh-inges grewe to unquyett longinges: when hee coulde fixe his thoughtes uppon no thinge, but that within a litle varrying, they shoulde ende with *Philoclea*. When eche thing hee sawe seemed to figure oute some parte of his passions, and that hee hearde no worde spoken, but that he Imagined yt carryed the sounde of *Philocleas* name: Then did pore *Pyrocles* yelde to the burthen, fynding him self prisoner, before hee had leysure to arme him self, and that hee mighte well (like the Spanyell) gnawe upon ye Cheyne that tyes him, but hee shoulde sooner marr his teeth then procure liberty. Then was his cheef delighte, secretly to drawe his dere frend a walking to the desert of the twoo Lodges, where hee sawe no grass upon wch hee thoughte *Philoclea* mighte happ to treade, but that hee envyed ye happynes of yt: And yet, with a contrary folly wolde some-tymes recomend his whole estate unto yt, till at ye lengthe, Love, the Refyner of Invention putt in his heade, a way, howe

9

to come to the sighte of his *Philoclea*. For wch hee wth greate speede and secretsy prepared every thinge that was necessary for his purpose, but, yet woulde not putt yt in execucõn, till hee had disclosed yt to *Musidorus*, bothe to performe the true Lawes of Frendshipp and withall to have his Counseill and allowance: And yet oute of ye sweetenes of his Disposicõn was basshfully afrayde, to breake yt wth him, to whome (besydes other bondes) because hee was his Elder, hee bare a kynde of reverence, untill some fitt oportunity mighte, as yt were, drawe yt from him. Whiche occasion tyme shortly presented untó him, for *Musidorus* having informed him self fully of the strengthe and Riches of ye Contry, of the nature of the people, and of the manner of theyre Lawes, & seeyng the Dukes Courte coulde not bee visited, and that they came not wthoute danger to that place, (prohibited to all men, but to certeyn Shepeheardes) grewe no less weary of his aboade there, then merveyled of the greate delighte *Pyrocles* tooke in that place: Where uppon one day at *Pyrocles* earnest request, beeyng walked thether ageane, began in this maner to say unto him. A mynde well trayned and longe exercysed in vertue, (my sweete and worthy Cossen) dothe not easily chaunge any Course yt once undertakes, but uppon well grounded and well weyed Causes: For, beeyng witness to yt self of his owne Inwarde good, yt fyndes no thinge with oute yt of so highe a pryce, for wch yt shoulde bee altered: Even the very Countenaunce and behavyo^r of suche a man dothe shewe forthe Images of ye same constancy by meynteyning a right harmony betwixt yt, and the Inwarde good, in yeelding yt self sutable to the vertuous resolutions of the mynde. This speeche, I direct to yow, Noble frende *Pyrocles*, the excellency of whose mynde and well chosen course in vertue, yf I doo not sufficiently knowe, (havinge seene suche rare Demonstracyons of yt) yt ys my weykenes, and not youre unworthynes: But as in deede I knowe yt, and knowyng yt, moste derely love bothe yt, and him that hathe yt, so must I needes say, that since oure late comming into his Contrey I have marcked in yo^w, (I will not say an alteracyon) but a Relenting truely and slaking of ye mayne Carryer yo^w had so notably begun and allmoste performed. And y^t in suche sorte as I can not fynde sufficyent reasons in my greate love towardes yow howe to allowe yt: For, to leave of other secrett argumentes wch my acquayntance wth yow

makes mee easily fynde, this, in effect to any man, may bee
manifest, that whereas yow are wonte in all the places yow
came, to give youre self vehemently to knowledg of those thinges
wch mighte better youre mynde, to seeke the familiarity of excellent men in Learning and Souldyery, and lastly to putt all
these thinges in practize, bothe by continuall wyse proceedinges
and worthy enterpryses as occasions fell for them. Yow, now,
leave all these thinges undone, yow let youre mynde falle a
sleepe, besydes youre Countenaunce trubled wch surely comes
not oute of vertue, (for vertue like the cleare heaven ys withowte Clowdes) and lastly wch seemeth straunge unto mee, yow
haunte greatly this place : wherein besydes the Disgrace y^t
mighte falle of yt, (whiche that yt hathe not allredy fallen uppon yow, ys more rather luck then providence, the *Duke* having
sharply forbiden yt) yow subject youre self to solitarynes, the
slye Enimy y^t moste dothe seperate a man from well doyng.
These wordes spoken vehemently and proceeding from so
dearely an esteemed frende as *Musidorus* did so perce pore
Pyrocles, that his blusshing Cheekes did witnesse with him, hee
rather coulde not help, then did not knowe his faulte : Yet,
desyerus by degrees to bringe his frende to a gentler Consideracyon of him, and beginning wth twoo or three broken sighes,
answered him to this purpose. Excellent *Musidorus*, in the
prayses yow gave mee in the beginning of youre speeche I
easily acknoulledge the force of youre good will unto mee : For,
neyther coulde yow have thought so well of mee, yf extremity
of love had not somethinge daselled youre eyes, Nor yow coulde
have loved mee so entierly, yf yow had not beene apte to make
so greate, (thoughe undeserved) Judgmentes of mee. And eeven
so must I say of those Imperfections, to whiche, thoughe I
have ever throughe weykenes beene subject, yet, yow by the
dayly mending of youre mynde have of late bene able too looke
into them, wch before yow coulde not discerne : So that the
Chaunge yow spake of falles not oute by my ympayring, but by
youre bettering, and yet under the leave of youre better Judgment I must needes saye thus muche (my Deare Cossyn) that I
fynde not my self wholly to bee Condempned, bycause I doo
not with a Continuall vehemency followe those knowlledges w^ch
yow calle ye betteringes of my mynde. For, bothe the mynde
yt self must, (like other thinges) some tymes bee unbent, or else

yt will bee eyther weykened or broken, and these knowlledges, as they are of good use, so are they not all the mynde may stretche yt self unto: who knowes whether I feede my myndes with higher thoughtes?, truely, as I knowe not all the particularityes, so yet, see I the boundes of all these knoulledges, but the workinges of the mynde I fynde muche more infinite then can bee ledd unto by ye eye, or imagined by any that distract theyre thoughtes wthowte them selves, and in such Contemplacyons, or as I thincke more excellent I enjoye my solitarynes, and my solitarynes perchaunce ys the Nurse of these Contemplacyons. Egles wee see flye alone, and they are but sheepe wch allway heard together: Condempne not therefore my mynde some tyme, to enjoy yt self, nor blame not, the taking of suche tymes as serve moste fitt for yt. And here *Pyrocles* sodenly stopped, like a man unsatisfyed in him self, thoughe his witt mighte well have served to have satisfyed an other: And soo looking with a Countenaunce as thoughe hee desyered hee shoulde knowe his mynde, withoute hearing him speake, to breathe oute some parte of his Inwarde evell, sending ageane new blood to his face, hee continewed his speeche in this maner. And Lorde, deare Cossyn (sayde hee) dothe not the pleasantnes of this place, carry in yt self sufficyent Rewarde, for any tyme lost in yt or for any suche daunger that mighte ensewe? Doo yow not see how every thinge Conspires together to make this place a heavenly Dwelling? Doo yow not see the grasse, howe in Coloure they excell the Emeraudes every one stryving to passe his fellowe, and yet they are all kept in an equall heighte? And see yo^w not the rest of all these beutyfull flowers, eche of whiche woulde requyer a mans witt to knowe, and his lyfe to express? Doo not these stately trees seeme to meynteyne theyre florisshing olde age with the onely happynes of theyre seate beeyng clothed with a Continuall springe, bycause no beauty here shoulde ever fade? Dothe not the Ayer breath health whiche the Byrdes, (bothe delightfull bothe to the eare and eye) do dayly solempnize with the sweete consent of theyre voyces? Ys not every Eccho here a perfect Musick? and these fressh and delightfull brookes, ho^w slowly they slyde away, as, lothe to leave the Company of so many thinges united in perfection, and with how sweete a Murmer they lament theyre forc[ed] departure: Certeynly, certeynly Cossyn yt must needes bee,

that some Goddess this Dezert belonges unto, who ys the sowle
of this soile, for, neyther ys any lesse then a Goddess worthy to
bee shryned in suche a heape of pleasures, nor any less then a
Goddess coulde have made yt so perfect a Moddell of the
heavenly dwellinges: And so hee ended with a deepe sighe,
rufully casting his eye uppon *Musidorus*, as more desyerus of
pitty, then pleading. But *Musidorus* had all this while helde his
looke fixed uppon *Pyrocles* countenaunce and wth no less loving
attention, marcked, howe his wordes proceeded from him; But,
in bothe these hee perceyved suche straunge diversityes, that they
rather increased newe Doubtes, then gave him grounde to settle
any judgement. For besydes his eyes, sometyme eeven greate w^th
teares the ofte chaunging of his Coloure with a kynde of shaking
unstedfastnes over all his body, hee mighte see in his Countenaunce some greate determynacõn mixed with feare: And
mighte perceyve in him store of thoughtes rather stirred then
disgested, his wordes interrupted continually with sighes, w^ch
served as a Burthen to eche sentence, and the tenor of his
speache (thoughe of his wonted phrase) not knitt together to one
constant ende but rather dissolved in yt self, as the vehemency
of ye Inward passion prevayled, whiche made *Musidorus* frame
his answer nearest to that humor wch shoulde soonest putt oute
ye secrett. For having in ye beginning of *Pyrocles* speeche (whiche
defended his solitarynes) framed in his mynde a Reply ageanst
yt, in the prayse of Honorable action in shewyng that suche
kynde of Contemplacyon ys but a gloryous tytle to Idlenes:
That in action a man did not onely better him self, but, benefitt others. That the Goddes woulde not have delivered a sowle
into the body, whiche hathe armes and legges onely instrumentes of Dooynge, but that yt were intended, the mynde
shoulde employ them, and that the mynde shoulde best knowe
his owne good or evell by practize: whiche knowledge was the
onely way to encrease the one & correct the other, besydes, many
other better argumentes, whiche the plentyfulnes of the matter
yeelded to the sharpenes of his witt. When hee founde *Pyrocles*
leave that, and falle to suche an affected praysing of the place,
hee lefte yt likewyse, and joyned therein wth him, because hee
founde him in that humor, utter more store of passyon: And
even thus kyndely embracing him, hee sayde, youre wordes are
suche, Noble Cossen, so sweete and strongly handled in the

13

prayse of solitarynes, as they woulde make mee yeelde my self lykewyse up unto yt. But that the same wordes make mee knowe, yt ys more pleasant to enjoy the Company of him that can speake suche wordes, then by suche wordes to bee perswaded to followe solitarynes: And eeven so do I give yow leave sweete *Pyrocles*, ever to defend solitarynes, so longe, as to defend yt, yow ever keepe Company. But I merveyle at the excessive prayses yow give to this Dezart, in truthe yt ys not unpleasant, but, yet, yf yow woulde returne unto *Macedon*, yow shoulde see eyther, many heavens, or fynde this, no more then earthely: And, even *Tempe*, in my *Thessalia*, where yow and I to my greate happynes were brought up together ys nothinge inferior unto yt. But, I thincke yo^w will make mee see that the vigor of youre witt can shewe yt self in any subject, or else yow feede sometymes youre solitarynes, with the Conceyptes of the *Poetts*: whose liberall pennes can as easily traveyll over mounteynes as Mole hilles, and so like well disposed men, sett upp every thinge to the highest Noate, especially, when they putt suche wordes in the mouthe of one of these Fantasticall mynde infected people, y^t Children and Musicians calle Lovers. This worde Lover did no less pearse pore *Pyrocles*, then the righte Tune of musick tuched him, that ys sick of the *Tarantula*: there was not one part of his body, that did not feele a sodeyne motion, the harte drawyng unto yt self the lyfe of every parte to help yt distressed with the sounde of that worde: yet after some pawse, lifting up his eyes a litle from the grounde, and yet not daring to place them in the face of *Musidorus*, armed with the Countenaunce of the pore Prisoner at the barr whose answer ys no thing but guilty, with muche adoo hee brought forthe this question. And alas (saide hee) dere Cosyn what yf I bee not so muche y^e *Poett*, the freedome of whose penne can exercyse yt self in any thing, as even y^t miserable subject of his Conning, whereof yow spake. Nowe the Eternall goddes forbidd, maynely cryed oute *Musidorus*. But *Pyrocles* having broken the yce pursewde on in this maner: And yet suche a one am I sayde hee that in suche extremity as no man can feele but my self, nor no man beleeve, since no man ever could taste the hundreth parte of that wch lyes in the Innermoste parte of my sowle. For synce yt was the fatall overthrowe of all my Liberty, to see in the gallery of *Mantinea* the onely *Philocleas* picture, that beauty did pearse so through my eyes to my harte, that the Impression dothe not lye but live there in suche sorte, as the questyon ys not nowe, whether I shall love or no, but whether Loving I shall live or dye: *Musidorus* was no less astonished with these wordes of his frende, then yf thincking him in healthe hee had sodenly toulde him that hee felt the panges of deathe oppress him. So that amasedly looking uppon him, (eeven as *Apollo* ys paynted when hee sawe *Daphnes* sodenly turned into a Lawrell) hee was not able to say one worde, but gave *Pyrocles* occasion, havinge allredy made the breache, to passe on in this sorte: And bycause I have layde open my wounde (Noble Cossen sayde hee) I will shewe yoᵂ what my Melancholy hathe broughte forthe for the preparacyon at least of a salve, yf yt bee not in yt self a Medi- cyn. I am resolved (because all direct wayes are barred mee, of opening my sute to the Duke) to take uppon mee the estate of an *Amazon* Lady goyng aboute the worlde, to practize feates of Chivalry, and to seeke my self a worthy husband: I have all redy provyded all furniture necessary for yt, and my face (yow see) will not easily discover mee. And here aboute will I haunte, till by the help of this Disguysing, I may come to the presence of her, whose Imprisonment darkens the worlde, that myne owne eyen may bee wittnesses to my harte, yt ys good reason why, hee shoulde bee thus captived. And then as I shall have atteyned to the first degree of my happynes, so, will Fortune, occasion and myne owne Industry putt forwardes the rest: For the Principall poynte ys, to sett in a good way, the thinge wee desyer, for then will tyme yt self dayly discover newe secrett helpes: As for my name yt shall bee *Cleophila*, turning *Philoclea* to my self, as my mynde ys wholly turned and transformed into her. Nowe therefore, doo I submitt my self to youre Counsell, (deare Cossen) and crave youre help, and thus hee ended: As who shoulde say, I have toulde yow all, have pitty on mee. But *Musidorus* had by this tyme gathered his spirites, dismayed to see him, whome hee loved more then him self, plounged in suche a Course of misery: And so, when *Pyrocles* had ended, casting a gastfull Countenance upon him, as yf hee woulde conjure some straunge spirite hee sawe possess him, with greate vehe- mency uttered these wordes. And ys yt possible, that this ys *Pyrocles* the onely young Prince in the Worlde formed by Nature, and framed by education, to the true exercyse of vertue,? or ys yt in deede some *Amazon Cleophila*, that hathe counterfeited the face of my frend in this sorte to vexe mee? For likelyer sure I woulde have thoughte, that my owtewarde face mighte have beene disguysed, then that the face of so excellent a mynde coulde have beene thus blemisshed? O, sweete *Pyrocles* seperate youre self a litle, yf yt bee possible from youre self, and let youre owne mynde looke uppon youre owne proceedinges, so shall my woordes bee needeles & yow best instructed. See with youre self, how fitt yt will bee for yow in this youre tender youthe, (borne so greate a Prince, and of so rare not onely expectation, but proof) desyered of youre oulde Father & wanted of youre native Contry, (nowe so nere home) to direct youre thoughtes from the way of goodnes, to loose, nay, to abuse youre tyme? Lastly, to overthrowe all the excellent thinges yow have done, wᶜʰ have filled yᵉ worlde with youre fame, as yf yow shoulde drowne youre ship in the longe desyered haven, or like an yll player, shoulde marr yᵉ last acte of his tragedy: Remember, (for I knowe, yow knowe yt) that yf wee will bee men, the reasonable parte of youre sowle, ys to have absolute Comaundemᵗ, ageanst wᶜʰ yf any sensuall weykenes aryse, wee are to yeelde all oure sounde forces to the overthrowyng of so unnaturall a Rebellyon. Wherein, how can wee want corage, synce wee are to dealle ageanst so weyke an Adversary, that in yt self, ys no thing but weykenes: Nay, wee are to resolve, that yf reason direct yt, wee must doo yt, and yf wee must doo yt, wee will doo yt. For, to say I can not, ys Chyldish, and I will not, womanish: And, see, how extremely every way, yow endaunger youre mynde, for to take this womanly habite, (withoute yoʷ frame youre behavyour accordingly) ys wholy vayne, youre behavyour can never come kyndely from yow, but as the mynde ys proportyoned unto yt: So that yow must resolve, yf that yoʷ will play youre parte to any purpose, (what soever peevish Imperfections are in that sexe) to soften youre harte for to receyve them, the very first downestepp to all wickednes. For, doo not deceyve youre self, my deare Cossen, there ys no man sodenly eyther excellently good, or extremely evill, but growes eyther as hee holdes him self up in vertue, or lettes him self slyde to vicyousnes: And let us see, what power ys the Author of all these trubles, forsoothe, Love, Love, a passyon, and the barest and fruitlessest of all passyons, feare breedeth witt, Anger ys the

Cradle of Corage, Joy openeth and enhableth the harte, Sorow as yt closeth yt, so yet, draweth yt inwarde to looke to the correcting of yt self, and so, all of them generally, have power, towarde some good by the direction of reason. But this basterd Love, (for in deede the name of Love ys unworthely applyed to so hatefull an humor) as yt ys ingendred betuixt lust and Idlenes, as ye matter yt worckes uppon ys no thing but a certeyn base weykenes whiche, some gentle fooles calle a gentle harte: As his adjoyned Companyons bee, unquietnes, longinges, fonde Comfortes, faynt discomfortes, hopes, Jealosyes, ungrounded rages, Causeles yeeldinges, so ys the highest ende yt aspyers unto, a litle pleasure wth muche payne before, and greate repentance after: But that ende, (how endles yt ronnes to infinite evills) were fitt ynoughe for the matter wee speake of, but, not for youre eares, in whome in deede, there ys so muche true disposicõn to vertue. Yet thus muche of his worthy effectes in youre self ys to bee founde, that yt utterly subvertes the Course of Nature, in making reason give place to sence, and man, to woman. And truely, hereuppon (I thinck) yt first gott the name of Love, for in deede the true Love hathe that excellent nature in yt, that yt dothe transforme the very essence of the Lover, into the thinge loved, uniting, and as yt were incorporating yt, with a secrett, and Inward worcking, and herein doo these kyndes of Love imitate ye excellent. For, as the Love of heaven makes one heavenly, the love of vertue vertuous, so dothe the love of the Worlde make one become worldly, and this effeminate love of a Woman, dothe so womanish a man, that, yf yow yeelde to yt, yt will not onely make yow a famous Amazon but a Launder, a Distaff spinner, or whatsoever other vyle occupacyon theyre idle heades can imagyn, and theyre weyke handes performe: Therefore, to truble yow no longer wth my tedyous, but, loving wordes, yf eyther yow remember, what yow are, what yow have beene, or what yow must bee, yf yow Consider, what yt ys, that mooves yo^w, or with what kynde of Creature yow are mooved, yow shall fynd ye cause so smalle, the effectes so daungerus, youre self so unworthy to ronne into the one, or to bee driven by the other, that, I doubte not, I shall quickly have occasyon, rather to prayse yow, for having Conquered yt, then to give yow further Counsell howe to doo yt. *Pyrocles* mynde was all this while so fixed uppon an other Devotion, that, hee

no more attentively marcked his frendes discourse, then the
Chylde, that hathe leave to play, marckes the last parte of his
Lesson, or the diligent Pylott in a daungerus tempest, dothe
attend to the unskillfull passinger: yet the very sounde having
lefte the generall poyntes of his speeche in his mynde, the respect hee bare to his frende, broughte forthe this Answer, (having
first payde up his late accustomed tribute of Syghes) Dere and
worthy frende, what soever good disposicõn nature hathe bestowed on mee, or howsoever that disposicõn hathe bene by
bringing up Confirmed, This must I confess, that I am not yet
come to that degree of Wisdome, to thincke lighte of the
sexe of whome I have my lyffe: Synce, yf I bee any thinge
(whiche youre Frendship rather fyndes, then I acknowlledg),
I was to come to yt, borne of a woman, and nurced of a woman,
and certeynly (for this poynte of youre speeche dothe nearest
tuche mee) yt ys straunge to see the unmanlike cruelty of mankynde. Who, not content with theyre tyrannous ambicion, to
have broughte the others vertuous pacyence under them, like
Chyldish Masters thincke theyre Masterhood nothing, withoute
doyng injury unto them who, (yf wee will argue by reason) are
framed of nature, with the same partes of the mynde, for the
exercyse of vertue, as wee are: And for example, even this estate
of *Amazons* (whiche I now for my greatest honor, do seeke to
counterfeit) dothe well witness, that yf generally the sweetnes
of theyre Disposicõn did not make them see the vaynes of these
thinges, (whiche wee accompte gloryous) they neyther want valure
of mynde, nor yet, dothe theyre fayrenes take away theyre force.
And truely, wee men, and praysers of men shoulde remember,
that yf wee have suche excellencyes, yt ys reason, to thincke
them excellent Creatures of whome wee are, synce a Kyte never
broughte forthe a good flyinge Hawke: But, to tell yow true,
I doo bothe disdayne to use any more wordes of suche a Subject,
whiche ys so praysed in yt self, as yt needes no prayses, and
withall, feare leste my Conceipte (not able to reache unto them)
bringe forthe wordes, wch for theire unworthynes may bee a
Disgrace unto them, I so inwardly honor. Let, this suffise,
that they are Capable of vertue, and vertue (yow youre self say)
ys to bee loved, and I too, truely: But this I willingly confess,
that yt likes mee muche better, when I fynde vertue in a fayre
Lodging, then when I am bounde to seeke yt in an yll favored

18

Creature, like a Pearle in a Doungehill. And here, *Pyrocles*
stayed, as, to breathe him self having bene transported wth a litle
vehemency, bycause, yt seemed him, *Musidorus* had over bitterly
glaunsed ageanst the reputacõn of womankynde: But then quyet-
ing his Countenaunce, aswell, as oute of an unquyet mynde, yt
mighte bee, hee thus proceeded on. And, pore Love (sayde hee)
Dere Cossyn, ys litle beholding unto yow, since yow are not
contented to spoyle yt of ye honor, of the highest power of the
mynde, wch notable men have attributed unto yt, but yow
deject yt, belowe all other passions (in truthe) some thinge
straungely; Synce, yf Love receyve any disgrace, yt ys by y^e
Company of those passyons yow preferr unto yt. For those
kynde of bitter objections, as, that Lusty Idlenes, and a weyke
harte shoulde bee as yt were the matter and forme of love,
rather tuche mee, (*Musidorus*) then Love: But, I am good
witnes of my owne Imperfections, and therefore will not defend
my self, but, herein I must say, yow deale contrary to youre self,
for, yf I bee so weyke, then can yow not with reason stirr mee
up, as yow did by the remembrance of myne owne vertue, or
yf in deede I bee vertuous, then must yow Confess, that love
hathe his worcking in a vertuous harte, and so no doubt hathe
yt what soever I bee. For, yf wee love vertue, in whome shall
wee love yt, but in vertuous Creatures, withoute youre meaning
bee, I shoulde love this worde of *Vertue*, when I see yt written
in a Booke: Those trublesome effectes yow say yt breedes bee
not the faultes of Love, but of him, that loves, as an unable
vessell to beare suche a power, lyke evell eyes not able to looke
on the sunne, or like a weyke brayne soonest overthrowne with
the best wyne. Eeven that heavenly love yow speake of ys
accompanyed in some hartes with hopes, greeffes, Longinges
and Dispayres, and in y^t heavenly love synce there are twoo
partes, the one the Love of yt self, the other, the excellency of
the thing loved, I (not able at the first leape, to frame bothe in
my self) doo now like a diligent worckman, make redy the
cheef Instrument, and first parte of that great worcke wch ys
love yt self: whiche, when I have a while practized in this
sorte, then, yow shall see mee turne yt to greater matters. And
thus gently, yow may, yf yt please yow, thincke of mee, neyther
doubte yow, because I werre a womans apparrell, I will bee the
more womannish, since I assure yo^w (for all my apparell) there

ys no thing I desyer more, then fully to proove my self a man, in this enterpryse: Muche mighte bee sayde in my defence, muche more for love, and moste of all for that Devyne Creature, wch hathe joyned mee and love together. But these Disputacions are fitter for quyett Schooles then my trubled braynes, wch are bent rather in deedes to performe then in wordes to defend the noble desyer y^t possesseth mee: O Lorde, (saide *Musidorus*) howe sharpp witted yo^w are to hurt youre self: No aunswered hee, but yt ys the hurte yo^w spake of, wch makes mee so sharpp witted. Even so (sayde *Musidorus*) as every base occupacyon makes one sharp in theyre practize and foolish in all the rest: Nay, rather (answered *Pyrocles*) as eche excellent thinge once well learned, serves for a measure of all other knowlledges. And ys that become (sayde *Musidorus*) a measure for other thinges, whiche never receyved measure in ytself? yt ys coumpted withoute measure (answered *Pyrocles*) bycause ye workinges of yt are withoute measure, but, otherwyse, in nature, yt hathe measure, synce yt hathe an ende allotted unto yt. The beginning beeyng so exellēt I wolde gladly knowe the ende enjoying (answered *Pyrocles* with a deepe sighe:) O, (saide *Musidorus*) now yow sett forthe the basenes of yt, since, yf yt ende in enjoying, yt shewes all the rest was nothing. You mystake mee (answered *Pyrocles*) I spake of the ende, to whiche yt ys directed, wch ende endes not, no sooner then the lyfe: Alas, lett youre owne brayne disenchaunt yo^w, saide *Musidorus*. My harte ys to farr possessed, sayde *Pyrocles*, but the head gives yo^w direction and the harte gives mee lyfe answered *Pyrocles*. But *Musidorus* was so greeved, to see his beloved frende obstinate (as hee thought) to his owne destruction, that yt forced him, with more then accustomed vehemency to speake these wordes. Well, well, sayde hee, yow list to abuse youre self, yt was a very white and redd vertue, wch yow coulde pick oute by the sighte of a picture, Confess the truthe, and yow shall fynde the uttermoste was but beauty: A thinge wch though yt bee in as greate excellency in youre self, as may bee in any, yet, am I sure, yo^w make no further reconing of yt, then of an owtewarde fading benefit nature bestowed uppon yow. And yet, suche ys youre wante of a true grounded vertue, wch must bee like yt self in all poyntes that what yow wysely coumpte a tryfle in youre self, yow fondly become a slave unto,

20

in an other: For, my parte, I now protest, I have lefte no thinge unsayde, wch my witt coulde make mee knowe, or my moste entire frendship to yow requyres of mee. I do now beseeche yow, even for the love betuixte us (yf this other Love have lefte any in yow towardes mee) and for the remembrance of youre oulde Carefull Father, (yf yow can remember him, that forgettes youre self) Lastly for *Pyrocles* sake, who ys now uppon the poynte of falling or rysing, to purge youre heade, of this vyle infection: Otherwyse, give mee leave rather in absence to bewayle youre myshapp, then to abyde the continuall pange of seeyng youre daunger with my eyes. The lengthe of these speeches before had not so muche cloyed *Pyrocles*, thoughe hee were very Impacyent of longe deliberacōns, as this last farewell of him, hee loved as his owne lyfe, did wounde his sowle: As in deede, they that thincke them selves afflicted, are apte to conceyve unkyndnes deepely, in so muche, that skaking his heade, and deliveringe some shewe of teares, hee thus uttered his greefes. Alas (saide hee) Prince *Musidorus*, howe crewelly yow deale with mee, yf yow seeke the victory, take yt, and yf yow list Tryumphe: Have yow all the reason of the Worlde, and with mee remayne all the Imperfections? Yet suche as I can no more lay from mee, then ye Crowe can bee perswaded by the Swann, to cast of his blacknes. But, truly yow deale with mee like a Phisicion, that, seeyng his patient in a pestilent feyver, shoulde chyde him, in steade of ministring help, and bid him bee sick no more: Or rather, like suche a frend, that vizitting his frende condempned to perpetuall prison, and loaded with greevous fetters, shoulde will him to shake of his Fetters or hee woulde leave him. I am sicke, and sick to the deathe, I am a Prisoner, neyther ys there any Redress, but, by her, to whome I am a slave: Now, yf yow list, Leave him, that loves yow in ye highest degree, but, remember ever, to carry this wth yow, that yow abandon youre Frende in his greatest neede. And herewith the deepe wounde of his Love beeyng rubbed a fressh, with this newe unkyndenes, began as yt were to bleede ageane, in suche sorte that hee was unable to beare yt any longer: But, gusshing oute abundance of teares, and Crossing his armes over his wofull harte hee sancke downe to the grounde. Whiche soden traunce, went so to the hart of *Musidorus*, that falling downe by him, & kissing the weeping eyes of his Frende, hee besoughte him, not to make accoumpte of his speeche, whiche, yf yt had bene over vehement, yet, was yt to bee borne withall bycause yt came oute of a Love muche more vehement, that, hee had never thoughte, fancy coulde have receyved so deepe a wounde: But, now fynding in him the force of yt, hee woulde no further contrary yt, but employ all his service, to medcyn yt in suche sorte, as the nature of yt requyred. But, even this kyndenes made *Pyrocles* the more melt in the former unkyndenes, whiche his manlike teares well shewed with a sylent looke upon *Musidorus*: As who shoulde say, and ys yt possible, that *Musidorus*, shoulde threaten to leave mee? And this stroke *Musidorus* mynde, & sences so dombe, too, that for greef, not beeyng able to saye any thinge, they rested, with theyre eyes placed one upon an other in suche sorte, as mighte well paynte oute the true passyon of unkyndenes, whiche ys, never a righte, but betuixte them y^t moste dearely love. And thus remayned they a tyme, till at lengthe, *Musidorus* embracing him, sayde, and will yow thus shake of youre Frende? yt ys yow y^t shake of mee (saide *Pyrocles*) beeyng for myne unperfectnes unworthy of youre Frendship: But this (saide *Musidorus*) shewes yow^w muche more unperfect, to bee crewell unto him, that submitteth himself unto yow^w, but, since yow^w are unperfect (sayde hee smylinge) yt ys reason yow^w bee governed by us wyse and perfect men. And that authority will I begin to take uppon mee with three absolute Comaundementes: the first That, yow encrease not youre evell with further greefes, The second that yow^w love *Philoclea*, with all the powers of youre mynde, and the last Commaundement shall bee, that yow commaunde mee to doo yow^w what service I can, towarde the obteyning of youre Desyers. *Pyrocles* harte was not so oppressed wth the twoo mighty passions of Love & unkyndenes, but, that yt yeelded to some myrthe at this Comaundem^t of *Musidorus*, that hee shoulde love *Philoclea*: So that, some thing clearing his face from his former shewes of greef, well, saide hee Deare Cossen, I see by the well chosinge of youre Commaundementes that yow are farr fitter to bee a Prince, then a Counsellor. And therefore, I am resolved to employ all my Indevoure to obay yow^w wth this Condicion, that the Commaundementes yow^w commaunde mee to lay uppon yow^w shall onely bee that yow^w continew to loove mee, and looke upon my Imperfections, with more affection then

Judgm[t]: Love yo[w], saide hee? Alas how can my harte bee seperated from the true embracing of yt, withoute yt burst, by beeyng to full of yt. But, saide hee let us leave of these flowers of newe begun frendship, and synce yo[w] have founde oute that way as youre redyest remedy, Let us goo putt on youre transforming apparell: For my parte, I will ever remayne hereaboutes, eyther to help yow in any necessity, or at leste to bee partaker of any evell may falle unto yow. *Pyrocles*, accepting this, as a moste notable testimony of his long approoved frendship, & returning to *Mantinea*, where having taken leave of theyre Hoste, who thoughe hee knewe them not was in love wth theyre vertue, and leaving wth him some apparrell and Jewells, with opinion they woulde returne after some tyme unto him: They departed thence to the place, where hee had lefte his womanish apparell, whiche wth the help of his frende, hee had quickly putt on, in suche sorte, as yt mighte seeme Love had not onely sharpened his wittes, but nymbled his handes in any thinge, whiche mighte serve to his service. And to begyn with his heade, thus was hee dressed; His heyre, w[ch] the younge men of *Greece* ware very longe, (accoumpting them moste beutyfull, that had yt in fayrest quantity) lay uppon the uppermoste parte of his foreheade in Lockes, some curled, and some, as yt were forgotten: with suche a Careles care and wth suche an arte so hyding arte, that hee seemed hee woulde lay them for a Patern whether nature simply or nature helped by cunning bee the more excellent, the Rest wherof was drawne into a Coronet of golde wyers, and covered with fethers of dyvers Coloures, that yt was not unlike to a hellmett, suche a glittering shewe yt bare, and so bravely yt was helde up from the heade. Uppon his body hee ware a kynde of Dublett of skye coloured Satyn, so plated over with plates of Massy golde, that hee seemed armed in yt: His sleeves of the same in steade of plates, was covered wth purled Lace, and suche was the nether parte of his garment, but that made so full of stuffe, and cutt after suche a fashyon, y[t] thoughe the lengthe fell under his anckles, yet in his goyng one mighte well perceyve the smalle of his Legg, w[ch] with the foote, was covered wth a litle short payre of Crimson vellvet buskyns, in some places open, as the auncyent maner was, to shew y[e] fayrenes of his skynn. Over all this, hee ware a certeyne Mantell of like stuffe, made in suche maner, that coming under his righte arme, and covering moste parte of that syde, yt tuched not the lefte syde, but uppon ye topp of ye shoulder, where the twoo endes mett, and were fastened together, wth a very riche Jewell the Devyse whereof was this : An Egle covered with the fethers of a Dove, and yet lying under an other Dove, in suche sorte, as yt seemed, the Dove prayed uppon the Egle, the Egle casting up suche a looke, as thoughe the state hee was in, liked him, thoughe the payne greeved him. Uppon the same syde uppon his thighe, hee ware a sworde, suche as wee now calle Scimitares, the pomell wherof was so richely sett with precyous stones, as they were sufficyent testimonyes, yt coulde bee no meane personage that bare yt; Suche was this *Amazons* attyre, and thus did *Pyrocles* become *Cleophila*, whiche name for a tyme, hereafter I will use. For, I my self feele suche Compassion of his passyon, that, I fynde even parte of his feare, leste his name shoulde bee uttered before fitt tyme were for yt : whiche yow faire Ladyes, that vouchesave to reade this (I doubte not) will accoumpte excusable. But *Musidorus* that had helped to dress his frende coulde not satisfy him self wth looking uppon him, so did hee fynde his excellent beuty sett oute with this newe chaunge, lyke a Dyamond sett in a more avantagious sorte, in somuche that hee coulde not chuse, but, (smyling) sayde unto him : Well, (saide hee) sweete Cossen, since yow are framed of suche a Loving mettell, I pray yo^w take heede of looking youre self in a glasse, leste *Narcissus* fortune falle unto yo^w. For my parte, I promyse yo^w, yf I were not fully resolved, never to submitt my hart to those fancyes, I were like ynoughe, while I dressed yow, to become a young *Pigmalion* : Alas, answered *Cleophila*, yf my beauty bee anythinge, then, will yt help mee to some parte of my Desyers, otherwyse, I am no more to sett by yt then ye Orator by his eloquence, that perswades no body. Shee ys a very invincible Creature then (saide hee), for I doubt mee muche (under youre pacyence) whether my Mistres youre Mistres have a greater portion of beuty : Speake not that blasphemy, deare frende (saide *Cleophila*) for, yf I have any beauty, yt ys the beauty wch the Imaginacyon of her strikes into my fancyes, whiche in parte shynes throughe my face into youre eyes. Truly saide *Musidorus* yow are growne a notable *Philosopher* of fancyes : *Astronomer*, (answered *Cleophila*) for they

24

are heavenly fancyes. In suche frendly speeches they returned
ageane to the Dezart of the twoo Lodges, where *Cleophila*
desyered *Musidorus* hee woulde hyde him self in a litle grove,
where hee mighte see howe shee coulde play her parte: For,
there, (shee sayde) shee was resolved to remayne, till, by some
good favoure of fortune shee mighte obteyne the sighte of her,
whome shee bare continually in the eyes of her mynde.
Musidorus obayed her request, full of extreme greef to see so
worthy a mynde thus infected, besydes hee coulde see no hope
of success, but great apparaunce of daunger: yet fynding yt so
deepely grounded, that, stryving ageanst yt, did rather anger
then heale the wounde, and rather calle his frendship in question,
then give place to any frendly Counsell, hee was content to
yeelde to the force of the present streame, with hope afterwardes,
as occasion fell to preveyle better with him, or at leste, to
adventure his lyfe in preserving him from any injury mighte
bee offered him. And with ye beating of those thoughtes,
remayned hee in the grove, till with a new fullnes hee was
emptyed of them, as yo^w shall after heare. In the meane tyme
Cleophila walking up and downe in that solitary place, with
many intricate determinacōns, at last, wearyed bothe in mynde
& body satt her downe: And beginning to tune her voyce, w^th
many sobbes and teares, sange this songe, wch shee had made,
synce her first determinacyon, thus to chaunge her estate.

> *Transformde in shewe, but more transformde in mynde,*
> *I cease to stryve, with duble Conquest foylde;*
> *For, woe ys mee, my powers all (I fynde)*
> *With owtewarde force, and inward treason spoylde.*

> *For, from withoute, came to myne eyes the blowe,*
> *Whereto, myne Inwarde thoughtes did faintly yeelde:*
> *Bothe these conspirde pore Reasons overthrowe,*
> *False in my self, thus have I lost the feelde.*

> *And thus myne eyes are plaste still in one sighte,*
> *And thus my thoughtes can thinck but one thing still:*
> *Thus, reason to his servantes gives his righte,*
> *Thus ys my power transformed to youre will.*
> *What marvell then I take a Womans hewe?*
> *Since, what I see, thincke, knowe, ys all but yow?*

I might enterteyne yo^w, (faire Ladyes) a greate while, yf I shoulde make as many interruptions in the repeating, as shee did in the singing: For no verse did pass oute of her mouthe, but that yt was wayted on wth suche abundance of sighes, and (as yt were) witnessed with her flowing teares, that thoughe the wordes were fewe, yet the tyme was long shee employed in uttering them, Allthoughe her pawses chose so fitt tymes, that they rather strengthened a sweeter passyon then hindered the harmony. *Musidorus* him self that lay so, as hee mighte see and heare these thinges, was yet more mooved to pitty by the maner of *Cleophilas* singing, then with any thinge hee had ever seene, so lyvely an action dothe the mynde, truely tuched, bringe forthe: But, so fell yt oute, that, as with her sweete voyce, shee recorded once or twyce the last verse of her songe, yt awakened the Shepeardes *Dametas*, who at that tyme had layde his sleepy back uppon a sunnye banck, not farr thence, gaping as farr, as his Jawes woulde suffer him. But beeyng trubled oute of his sleepe (the best thinge his lyfe coulde bringe forthe) his dull sences coulde not convey the pleasure of ye excellent Musick to his rude mynde, but that hee fell into a notable rage: In so muche, that, taking a hedging bill lay by him, hee guyded him self by the voyce, till hee came to the place, where hee sawe *Cleophila* sitting and wringing her handes, and with some fewe wordes to her self breathing oute to her self parte of the vehemency of y^t passion whiche shee had not fully declared in her songe. But, no more were his eyes taken wth her beauty then his eares with her musick, but beginning to sweare by the pantaple of *Pallas*, *Venus* wastecoate & suche other Oathes as his rusticall bravery coulde imagyn, leaning his handes uppon his bill and his Chinne uppon his handes, hee fell to mutter suche Cursinges and Raylinges ageanst her, as a man mighte well see hee had passed throughe the discipline of an Alehowse: And bycause yo^w may take the better into youre fancyes his mañerlynes, the maner of the man shall in fewe wordes bee described.

Hee was a short, leane fellowe, of black hayre, and notably backt for a burden, one of his eyes oute, his nose turned up to take more ayer, a seaven or eighte long black hayres uppon his chinne, wch hee called his bearde, his brest hee ware allwayes unbuttoned, for heate, and yet, a stomacher before yt for colde, ever untrust, yet, poyntes hanging downe, bycause hee mighte bee trust, yf hee list, yll gartered for a Courtelike Carelesnes,

onely well shodd for his fathers sake, who had uppon his deathe
bed charged him to take heede of goyng wett. Hee had for love,
chosen his wyfe, *Miso*, yet, so handsome a belldame, that shee was
counted a Witche, onely for her face, and her splay foote, neyther
inwardly nor owtewardly, was there any good thing in her, but,
that shee observed *Decorum*; having in a wretched body a froward
mynde, neither was there any humor, in wch her husband and
shee coulde ever agree, but in disagreeyng: Betuixt these twoo
issewed forthe Mistris *Mopsa*, a fitt woman to participate of bothe
theyre perfections. But bycause *Alethes* an honest man of that
tyme sett forthe her prayses in verse, I will onely repeate them,
and spare myne owne peññ, because shee bare the Sexe of a
Woman, and these they were.

What lengthe of verse can serve, brave Mopsas *good to showe,*
Whose vertues strange, & beutyes suche, as no man them may
knowe :
Thus shrewdly burdened then, how can my Muse escape ;
The godds must help, and precyous thinges must serve to shew her
shape.

Like great god Saturne, *faire, and like faire* Venus *chaste,*
As smoothe as Pan, *as* Juno, *mylde, lyke goddess* Iris *faste.*
With Cupid *shee foresees, and goes god* Vulcans *pace,*
And for a taste of all these giftes shee borowes Momus *grace.*

Her forehead Jacincth *lyke, her cheekes of* Opall *hewe,*
Her twinckling eyes bedect wth perle, her lippes of Saphire *blewe.*
Her heare pure Crapall *stone, her Mouthe, O heavenly wyde,*
Her skinne like burnisht golde, her handes like silver Owir *untryde.*
As for those partes unknowne, whiche hidden sure are best
Happy bee they wch well beleeve, and never seeke the rest.

The beginning of *Dametas* credit with *Basilius*, was by the
Dukes straying oute of his way one tyme, a hunting, where,
meeting this fellow and asking him the way, and so falling into
other questions, hee founde some of his answers tuching husbandry
matters (as a Dogg, sure yf hee coulde speake had witt ynoughe
to describe his kennell) not unsensible: And all uttered wth suche
a rudenes, wch the Duke interpreted playñes (allthoughe there
bee great difference betwixt them), that the Duke conceyving
a sodeyn delighte in his enterteynement, tooke him to his Courte,

with aparant shewe of his good opinion. Whence the flatering Courtyer had no sooner taken the Princes mynde, but y[t] there were streight reasons to confirme the *Dukes* dooyng, and shadowes of vertues founde for *Dametas*: His silence grewe witt, his bluntnes integrity, his beastly ignorance, vertuous simplicity. And the *Duke* (acording to the nature of great persons) in love with that hee had done him self, fancyed, that, the weykenes was in him wth his presence woulde growe wisdome, and so like a creature of his owne making hee liked him more and more. And thus gave hee him self the office of Principall *Heardman*, and thus lastly did hee putt his lyfe into his handes, allthoughe hee grounded uppon a greate errur: For his quality was not to make men, but to use men according as men were, no more then an Asse woulde bee taughte to manneage a horse to hunt, or a hounde to beare a saddle, but, eche to bee used acording to y[e] force of his owne nature. But, *Dametas*, (as I sayde) sodenly awaked, remembred the *Dukes* commaundement, and glad hee mighte use his authority in chyding, came swearing to the place, where *Cleophila* was, with a voyce like him, that playes *Hercules* in a play and god knowes never had *Hercules* fancy in his heade: The first worde hee spake after his rayling oathes was, Am not I *Dametas*? why, am not I *Dametas*? These wordes made *Cleophila* lifte up her eyes uppon him, and seeyng what maner of man hee was, the heighte of her thoughtes woulde not suffer her, to yeelde any answer to so base a Creature, but Casting ageane downe her eyes, leaning uppon the grounde, and putting her Cheeke in y[e] Palme of her hande, fetched a great sighe, as yf shee had answered him, my heade ys trubled with greater matters: whiche, *Dametas* (as all persons, witnesses of theyre owne unworthynes are apte to thincke they are contempned) tooke in so haynous a Chafe, that standing uppon his tiptoes, and staring, as yf hee woulde have had a moate pulled oute of his eye, why, sayde hee, Thow woman, or boy, or bothe, or whatsoever thow bee, I tell thee there ys no place for thee, gett thee gone, I tell thee yt ys the *Dukes* pleasure, I tell thee yt ys Mr *Dametas* pleasure. *Cleophila* coulde not chuse but smyle at him, and, yet taking her self wth the maner, spake these wordes to her self: O *Spirite*, (saide shee) of myne, how canst thow receyve my myrthe in the mydest of thyne agonyes, and thow myrthe howe darest thow enter into a mynde so growne of late thy professed enimy? Thy spirite, (sayde *Dametas*) dooest

28

thow thincke mee a Spirite? I tell thee, I am the *Dukes* officer,
and have the charge of him & his Daughters. O Perle (saide
sobbinge *Cleophila*) that so vyle an Oyster shoulde keepe thee?
By the Combecase of *Diana*, sware *Dametas*, this woman ys madd.
Oysters and Pearles? Doest thow thincke I will buy Oysters?
I tell ye gett thee packing, or else I must needes bee offended.
O Sunne, sayde *Cleophila*? howe long shall this Cloude live to
darcken thee? and the pore Creatures that live onely by thee bee
deprived of thee? These speeches to her self putt *Dametas* oute
of all patience: So that hitting her upon ye brest with the blunt
ende of his Bill, Mayde Maryan (saide hee) am not I a person to
bee answered? But *Cleophila*, no sooner felte the blowe, but that
the fyer sparckling oute of her eyes, and rysing up wth a right
Pyrocles Countenaunce in a *Cleophila* face; vyle Creature (saide
shee, laying her hande uppon her sworde) force mee not to defyle
this sworde in thy base blood? *Dametas* that from his Chyldehood
had ever feared ye blade of a sworde, rann backward with his
handes above his heade at least xx^{ti} paces, gaping and staring with
the very Countenaunce of those Clownish Churles, that, by *Latonas*
prayer were turned into Frogges: At lengthe, staying hee came a
litle nearer her ageane, but still wthoute the Compas of blowes,
holding one legg, as yt were, redy to runne away and then fell to
scolding and rayling, swearing, that yt was but a litle bashfullnes
in him, that had made him goo back. And that yf shee stayed
any longer, hee woulde make her see, his blood come oute of the
eldest shepeardes howse in that Contry, but, seeyng her walke up
and downe, wthout marcking what hee sayde, hee went for more
help to his Lodg: where knocking a good while, at lengthe hee
cryed to his wyfe *Miso*, that in a whores name shee shoulde come
oute to him; but in steade of that hee might heare a hollow rotten
voyce, that byd him lett her alone, like a knave as hee was for
shee was busy aboute my Lady *Pamela*. This dasshed pore *Dametas*
more then any thinge, for oulde acqueyntance had taughte him,
to feare that place, and therefore, calling with a more pityfull
voyce, to his Daughter, hee mighte see a face looke oute of a
wyndow, ynoughe to have made any blynde man in Love: yt
was Mistris *Mopsa*, that in stede of answer asked him whether
hee was madd to forgett his Dewty to her Mother? *Dametas*
shroncke downe his shoulders, like the pore Asse, that layes downe
his eares, when hee must needes yeelde to the Burthen: And yet

his tounge the valyantest parte of him coulde not forbeare to say
these wordes, Here ys forreyn warres abroade and uncivill warres
at home, and all wth woemen, Now, (saide hee) the black Jaunders,
and the red flixe take all the wrabbed kynde of yo^w. And with
this prayer hee went to the other Lodge, where the *Duke* at that
tyme, was sleeping, as yt was in the heate of the day, and there
hee whistled, and stamped, and knocked, Cryinge, O my Leege,
with suche faces, as mighte well shewe, what a deformity a passion
can bringe a man into, when yt ys not governed wth reason: Till
at lengthe, the faire *Philoclea* came downe, in suche lose aparell
as was ynoughe to have bounde any mans fancyes, and wth a
sweete looke asking him, what hee woulde have? *Dametas* withoute
any reverence, comaunded her in the *Dukes* name, shee should
teell the *Duke*, he was to speake with the *Duke*, for hee, forsoothe
had thinges to tell the *Duke*, wch perteyned to the *Dukes* service:
Shee answered him hee shoulde bee obeyed, since, suche was the
fortune of her and her Sister. And so went shee to tell her father
of *Dametas* beeyng there, leaving him chafing at ye dore, and
whetting his bill, swearing, yf hee mett her ageane, neyther shee
nor the tallest woman in the parish shoulde make him ronne away
any more: But, the *Duke* understanding by his Jewell *Philoclea*,
that some thing there was, whiche greatly trubled *Dametas* conscyence, came downe presently unto him, to knowe the matter.
Where hee founde *Dametas* talking to him self and making faces
like an Ape, that had newly taken a purgacyon, pale, shaking,
and foming at the mouthe, and a greate while yt was before the
Duke coulde gett any worde of him: At lengthe, putting his legg
before him, (wch was the maner of his Cursy) hee tolde the *Duke*,
that, saving the reverence of his Duety, hee shoulde keepe him
self from henceforward, hee woulde take no more charge of him.
The *Duke* accustomed to take all well at his handes, did but
laughe, to see his rage, and stroaking his heade, desyered him of
fellowship to lett him knowe the matter: I tell yo^w (saythe
Dametas) yt ys not for mee to bee an officer, withoute I may
bee obayed. But, what trubles thee my good *Dametas*, (saythe the
Duke), I tell yow, saide *Dametas*, I have bene a man in my dayes
what soever I bee nowe: And reason (answered the *Duke*) but let
mee knowe, that I may redress thy wronges: Nay sayde *Dametas*,
no wronges neyther, but, thus falles oute the Case, my Leege.
I mett with suche a Mankynde creature yonder with her sworde

by her hipp, and with suche a visage, as, yf yt had not bene for mee and this bill, god save yt) shee had come hether, and killed yo^w and all youre howse: What? stryke a woman, sayde the *Duke*? In deede saide *Dametas*, I made her but a litle weepe, and after I had pity on her. It was well and wysely done sayde the *Duke*, but, I pray thee shewe mee her: I pray yow saide *Dametas* first, calle for more Company, to holde mee from hurting her, for my stomack ryseth ageanst her. Let mee but see the place (saide the *Duke*) and then yow shall knowe whether my wordes or youre bill bee the better weapon: *Dametas* went stalcking on before the *Duke*, as yf hee had bene afrayde to wake his Chylde, and then poynting with his bill towardes her, was not hasty to make any nere approches. But the *Duke* no sooner sawe *Cleophila*, but, that hee remayned amased at the goodlynes of her stature, and ye statelynes of her Marche (for at that tyme shee was walking with a countenaunce well setting forthe an extreme distraction of her mynde) And as hee came nerer her, at the excellent perfection of her beauty: In somuche, that forgetting any anger hee conceyved in *Dametas* behalf and dooyng reverence to her as to a Lady in whome hee sawe much worthy of greate respect. Fayre Lady saide hee, yt ys no thinge straunge that suche a solitary place as this shoulde receyve solitary persons, but muche do I marveyle, howe suche a beauty as youres ys, coulde bee suffered to bee thus alone: Shee looking with a grave majesty uppon him, as yf shee founde in her self, Cause, why, shee shoulde bee reverenced; They are never alone (sayde shee) that are accompanyed with noble thoughtes. But, those thoughtes (sayde y^e *Duke* replying for the delighte hee had to speake further with her) can not in this youre Lonelynes, neyther warrant yo^w from suspicion in others, nor defend yo^w from Melancholy in youre self: *Cleophila* looking upon him as thoughe hee pressed further then hee needed, I seeke no better warraunte sayde shee, then myne owne conscyence, nor no greater pleasure then myne owne contentacyon. Yet vertue seekes to satisfy others, saide *Basilius*: Those that bee good, aunswered *Cleophila* and they will bee satisfyed so long as they see no evill. Yet will the best in this Contry saide the *Duke*, suspect so excellent a beauty, beeyng so weykely guarded: Then are the best but starck naughte answered *Cleophila*, for open suspecting others comes of secret condempning them selves. But in my Contry (sayde shee) continewing her

31

speeche with a brave vehemency (whose maners I am in all places to meynteyne, and reverence) the generall goodnes wch ys norished in oure hartes, makes every one thinck that strengthe of vertue in an other, wherof they fynde the assured foundacion in them selves. But, *Basilius*, who began to feele the sparckles of those flames, wch shortly after burned all other thoughtes oute of his harte, felt suche a musick, as hee thoughte, in her voyce, and suche an eye pleasing in her face, that hee thoughte his retyring into this solitary place was well employed, yf yt had bene onely to have mett wth suche a guest : And therefore, desyerus to enter into nerer poyntes with her, Excellent Lady (sayde hee) yo^w prayse so greatly and yet so wysely youre Contry that I must needes desyer to knowe what the Nest ys oute of wch suche byrdes do flye. Yow must first deserve that knouledge (saide shee) before yow obtayne yt : And by what meanes saide *Basilius*, shall I deserve to know youre estate? By letting mee first know youres saide shee. To obay yo^w, saide hee, I will doo yt, all-thoughe yt were so muche more reason youres shoulde be knowne first, as yo^w do deserve in all poyntes to bee preferred : Knowe yo^w faire Lady (saide hee) that my name ys *Basilius*, unworthely Duke of this Contry, the rest eyther fame hathe all redy broughte to youre eares, or yf yt please yo^w, To make this place happy by youre presence, at more Leysure yo^w shall understand of mee. *Cleophila*, who had from the beginning suspected, yt shoulde bee hee but, woulde not seeme shee did so, (to keepe her Matie the better) making some Reverence to him, Mighty Prince (saide shee) Let my not knowyng of yo^w serve for the excuse of my boldenes, and the litle reverence I doo to yo^w, impute yt to the maner of my Contry, whiche ys the Invincible Lande of the *Amazons*, my self neece to *Semicia*, queene of that Contry, lineally discended of the famous *Penthesilea*, slayne before *Troy*, by the bloody hande of *Pyrhus*. I having in this my yowthe determyned to make the worlde see the *Amazons* excellencyes, aswell in private, as in publique vertues, have passed many daungerus adventures in dyvers Contryes : Till the unmercyfull sea deprived mee of all my Company, so that Shipwrack broughte mee to this Realme, and uncerteyne wandering guyded mee to this place. Whosoever sawe a man, to whome a beloved Chylde longe lost did (unlooked for) returne, mighte easily figure unto his fancy, the very fashion of *Basilius* Countenaunce, so farr had Love

32

become his Master, and so had this younge *Syren* charmed his olde eares: Insomuche, that wth more vehement importunacy, then any greedy Hoste woulde use to well acqueynted passingers, hee fell to intreate her aboade there for some tyme. Shee, allthoughe no thing coulde come fitter to the very poynte of her desyer, yet had shee all redy learned that womanish quality to counterfet backwardnes, in that shee moste wished: So that hee desyerus, to proove, whether intercession coming oute of fitter mouthes mighte better preveyle, called to *Dametas*, and comaunded him, to bringe forthe his wyfe and twoo Daughters, three Ladyes, allthoughe dyvers, yet all of excellent beauty. The *Duches Ginecia* in grave Matrone like attire with a countenaunce and behavyour farr unlike to falle into those inconvenyences shee afterwardes tasted of. The faire *Pamela* whose noble hart had longe disdayned to fynde the trust of her vertue reposed in the handes of a Shepeheard, had, yet (to shewe an obeydyence) taken on a Shepeardish apparrell, wch was of Russet vellvet, cutt after theyre fashion with a streyte body open brested the nether parte full of pleytes with wyde open sleeves hanging downe very lowe, her hayre at the full lengthe wounde aboute wth golde Lace: By the Comparyson, to shewe, how farr her hayer did excell in coloure, betwixt her brestes, whiche sweetly ryse up like twoo faire mounteynettes in the plesaunt vale of *Tempe*, there hanging downe a Jewell whiche shee had devysed as an *Impresa*, of her owne estate, yt was a perfect white Lambe tyed at a stake, with a great nomber of Chaynes, as yf yt had bene feared leste the silly Creature shoulde do some great harme, neyther had shee added any worde unto yt, (whiche ys as yt were the lyfe of an Impresa) but eeven tooke syilence as the worde of the pore Lambe, shewing suche humblenes, as not to use her owne voyce for compleynte of her misery. But, when the Ornament of the earthe, younge *Philoclea* appeared in her nymphelike apparell, so nere nakednes, as one might well discerne parte of her perfections: And yet so apparelled as did shewe, shee kept the best store of her beautyes to her self, her excellent faire hayer drawen up into a nett, made onely of yt self, A nett in deede to have caughte the wyldest Disposicõn, her body covered with a lighte taffita garment, so cutt, as the wrought smock came throughe yt in many places, ynoughe, to have made a very restrayned imaginacyon have thoughte what was under yt: with the sweete cast of her black eye, whiche seemed to make a Contention whether that in perfect blacknes, or her skinne in perfect whitenes were the moste excellent. Then I say the very Cloudes seemed to give place to make the heaven more faire, at least, the Cloudes of *Cleophilas* thoughtes quyte vanisshed, and so was her brayne fixed: w^thall that her sighte seemed more forcible and clere, then ever before, or since shee founde yt. With suche straunge delighte unto her (for still faire Ladyes, you remember that I use the Shee tytle to *Pyrocles* since so hee woulde have yt) that shee stoode like a well wrought image, with showe of lyfe, but withoute all exercyse of lyfe: So forcibly had love transferred all her Spirites into the present Contemplacyon of the Lovely *Philoclea*, and so had yt bene like ynoughe shee woulde have stayed longe tyme, but y^t by chaunce *Ginecia* stepped betwixte her sight, and the Lady *Philoclea*. And the chaunge of the object made her recover her sences, so that shee coulde with good manner receyve the salutacyon of y^e *Duchess* and the *Princess Pamela*: Doyng them yet, no further reverence then one Princess useth to an other. But when shee came to ye Lady *Philoclea*, shee fell downe on her knees, taking by force, her faire handes, and kissing them with great shewe of extreme affection, and with a bowed downe countenaunce began this speech unto her. Devyne Lady, (saide shee) let not the worlde nor this greate Princess merveyle, to see mee contrary to my maner, doo this especiall honor unto yow, since all bothe men and woemen owe this Homage to the perfection of youre beauty. *Philocleas* blusshing cheekes quickly witnessed, ho^w muche shee was abasshed, to see the singularity used to her self, & therefore, causing *Cleophila* to ryse, Noble Lady (saithe shee) yt ys no merveyle, to see youre judgment muche mistaken in my beauty, since yow begin with so greate an error, as to doo more honor unto mee, then unto them, to whome I my self owe all service: Rather (answered *Cleophila*) that shewes the power of youre beuty wch hathe forced mee, to falle into suche an error, yf yt were an error. Yo^w are so acquaynted (saide *Philoclea*, sweetely smyling) with youre owne beauty, that yt makes yow easely falle into the Discourse of beauty: Beauty in mee (saide *Cleophila*? deeply sighing), alas yf there bee any, yt ys in my eyes, whiche youre happy presence hathe imparted unto them. *Basilius* was eeven transported wth delighte to here these speeches, betuixt his wellbeloved Daughter, and his better-Loved Lady,

34

& so made a signe to *Philoclea*, that shee shoulde intreate her to remayne with them: whiche, shee willingly obeyed, for all redy shee conceyved delighte in *Cleophilas* presence, and therefore sayde unto her: It ys a greate happynes (I confess) to bee praysed or them, that are them selves moste prayse worthy; and well I fynde yow an Invincible *Amazon*, synce yow will overcome in a wrong matter: But, yf my beuty bee any thing saide shee, then let yt obteyne thus muche of yow, That, yow will remayne in this Company, some tyme to ease youre owne travell, and oure solitarynes. First, let mee dye saide *Cleophila*, before any worde spoken by suche a mowthe shoulde come in vayne, I yeelde wholly to youre Commaundement, fearing no thing, but y^t yo^w commaunde that wch may bee trublesome to youre self. Thus wth some other wordes of enterteyning, her staying was concluded to ye inspeakeable joy of the *Duke*, allthoughe perchaunce wth some litle envy in the other Ladyes, to see younge *Philocleas* beuty so advaunced.

Yow Ladyes knowe best whether sometymes yo^w feele impression of that passion, for my parte, I wolde hardly thincke that the affection of a mother and the noble mynde of *Pamela* coulde bee over throwne wth so base a thing as envy ys: Especially, *Pamela*, to whome fortune had all redy framed an other, who no less was dedicated to her excellencyes, then *Cleophila* was to *Philocleas* perfection, as yo^w shall shortly heare. For, the *Duke* goynge into the Lodge wth his wyfe and Daughters, *Cleophila* desyered them excuse her for a while, for that shee had thoughtes to pass over with her self, & that shortly after shee woulde come unto them: In deede meaning to fynde her frende *Musidorus*, and to glory with him of ye happynes of her choyce, but when shee looked in the grove, and coulde no where fynde him, merveyling something at yt, shee gave her self to feede on those sweete thoughtes, wch now had the full possession of her hart: sometymes thinckyng how farr *Philoclea* her self passed her picture, sometymes fore imagening wth her self, howe happy shee shoulde bee yf shee coulde obteyne her desyers. Till having spent thus an hower or twoo, shee mighte perceyve a farr of, one coming towardes her in the apparrell of a Shepeard, wth his Armes hanging downe goyng, a kynde of Languisshing pace, with his eyes some tymes cast up to heaven, as thoughe his fancyes strave to mounte up higher, some tymes throwne downe to the grounde: As yf the earthe coulde not beare the burden of his paynes; at lengthe shee hearde him wth a Lamentable tune singe these fewe verses.

> Come Shepearde weedes become youre Masters mynde,
>   Yeelde owteward shewe, what Inwarde chaunge hee tryes:
> Nor bee abashed, synce suche a guest yow fynde,
>   Whose strongest hope in youre weyke comforte lyes.
>
> Come Shepeard weedes attend my woofull Cryes,
>   Disuse youre selves from sweete Menalcas voyce:
> For others bee those Tunes wch sorrowes tyes,
>   From those clere notes wch freely may rejoyce.
>
> Then powre oute pleynte, and in one worde say this:
> Helples his pleynte, who spoyles him self of blis.

And having ended, shee mighte see him stryke him self upon ye brest, uttering these wordes: O myserable Wretche, whether doo thy Destenyes guyde thee? yt seemed to *Cleophila*, shee knewe ye voyce, and therefore, drawyng nearer that her sighte mighte receyve a perfect discerning, shee sawe playnely, to her greate amasement, yt was her dere frende *Musidorus*. And nowe, having named hym, mee thinckes yt reason, I shoulde tell yo^w, what chaunse broughte him to this chaunge: I lefte him lately (yf yo^w remember fayre Ladyes) in the grove, by the twoo Lodges, there to see what shoulde befalle to his dere new transformed Frende. There hearde hee all the Compleyntes (not withoute greate Compassion) that his frende made to him self, and there, (not withoute some Laughter) did hee see what passed betuixt him and *Dametas*, and howe stately hee playde ye parte of *Cleophila*, at the *Dukes* first comming: And falling into many kynde of fancyes towardes him, sometyme pitying his Case, sometymes praysing his behavyour, hee woulde often say to him self. O sweete *Pyrocles* how arte thow bewitched? where ys thy vertue? where ys the use of thy reason? Howe muche am I inferior unto thee in all the powers of thy mynde? And yet knowe I, that all the heavens, can not bring mee to suche a thraldome. Scarsely (thinck I) hee had spoken these wordes, but that the *Duchess* (beeyng sent for to enterteyne *Cleophila*) came oute with her twoo Daughters: Where the beames of ye Princess *Pamelas* beauty, had no sooner stricken into his eyes, but, that hee was wounded with more

36

sodeyn vyolence of Love then ever *Pyrocles* was. Whether in deede yt were that this straunge power woulde bee bravely revenged on him, for the bitter wordes hee had used, or that his very resisting made the wounde the crewellar: As wee see the Harquebush dothe moste endomage the stiffest mettall, or rather that ye continuall healthfullnes of his mynde made this sodeyn evill the more incurable: As the soundest bodyes once infected, are moste mortally endaungered. But, howesoever the Cause was, suche was the effect, that not beeyng able to beare the vehement payne, hee ranne away throughe ye grove like a madd man: Hoping perchaunce (as the fever sick folckes doo), that the chaunge of places mighte ease his greef, but therein was his Luck in deede better then his providence. For, hee had not goñ a litle, but that hee mett with a Shepearde (according to his estate) handsomely apparrelled, who was as then goynge to meete with other Shepeardes (as uppon certeyne dayes they had accustomed) to doo exercyses of activity, and to play newe invented Ecclogues before the *Duke*: whiche, when *Musidorus* had learned of him (for Love ys full of desyer, and desyer ys allwayes inquisitive) yt came streyghte into his heade, that there was no better way for him to come by the often enjoying of the Princess *Pamelas* sighte, then to take the apparell of this Shepearde uppon him. Whiche hee quickly did giving him his owne muche richer, and withall, leste the matter by him bee discovered, hyered him withowte stay to goo into *Thessalia*, wryting twoo or three wordes by him, (in a payre of Tables well closed up) to a servaunt of his, that hee shoulde uppon the receipte, arrest and keepe him in good order, till hee hearde his further pleasure: yet before *Menalcas* departed, (for so was his name) hee learned of him bothe his owne estate, and the maner of theyre pastymes and Egglogues. And thus furnished hee returned ageane to the place, where his harte was pledged, soo oppressed in mynde, that, yt seemed unto him his Legges were uñeth able to beare him: whiche greef hee uttered wth the Dolefull songe I tolde yow of before, and was Cause that his dere hee shee frende *Cleophila* came unto him. Who, when shee was assured yt was hee (with wonted entiernes embrasing him) demaunded of him what sodeyn chaunge, had thus sodeynly chaunged him? whether the goddess of those woodes had suche a power, to transforme every body, or whether in

Deede, as hee had allwayes in all enterpryzes moste faythfully accompanyed her, so hee woulde continew to matche her in this new *Metamorphosis*. But *Musidorus* looking dolefully uppon her, wringing his handes, and powring oute abundance of teares, begañ to recoumpt unto her all this I have allredy toulde yow: But with suche passionate delating of yt, that, for my parte I have not a feeling Insighte enoughe into the matter, to bee able lyvely to express yt, suffyseth yt, that what so ever a possessed hart, with a good tongue to a dere frende coulde utter, was at that tyme largely sett forthe. The perfect frendship *Cleophila* bare him, and the greate pity shee by good experience had of his Case, coulde not keepe her from smyling at him, remembring howe vehemently hee cryed owte ageanst ye folly of Lovers, so that shee thoughte good a litle to punish him, playing with him in this maner: Why, howe now Dere Cossen saide shee yow that were even now so highe in the pullpett, ageanst Love, are yow now become so meane an Auditor? Remember, that love ys a passion, and that a worthy manns reason must ever have the Masterhod. I recant, I recant, cryed *Musidorus*, and with all falling downe prostrate O thow Celestiall, or infernall Spirite of Love (saide hee) or what other heavenly or hellish tytle thow list to have (for bothe those effectes I fynde in my self) have Compassion of mee, and let thy glory bee as greate in pardoning them that bee submitted to thee, as in Conquering those that were rebellyous: No no, saide *Cleophila* (yet further, to urge him) I see yow well enoughe, yow make but an enterlude of my myshappes, and doo but counterfeit thus, to make mee see the deformity of my passyons, but, take heede (saide shee) Cossen, that this Jeste doo not one day turne to earnest. Now, I beseeche yee saide *Musidorus* taking her fast by the hande, even for the truthe of oure Frendship, of whiche (yf I bee not alltogether an unhappy man) thow haste some remembrance, And by those secret flames whiche (I knowe) have likwyse nerely touched thee, make no Jeste of that, wch hathe so earnestly persed mee throughe, nor let that bee light unto thee wch ys to mee so burdenous that I am not able to beare yt? *Musidorus* did so lyvely deliver oute his inwarde greeffes, that *Cleophilas* frendly harte felt a great Impression of pity withall, as certeynly all persons that fynde them selves afflicted, easely falle to Compas-

38

sion of them who taste of like misery, partely ledd by the comon Course of humanity; But principally bycause under the Image of them, they Lament theyre owne mishappes, and so the Compleyntes that others make, seeme to tuche the righte tune of theyre owne woes, wch did mutually worck so in these twoo young Princes that, looking rufully, one uppon the other, they made theyre speeche (a greate while) no thinge but Dolefull sighes, yet, some tymes they woulde yeelde oute suche like Lamentacions: Alas what farther evill hathe fortune reserved for us? what shall bee the ende of this oure tragicall pilgrimage? Shipwrackes, Daily daungers, absence from oure Contry, have at lengthe broughte forthe this Captiving of us within oure selves, whiche hathe transformed the one in Sexe, and the other in state, as muche as the uttermoste worcke of chaungeable fortune can bee extended unto. And then woulde they kisse one an other, vowyng to continew partakers of all eyther good or evell fortune, & thus perchaunce woulde they have forgotten them selves some longer tyme; But that *Basilius*, whose harte was now sett on fyer wth his newe Mistris, fynding her absence longe, sent oute *Dametas*, to her, to knowe yf shee woulde comaunde any thinge, and to invite her to goo with his wyfe and Daughters to a fayre Meadowe, there by, to see the Sportes and heare the Eglogues of his Contry Shepeardes. *Dametas* came owte with twoo or three swordes aboute him, his hedging bill on his neck, and a chopping knyfe under his girdle, armed onely behynde, as fearinge moste the blowes that mighte falle on the raynes of his back: For, in deede *Cleophila* had putt suche a sodeyn feare into his heade, that from thenceforthe he was resolved, never to come oute any more yll provyded, yet, had his blunt braynes perceyved some favoure the Duke bare to this newe come Lady. And so framing him self thereunto, (as withoute doubte the moste servile flatery ys moste easily lodged in the moste grosse Capacity, for theyre ordinary Conceipte drawes a yeelding to theyre greaters, and then have they not witt to discerne the right degrees of goodnes) hee no sooner sawe her, but with hed and armes hee layde his reverence before her, enoughe to have made any man forsworne all Curtesy: And then, in the *Dukes* name did hee requyer her, shee wolde take paynes to see theyre pastoralls, for so theyre sportes were termed, But when hee espyed *Musidorus* standing by her, (for his eye had bene placed all this while uppon her) not knowing him, hee woulde fayne have perswaded him self to have bene angry, but y[t] hee durst not. Yet muttering and Champing as thoughe his Cudd trubled him, hee gave occasion to *Musidorus* to come nerer him, and to frame a Tale of his owne lyfe, that hee was a younger brother of the Shepeard *Menalcas*, by name *Dorus*, sent by his Father in his tender age to *Athens*, there to learne some Cunning more then ordenary, for to excell his fellowe Shepeardes in theyre Eglogues: And that his brother *Menalcas* latily gone thether to fetche him home, was deceassed, where uppon his Deathe bed hee had charged him to seeke the service of *Dametas*, and to bee wholly and onely guyded by his Counsell, as one in whose Judgm[t] and integrity the *Duke* had singuler Confidence. For token whereof hee gave him a Some of golde in redy Coyne, whiche *Menalcas* had bequeathed him, uppon Condicõn, hee shoulde receyve this pore *Dorus* into his service, that his mynde and maners mighte growe the better, by his daily ensample: *Dametas*, no sooner sawe the golde, but that his harte was presently infected with the self conceipte hee tooke of yt, whiche beeyng helped by the tickling of *Musidorus* prayses, so turned y[e] brayne of good *Dametas*, that hee became slave to that whiche hee that wolde bee his servaunt bestowed uppon him. And gave in him self an ensample for ever, that the foole can never bee honest, since (not beeynge able to ballance what poyntes vertue standes uppon) every present occasion catches his senses, and his senses are Masters of his silly mynde: yet for countenaunce sake, hee seemed very squeymish (in respect hee had y[e] chardge of the Princes *Pamela*) to accept any new servaunt into his howse. But, suche was the secret operacyon of the golde, helped wth the perswasion of the Amazon *Cleophila* (who saide yt was pity so proper a younge man shoulde bee any where else, then with so good a Master) that, in the ende hee agreed to receyve him for his Servaunt: So as, that day in theyre pastoralles, hee prooved him self active in mynde and body: And thus went they to the Lodge, wth greater joy to *Musidorus* (nowe onely pore Shepearde *Dorus*) then all his lyfe before had ever brought forthe unto him; so manifest yt ys, that the greatest poynte owteward thinges can bringe a man unto, ys the Contentment of mynde (w[ch] once obteyned) no estate ys miserable, and wthoute y^t no Princes state restfull. There founde they *Ginecia* with her twoo Daughters, redy to goo to the Meadowe, whither allso, they went: For, as for *Basilius* hee desyered to stay behynde them, to debate a litle wth him self of this newe guest that had entered and possessed his braynes: There yt ys sayde the pore olde *Basilius* beeyng nowe alone (for as I sayde, the rest were goñ to see the Pastoralles) had a sufficyent Eglogue in his owne head, betuixt Honor, with the longe experience hee had had of the worlde on the one syde, and this new assaulte of *Cleophilas* beauty, on the other syde. There hard by the Lodge walked hee, carrying this unquyet contention aboute him, but, passion ere longe, had gotten the absolute Masterhood, bringing wth yt the shewe of present pleasure fortifyed wth ye autority of a Prince, whose power mighte easily satisfy his will ageanst ye farr fett (thoughe true) reasons of the Spirite, whiche in a man not trayned in the way of vertue, hathe but slender worcking: So that ere longe hee utterly gave him self over to the Longing desyer, to enjoy *Cleophila*, whiche fynding an olde broken vessell of him, had more power in him then perchaunce yt would have had in a younger man, and so, as all vyce ys foolish, yt wroughte in him the more absurde follye. But, thus as I say, in a nomber of intermixed imaginacyons hee stayed solitary by the Lodge, wayting, for the returne of his Company from ye pastoralles some good space of tyme: Till hee was sodenly stirred oute of his deepe muses, by the hasty and fearefull ronning unto him, of moste parte of the Shepeardes, who came flying from the pastorall sportes, cryinge one to an other, to stay and save the *Duchess* & younge Ladyes. But, even whilest they cryed so, they ranne away as fast as they Coulde so that the one tumbled over the other, eche one shewing hee woulde bee glad, his fellow shoulde doo valyantly, but his owne harte served him not. The *Duke* amased to see suche extreme shewes of feare asked the matter of them, but, feare had so possessed theyre Inwarde partes, that theyre breathe coulde not serve to tell him, But after suche a broken maner, that I thinke yt not best, to truble yo^w, fayre Ladyes, with theyre panting speeches, but, to make a full Declaracõn of yt my self, and thus yt was. *Ginecia* with her twoo Daughters, *Cleophila* the Shepeardes *Dorus* and *Dametas* beeyng parted from y^e *Duke* whome they lefte solitary at the Lodge, came into the fayre Meadowe appoynted for theyre Shepeardish pastymes: It was in deede a place of greate delighte, for throughe the middest of yt there ranne a sweete brooke, whiche did bothe holde the eye open wth her beutyfull streames, and close the eye with the sweete purling noyse yt made upon ye pible stones yt rañ over. The Meadow yt self yeelding so liberally all sortes of flowers, that yt seemed to norish a Contention betuixt the Coloure and the smell, whether in his kynde were the more delightfull: Rounde aboute the Meadowe (as yf yt had beene to enclose a Theater) grewe all suche sorte of Trees, as eyther excellency of fruite, statelynes of grouthe, continuall greeñes, or Poeticall fancyes have made at any tyme famous. In moste parte of wch Trees, there had bene framed by Arte, suche plesant Arboures, that yt became a gallery a lofte from one Tree to the other, allmoste rounde aboute, whiche beelowe yeelded a perfect shadowe, in those whott Contryes counted a greate pleasure: In this place, under one of these Trees the Ladyes satt downe, inquiring many questyons of younge *Dorus*, now newly perceyved of them. Whilest the other Shepeardes made them redy to the pastymes, *Dorus* keeping his eye still uppon ye Princess *Pamela*, answered with suche a trembling voyce, and abasshed Countenaunce, and often tymes so farr from the matter, that yt was some sporte to the Ladyes, thinking yt had bene wante of education wch made him so discountenaunced with unwonted presence: But *Cleophila* that sawe in him the glasse of her owne misery, taking ye faire hande of *Philoclea*, and with more then womanish ardency, kissing yt began to say these wordes. O Love, sithe thow arte inchangeable to mens estates, howe arte thow so Constant in theyre tormentes? when, sodenly, there came oute of the wood, a monsterus Lyon, with a shee Beare, of litle less fercenes, whiche having beene hunted in forrestes farr of had by chaunce cõme to this place, where suche Beastes had never before bene seene. Whiche when the Shepeardes sawe, like silly wretches that thinke all evill ys ever next them selves, rañ away in suche sorte, as I have tolde yo^w, till they came to y^e *Dukes* presence: There, mighte one have seene at one instant, all sortes of passyons lyvely paynted oute in the younge Lovers faces, an extremity of Love shyning in theyre eyes, feare for theyre Mistresses, assured hope in theyre owne vertue, Anger

42

ageanst the Beastes, Joy, that occasion employed theyre services, sorrowes, to see theyre Ladyes in agony: For in deede, the sweete *Philoclea* no sooner espyed the Ravenus Lyon, but, that, opening her armes shee fell so righte upon the brest of *Cleophila*, sitting by her, that theyre faces at unawares closed together whiche so transported all what so ever *Cleophila* was, that shee gave leysure to the Lyon to come very nere them, before shee ridd her self from the dere Armes of *Philoclea*. But, necessity, the onely over Ruler of affections did force her then gently to unfolde her self from those sweete embracementes, and so drawing her sworde wayted the present assaute of the Lyon: who seeyng *Philoclea* flee away, sodenly turned after her, for as-soone as shee had risen up with *Cleophila*, shee rañ as fast as her delicate legges woulde carry her towardes the Lodge, after the fugitive Shepeardes. But *Cleophila*, seeyng how greedily the Lyon went after the Praye (shee her self so muche desyered) yt seemed all her Spirites were kindled with an unwonted feare, so that, equalling the Lyon, in swiftnes, shee overtooke him, as hee was redy to have seized him self of this beutyfull chase: And disdeynfully saying, are yow become my Competitour?, thrust the Lyon throughe the brest, farr into the body, yet, the valyant Beast came with all so farr upon the weapen, that with his pawe, hee gave a sore wounde to the lefte shoulder of *Cleophila*: And mortall yt woulde have bene, had not the Deathe wounde hee receyved, allredy, taken away the greatest effect of his force, but, therewithall hee fell downe, and gave *Cleophila* leysure to take of his heade, to carry yt for a present to her Lady *Philoclea*. Who, all this while, not knowyng, what was done behynde her, kept on her Course, as *Arethusa*, when shee rañ from *Alpheus*, her light *Nimphlyk* apparell beeyng carryed up with the wynde, that, muche of those beutyes shee woulde at an other tyme have willingly hidden, were presented to the eye of the twyce wounded *Cleophila*: wᶜʰ made *Cleophila* not followe her over hastely, leste shee shoulde too soone deprive her self of that pleasure. But carrying the Lyons heade in her hande, did not fully over take her, till, they came, bothe into yᵉ presence of *Basilius*, at that tyme examening the Shepeardes, of what was past, and preparing him self to come to theyre succoure: Neither were they longe there, but, that *Ginecia* came to them, whose looke had all this while bene uppon the

Combate eying so fixedly *Cleophilas* maner of feighting, that no feare did preveyle over her. But, assoone as *Cleophila* had cutt of his heade, and rañ after *Philoclea*, shee coulde not fynde in her harte, but to ronne likewyse after *Cleophila*, so that yt was a newe sighte fortune had prepared to those woodes, to see these three greate Personages thus rone one after the other: Eche carryed away with the vyolence of an Inwarde evell, the sweete *Philoclea*, with suche feare, that shee thoughte shee was still in the Lyons mowthe, *Cleophila* with a paynefull delighte shee had to see, withoute hope of enjoying, *Ginecia*, not so muche with the love shee bare to her best beloved Daughter, as with a newe wonderfull passionate love had possessed her harte of the goodly *Cleophila*. For so the truthe ys that, at the first sighte shee had of *Cleophila*, her harte gave her, shee was a man, thus for some straunge Cause disguysed, whiche now in effect this Combate did assure her of, bycause shee measured the possibility of all woemens hartes, oute of her owne. And this Doubte framed a Desyer in her to knowe, and desyer to knowe brought forthe shortly suche a longing to enjoy, that yt reduced her whole mynde to an extreme and unfortunate slavery, pitifully truely considering her beuty and estate. But for a perfect marcke of the Tryumphe of Love, who coulde in one moment overthrowe the harte of a wyse Lady, so, y^t neyther Honor longe meynteyned, nor Love of husband and Children coulde withstand yt, but of that yo^w shall after heare: For, now, they beeyng come before the *Duke*, and the fayre *Philoclea* scarcely then stayed from her feare, *Cleophila* kneeling downe presented the heade of ye Lyon unto her wth these wordes. Onely Lady saide shee, here see yo^w the punishment of that unnaturall beast, wch contrary to his owne kynde woulde have wronged Princess blood, neither were his eyes vanquishd with the Duety all eyes beare to youre beuty: Happy am I and my beuty bothe answered the faire *Philoclea* (the blood coming ageane to her Cheekes pale before for feare) that yow Excellent Amazon were there to teache him good mañers. And even thancke that beuty, saide *Cleophila*, wch forceth all noble swordes to bee redy to serve yt. Having finisshed these wordes the Lady *Philoclea* perceyved the blood that rañ abundãtly downe uppon *Cleophilas* shoulder, so that starting asyde wth a countenãce full of sweete

44

pity: Alas, (saide shee) now I perceyve my good happ ys wayted on with great misfortune, synce my savety ys wroughte wth the Daunger of a muche more worthy person. Noble Lady (answered shee) yf youre Inward eyes coulde discerne the woundes of my sowle, yow shoulde have a plentifuller Cause to exercyse youre Compassyon: But yt was sporte to see howe in one instant bothe *Basilius* & *Ginecia* (like a Father and Mother to a beloved Chylde) came ronning to see the wounde of *Cleophila*, into what rages *Basilius* grewe, and what teares *Ginecia* spent: For yt seemed that Love had purposed, to make in those solitary woodes, a perfect Demonstration of his unresistable force, to shewe that no Dezart place can avoyde his Darte hee must flie from him self that will shonne his evill. But so wonderfull and in effect incredible, was the passion wch rayned aswell in *Ginecia*, as *Basilius* and all for the pore *Cleophila* dedicated, an other way: That yt seemes to my self I use not wordes enowe to make yow see, how they coulde in one moment bee so overtaken. But, yow worthy Ladyes, that have at any tyme feelingly knowne what yt meanes, will easily beleeve the possibility of yt, let the ignorant sorte of people give credit unto them that have passed the Dolefull passage, and duely fynde, that quickly ys the infection gotten, whiche in longe tyme ys hardly cured: *Basilius* woulde kisse her forehead, blessing the Destenyes that had joyned suche beuty and valour together, *Ginecia* woulde kisse her more boldly by the liberty of her womanish shewe, allthough her hart were sett on no thinge Lesse. For allredy was shee fallen into a Jelous envy agenst her Daughter *Philoclea*, bycause shee found *Cleophila* shewed suche extraordenary dutifull favour unto her, and even that setled her opinion ye more of her Manhood: And this doubtfull Jelousy served as a Bellowse to kyndle the vyolent Coles of her passion, but as the overkynde Nurse may some tymes with kissing forgett to give the Chylde suck, so had they with twoo muche kyndenes unkyndly forgotten the wounde of *Cleophila*, had not *Philoclea* (whose harte had not yet goñ beyond the limittes of a right good will) advysed her self, and desyerd her Mother to help her, to dress the wounde of *Cleophila*. For bothe those greate Ladyes were excellently seene in that parte of surgery, an Arte in that Age greatly esteemed, bycause yt served as a Minister to vertuous Corage: whiche in those worthy dayes, was even by Ladyes more beloved, then any owteward bewty. So that to the great Comfort of *Cleophila* more to feele the delicate handes of *Philoclea*, then for ye Care shee had of her wounde, these twoo Ladyes had quickly dressed yt, applying so precyous a balme, as all the heate and payne was asswaged with aparant hope of some amendement: In wch dooyng I know not whether *Ginecia* tooke some greater Conjectures of *Cleophilas* sexe. But even then and not before, did *Cleophila* remember her self of her dere frende *Musidorus*, for having onely had Care of ye excellent *Philoclea*, shee neyther missed her frende, nor the Princess *Pamela*: Not somuche to bee marveyled at in her, since bothe the *Duke* and *Duchess* had forgotten theyre Daughter, so were all theyre thoughtes plunged in one place. Besydes *Cleophila* had not seene any daunger was like to falle unto him, for her eye had still bene fixed uppon *Philoclea*, and that made her ye more Careles: But nowe with a kynde of rysing in her harte, leste some evill shoulde befalle unto her chosen frende, shee hastely asked what was become of the Princess *Pamela* with the twoo Shepeardes *Dametas* & *Dorus*. And then the *Duke* and *Ginecia* remembred theyre forgetfullnes, and with greate astonishment made like inquiry for her: But of all the Company of the Shepeardes (so had the Lyons sighte putt them from them selves) there was but one, that coulde say any thinge of her, & all hee sayde was this, that as hee rañ away, hee might perceyve a greate Beare rone directly towardes her. *Cleophila* (whose corage was allwayes redy withoute deliberacyon) tooke up the sworde lyinge by her, with mynde to bestow her lyfe for the succour or Revenge of her *Musidorus* and the gracyous *Pamela*: But as shee had rone twoo or three steppes, they mighte all see *Pamela* coming betwixt *Dametas* & *Dorus*. *Pamela* having in her hand the pawe of the Beare, wch the Shepeard *Dorus* had newly presented unto her, desyering her to keepe yt as of suche a Beast, whiche thoughe shee was to bee punished for her over great Cruelty, yet, was her witt to bee esteemed, since shee coulde make so sweete a Choyse: *Dametas*, for his parte, came pyping and Daunsing, the merryest man of a parrishe, but when hee came so nere, as hee might bee hearde of the *Duke*, hee sange this Songe, for Joy of theyre success.

Now thancked bee the great god Pan,
　That thus preserves my loved lyfe:
Thancked bee I that keepe A man,
　Who ended hathe this fearefull stryfe.
So, yf my Man must prayses have;
　What then must I, that keepe the knave?

For, as the Moone the eye dothe please,
　With gentle beames not hurting sighte:
Yet hathe Sir Sunn *the greatest prayse,*
　Bycause from him dothe come her lighte.
So, yf my man must prayses have;
　What then must I, that keepe the knave?

Yt were a very superfluous thinge to tell yoᵂ, how glad eche
party was of the happy returning from those daungers: And
doubt yow not, fayre Ladyes, there wanted no questioning how
thinges had passed, but bycause I will have the thanckes my
self, yt shall bee I yow shall heare yt of, And thus the Auncyent
Recordes of *Arcadia* say, yt fell owte. The Lyons presence had
no sooner driven away the hartless Shepeardes, and followed, as
I tolde yoᵂ the excellent *Philoclea*, but that there came oute of
the same woodes a monsterus shee Beare, whiche fearing to
deale with the Lyons pray, came furyously towardes the
Princess *Pamela*: who whether yt were, shee had heard, that
suche was the best refuge ageanst yᵗ Beast, or that feare, (as yt
fell oute moste likely) broughte forthe yᵉ effectes of wisdome,
shee, no sooner sawe the Beare coming towardes her, but, shee
fell downe flatt uppon her face. Whiche when the Prince
Musidorus sawe (whome bycause suche was his pleasure, I am
bolde to calle the Shepearde *Dorus*) with a true Resolved
magnanimity allthoughe hee had no other weapon, but a great
Shepeardes knyfe, hee lepte before the heade of his dere Lady,
and (saying these wordes unto her, receyve here the sacrifice of
that harte, whiche ys onely vowed to youre service) attending
with a quyet Corage, the Coming of yᵉ Beare, whiche according
to the maner of that Beastes feighte (especially agenst A man
that resistes them) rose up uppon her hinder feete, so to take
him in her ougly pawes: But as shee was redy to give him a
mortall embrasement, The Shepeard *Dorus*, with a lusty strengthe
& good fortune thrust his knyfe so righte into the harte of the

Beaste, that shee fell downe Dead, withoute ever beeyng able to tuche him. Whiche beeyng done, hee turned to his Lady *Pamela*, at that tyme in a swounde with extremity of feare, and softely taking her in his Armes, hee tooke the advauntage to kisse and rekiss her a hundred tymes, with suche exceeding delighte that hee woulde often after say, hee thoughte the Joy woulde have carryed his lyfe from him, had not the greef hee conceyved to see her in suche Case some thing Diminisshed yt: But, longe, in that delightfull agony hee was not, for the Lady *Pamela*, beeyng come oute of her sounde, opened her fayre eyes, and seeyng her self in the handes of this Newcome Shepehearde, with greate disdayne putt him from her. But when shee sawe the Ougly Beare lying by her, starting asyde (for, feare gave not reason leave to determeyn whether yt were Deade or noo) shee forgatt her anger, and cryed to *Dorus* to help her: wherefore, hee cutting of the fore pawe of the Beare, and shewyng unto her ye bloody knyfe, toulde her, shee mighte well perceyve by this, that there was no harte so base, nor weapon so feeble, but, that the force of her beuty was well able, to enable them for the performance of great matters. Shee enquyring the maner, and whether him self were hurte, gave him great thanckes for his paynes, with promyse of Rewarde: But, beeynge asshamed to fynde her self so alone with this younge Shepearde, looked rounde aboute, yf shee coulde see any body, and at lengthe they bothe perceyved the gentle *Dametas*, lyinge with his head and brest, as farr as hee coulde thrust him self into a Busshe, drawyng up his Legges as close unto him, as hee coulde. For, in deede, assoone as hee sawe ye Beare coming towardes them, (Like a man that was very apte to take pitty of him self) hee ran headlonge into this Bussh, with full resolution, y^t at the worst hand hee woulde not see his owne deathe: And when *Dorus* pusshed him, bidding him bee of good Corage, yt was a great while, before hee coulde perswade him, that *Dorus* was not the Beare, so that, hee was fayne to pull him oute by the heeles, and shewe him her as Deade as hee coulde wishe her, whiche yow may beleeve was a very joyfull sighte unto him. And yet like a man of a Revengefull spirite, hee gave the deade body many a wounde, swearing by muche yt was pitty, suche Beastes shoulde bee suffered in a Comon Welthe: And then with as imoderate Joye, as before with feare (for his harte was

48

framed never to bee withoute a passyon) hee went by his fayre charge, daunsing, pyping, and singing, till they all came to the presence of the carefull Company, as before I tolde yow. Thus nowe this litle, (but Noble) Company united ageane together, the first thinge was done, was the yeelding of the greate thanckes and prayses of all sydes, to the vertuous *Cleophila*: The *Duke* tolde with what a gallant grace shee ranñ after *Philoclea* with the Lyons heade in her hande, like an other *Pallas* with the spoyles of *Gorgon*. *Ginecia* sware, shee sawe the very face of younge *Hercules* killing yᵉ *Nemean* Lyon, and all with a gratefull assent confirmed yᵉ same prayses; Onely pore *Dorus* (thoughe of equall desert) yet, not proceeding from equall estate, shoulde have bene lefte forgotten, had not *Cleophila*, (partely to putt by the occasion of her owne excessive prayses but principally for the true remembrance shee had of her professed frende), with great admiracion spoken of his hazardous acte, asking a fressh (as yf hee had never before knowne him) what hee was, and whether hee had haunted that place before: Protesting, that uppon her Conscyence, shee coulde not thinck, but that hee came of some very Noble blood, so noble a Countenaunce hee bare, and so worthy an acte hee had performed.

This, *Basilius* tooke, (as the Lovers harte ys apte to receyve all sodeyn sortes of impression) as thoughe his Mistris, had given him a secrett reprehension, that hee had not shewed more gratefullnes to yᵉ valiant *Dorus*: And therefore, as nymbly as hee coulde, began forthewith to enquyer of his estate, adding promyse of greate Rewardes, amonge the rest, offering him that, yf hee woulde exercyse his valure in Souldyery, hee woulde Committ some charge unto him under *Philanax* governour of his frontiers: But, *Dorus*, whose Ambicion stretched a quyte other way, having first answered (tuching his estate) that hee was brother to the Shepeard *Menalcas*, whome the *Duke* had well knowne and excused his goynge to Souldyery, by the unaptnes hee founde in him self that way, toulde the *Duke* that his Brother in his last Testament had commaunded him to dedicate his service to *Dametas*: And therefore, aswell for the Due obeydyence thereto as for the satisfaction of his owne mynde (whiche was wholly sett upon pastorall affaires) hee woulde thincke his service greatly rewarded, yf hee mighte by that meanes obtayne, to live in the sighte of yᵉ *Duke*, more then the rest of his fellowes, and yet practize that his chosen vocation. The *Duke* liking well of his modest maner charged *Dametas* to receyve him like a sonne in his howse telling hym, bycause of his tryed valor, hee woulde have him bee as a Guarde to his Daughter *Pamela*: To whome likewyse hee recomended him, sticking not to say, suche men were to bee cherisshed, since shee was in danger of some secrett mysadventure. All this while *Pamela* saide litle of him and even as litle did *Philoclea* of *Cleophila*, allthoughe every body else filled theyre mouthes with theyre prayses: Wherof seeking the Cause, yᵗ they whiche moste were bounde, sayde leste, I note this to my self (faire Ladyes) That, eeven at this tyme they did begin to fynde, they them selves coulde not tell, what kynde of inclinacyon towardes them. Whereof feeling a secret accusation in them selves, and in theyre simplicity not able to warraunt yt, closed up all suche motion in secrett, withoute daring scarcely to breathe oute the Names of them, who allredy began to breede unwonted warr in theyre Spirites: For in deede, Fortune had framed a very stage play of Love amonge these fewe folkes, making the Olde age of *Basilius* the vertue of *Ginecia*, and the simplicity of *Philoclea*, all affected to one. But, by a three kynde of passyon, *Basilius* assuring him self shee was (as shee pretended) a younge Lady, but greatly dispayring for his owne unworthynes sake, *Ginecia* hoping her Judgment to bee Righte of his disguysing: But, therein fearing a greater sore yf his harte were pledged to his Daughter. But, sweete *Philoclea* grewe shortly after of all other into worste Terme, for taking her to bee suche as shee professed, desyer shee did, but shee knewe not what: And shee longed to obteyne that, wherof shee her self coulde not imagyn the Name, but full of unquyet imaginacyons, rested onely unhappy, bycause shee knewe not her good happ. *Cleophila* hathe (I thincke) sayde ynoughe for her self, to make yow knowe (fayre Ladyes) that shee was not a litle enchaunted: And as for *Dorus*, a Shepeardes Apparell uppon the *Duke* of *Thessalia* will answer for him. *Pamela* was the onely Lady that woulde needes make open warr upon her self, and obteyne the victory, for, in deede even now fynde shee did, a certeyne worcking of a newe come Inclination to *Dorus*: But, when shee founde perfectly in her self whether yt must drawe her, shee did over master yt, with the Consideracyon of his meañenes: But, how therein *Dorus* soughte to satisfy her, yo^w shall after heare, For, now the Day beeyng closed up in darckenes the *Duke* woulde fayne have had *Cleophila* goñ to rest bycause of the late receyved wounde: But, shee that founde no better salve, then *Philocleas* presence, desyered first, that by Torche lighte, they mighte see some of the pastoralles the Lyons coming had disordered, whiche accordingly was done: whereof I will repeate a fewe, to ease yow fayre Ladyes of the tedyousnes of this longe discourse.

Here endes The Firste Booke, or Acte.

HERE BEGINS. THE FIRSTE EGLOGUES

The maner of the *Arcadian* Shepeardes was when they
mett, together, to pass theyre tyme eyther in suche Musick, as
theyre Rurall education woulde afforde them, or in exercyse of
theyre body, and tryinge of Masteryes: But, of all other thinges
they did especially delighte in Eglogues, wherein, they woulde
some tyme contend for a pryze of well singing, sometymes
lament the unhappy pursuite of theyre afflictions, some tymes
ageane under hidden formes, utter suche matter, as otherwyse
were not fitt for theyre Delivery. Neyther ys yt to bee
marveyled, that they did so muche excell other Natyons in that
quality, since from theire Chyldehood, they were brought up
unto yt, and were not suche base Shepeardes, as wee comonly
make accoumpte of: But, the very Owners of the Sheepe them
selves, whiche in that thrifty worlde, the substancyallest Men
woulde employ theyre whole Care uppon. And when they had
practized the goodnes of theyre Wittes in suche sportes, then
was yt theyre maner, ever to have one, who shoulde wryte up
ye substance of that they saide: Whose penñ having more
leysure, then theyre tungues, might perchaunce pullish a litle
the Rudenes of an unthought on songe. But the peace wherein
they did so notably florish (and specially the sweete enjoyng of
theyre peace to so pleasant uses) drew dyvers strauggers aswell
of greate, as meane howses; Especially suche, whome inwarde
Melancholyes, made weary of the Worldes eyes, to come and
live amonge them, applying them selves to theyre trade, whiche
likewyse was many tymes occasyon to beutify more, (then
otherwyse yt woulde have bene) this pastorall exercyse. But, no
thing did lifte yt up to so highe a key, as the presence of theyre
owne *Duke*, who not onely by looking on, but, by greate
Curtesy and Liberality animated the Shepeardes the more
exquisitely, to seek a worthy accomplishment, of his good liking:
As this tyme after the valyant killing of the Beastes, by the
twoo Disguysed Princes performed. The *Duke*, (because
Cleophila so woulde have yt) used the Artificiall day of Torches,
to lighten the sportes, theyre Inventions coulde minister: And
yet, bycause many mo Shepeardes were newly come, then at
5²

the first were, hee did with a gentle maner chastize the Cowardize of the fugitive Shepeardes, with making them (for that nighte) bee Torchebearers, and the others later come, hee willed with all freedome of speeche, and behavyour to keepe theyre accustomed Methode, whiche they prepared them selves to doo, whilest hee satt him self downe, having on the one syde the *Duchess*, but of his hart syde the faire *Cleophila*, whose eyes seemed to have chaunged sighte with *Philoclea's* eyes (whome *Ginecia* had of purpose placed by her self) so attentive Lookes were mutually fixed betweene them, to the greatest Corosy to *Ginecia*, that can bee imagined: whose Love open sighte did more and more perse into the knowledge of *Cleophila's* counterfeting, whiche likewyse more and more fortefyed her unlawfull Desyers, yet with so great, and vyolent a Combatt with her self, as the suppression of a longe used vertue comes to. But, an other place shall serve, to manifest her Agonyes, this beeyng dedicated onely to pastoralls, shall bend yt self y^t way, and leave all these Princely motions, to theyre Consideracyons, that (untoulde) can gess what Love meanes: Whereof the Princess *Pamela*, that sate next to *Cleophila* was moste free, having in her mynde used *Dorus* basenes, as a shielde ageanst his worthynes. But, they, beeyng sett in order, *Dametas*, who muche disdayned (since his late auctority) all his oulde Companyons, brought his servãt *Dorus* in good acqueyntance of them: And him self stoode like a Director over them, with nodding, gaping, wincking, or stamping, shewyng howe hee did like, or myslike those thinges hee did not understand. The first Sportes the Shepeardes shewed, were full of suche Leapes and gamboldes, (as beeyng accorded to the pype whiche they bare in theyre mouthes eeven as they daunsed) made a right picture of theyre Cheef god *Pan*, and his Companyons the Satyres: Then, woulde they cast away theyre pypes, and holding hand in hand, daunce as yt were in a Brawle, by the onely Cadence of theyre voyces. W^{ch} they woulde use in singing some shorte Couplettes whereto the one half beginning, the other half answered: As, the one half saying, *Wee love, and have oure Loves rewarded*; the others woulde answer, *Wee love, and are no whitt regarded*. The first ageane, *Wee fynde moste sweete affections snaire*: with like tyme, yt shoulde bee (as in a Quiere)

sent back ageane, *That sweete, but sowre dispayrefull care.* A
thirde tyme likewyse thus, *Who can dispayre, whome hope dothe
beare?*: The answer, *And who can hope, who feeles dispayre?*.
Then all joyning theyre voyces, and daunsing a faster measure,
they woulde conclude with some suche wordes, *As withoute
breathe, no Pype dothe moove; No Musick kyndly withoute Love.*
Having thus varyed bothe theyre Songes and Daunses into
dyvers sortes of Inventions, theyre last sporte was one of them
to provoke an other, to a more large expressing of his passyons:
For whiche, *Lalus* a Shepearde (accoumpted one of ye best
singers amonge them) having marcked in *Dorus* daunsing, no
less good grace and handsome behavyour, then extreme tokens
of a trubled mynde hee began first with his pype, and then with
his voyce thus to chalenge *Dorus*, and was by him answered in
the under written sorte.

Lalus. *Come* Dorus *come, Let Songes thy sorrowes signify,*
　　　　And, yf for want of use thy mynde ashamed ys,
　　　That very shame, with Loves hye tytle Dignify:
　　No style ys helde for base, where Love well named ys.
　　　　Eche eare suckes up the wordes a true Love scattereth,
　　　　*And playne speeche ofte, then quaynte phrase better
　　　　framed ys.*

Dorus. *Nightingales sildome singe, the Pye still chattereth,*
　　　　The wood cryes moste, before yt throwly kindled bee,
　　　Deadly woundes inward bleede, eche sleight sore mattereth:
　　Hardly they hearde, wch by good Hunters singled bee,
　　　　*Shallow brookes murmer moste, Depe sylent slyde
　　　　away,*
　　　　*Nor true Love Loves, his Loves with others mingled
　　　　bee.*

Lalus. *Yf thow wilt not bee seene, thy face goo hyde away,*
　　　　Bee none of us, or else meynteyne oure fashyon,
　　　Who frownes at others feastes, dothe better byde away,
　　　But yf thow haste a Love in that Loves passyon
　　　　I Challenge thee by shewe of her perfection
　　　　Whiche of us Twoo deserveth moste Compassyon.

Dorus. *Thy Chalenge greate, but greater my protection,*
    Singe then, and see, for now thow haste enflamed
      mee,
    Thy healthe to meane a Matche for my infection,
    No though the Heavens for highe Attempt have blamed
      mee
      Yet, highe ys myne Attempt (O Muse) *historify*
      Her prayse, whose prayse to learne, youre skill hathe
      framed mee.

Lalus. *Muse, holde youre peace, but thow my God* Pan *glorify,*
    My Kalas *giftes, who with all good giftes filled ys.*
    Thy Pype (O Pan) *shall help, thoughe I singe sorily,*
    A heape of sweetes shee ys where no thing spilled ys;
      Who, thoughe shee bee no Bee, yet full of hony ys
      A Litle feelde, with plowe of Rose wch tilled ys.

idem. *Mylde as a Lambe, more deynty than a Cony ys,*
    Her eyes my eye sighte ys, her Conversacyon,
    More glad to mee, then to a Myser mony ys :
    What Coy accoumpte shee makes of estimacyon,
      Howe nice to tuche, how all her speeches peized
      bee,
      A Nimphe *thus turned, but mended in translation.*

Dorus. *Suche* Kala *ys, but, Ah, my fancyes raysed bee,*
    In one whose name, to name were highe presumption,
    Synce vertues all to make her Tytle pleased bee,
    O happy goddes, wch by Inward assumption;
      Enjoy her sowle, in bodyes fayre possession,
      And keepe yt joyned fearing youre Seates consump-
      tion.

idem. *Howe ofte with rayne of teares, Skyes make Confession,*
    Theyre Duellers rapt with sighte of her perfection,
    From heavenly throane to her heaven use digression:
    Of best thinges then, what worlde can yeelde confection,
      To licken her, deck youres with youre Comparyson
      She ys herself of best thinges the Collection.

Lalus.   *Howe ofte my Dolefull* Sire, *cryed to mee, tarry, sonne,*
      (When firste hee spyde my Love) howe ofte hee saide to mee,
    Thow arte no Souldyer fitt for Cupides *guarryson,*
    My sonne keepe this, that my long toyle hathe layde to mee,
      Love well thyne owne (mee thincke) wolles whitenes passeth all.
      I never founde longe Love, suche wealthe hathe payde to mee,

idem.   *This wynde, hee spent, but when my* Kala *glasseth all*
      My sighte, in her faire Lym̃es, I then assure my self,
    Not rotten sheepe, but hye Crownes, shee surpasseth all,
    Can I bee pore, that her golde hayer procure my self.
      Want I white woolle, whose eyes her white skinne garnished?
      Till I gett her, shall I to keepe enure my self?

Dorus.   *Howe ofte when reason sawe Love of her harnished,*
      With Armor of my harte hee cryed, O, vanitye?
    To sett a Perle in steele, so meanely varnished?
    Looke to thy self, reache not beyonde humanity?
      Her mynde, beames, state, farr from thy weyke winges banished
      And Love whiche Lover hurtes ys inhumanity.

idem.   *Thus reason sayde, but shee came, reason vanished,*
      Her eyes so mastering mee, that suche objection
    Seemde but to spoyle the foode of thought longe famished;
    Her pereles heighte, my mynde to hye erection,
      Drawes up, and yf (hope fayling) ende lyves pleasure,
      Of fayrer Deathe how can I make election.

Lalus.   *Once my well wayting eyes espyed my treasure*
      With sleeves turnde up, loose hayer, and brestes enlarged,
    Her Fathers Corne mooving, her fayres Lym̃es measure,
    O (Cryed I) of so meane worcke bee discharged?
      Measure my Case, how by thy Beutyes fillinge
      With seede of woes, my harte brym̃full ys charged.

idem.   *Thy Father biddes thee save, and Chydes for spilling,*
     Save then my sowle, spill not my thoughtes well heaped,
     No Lovely prayse was ever gott by killinge,
     These bolde wordes shee did heare, this fruite I reaped,
       That shee whose Looke alone mighte make mee blessed
       Did smyle on mee, and then away shee leaped.

Dorus. *O sweete, once, I sawe with Drede oppressed,*
     Her whome I Drede, so that, with prostrate lying,
     Her Lengthe the earthe in Loves cheef Clothing dressed,
     I sawe that Richess falle, and fell a Cryinge,
       Lett not deade Earthe enjoy so deare a Cover,
       But Deck there with my sowle, for youre sake dyinge.

Idem.   *Lay all youre feare uppon youre Fearefull Lover;*
     Shyne eyes on mee, that bothe oure Lyves bee guarded;
     So I youre sighte, yo^w shall youre selves recover,
     I cryed, and was with open Rayes, rewarded,
       But, streight they fledd, summond' by crewell honor,
       Honor, the Cause, Desert ys not regarded.

Lalus. *This Mayde thus made for joyes, (O Pan) bemone her,*
     That withoute Love, shee spendes her yeares of Love,
     So fayre a feelde woulde well become an Owner,
     And yf enchauntement can a hard harte moove,
       Teache mee what Circle can acquaynte her spirite
       Affections charmes in my behalf to proove.
     The Circle ys my (Rounde aboute her) sighte
     The power I will Invoke dwelles in her eyes
     My Charme shoulde bee, shee haunte mee day and nighte.

Dorus. *Farr other Case, (O Muse) my sorrowe tryes,*
     Bent to suche one in whome my self must saye,
     No thing can mende one poynte, that in her lyes:
     What Circle then in so rare force beares sway,

57

Whose spirit all Spirites can spoyle, rayse, dampne or save,
No Charme holdes her, but well possess shee may
Possess shee dothe and makes my sowle her Slave,
My eyes the bandes, my thoughtes the fatall knott,
No thralles like them, that Inwarde bondage have.

Lalus. *Kala, at lengthe conclude my Lingering Lott,*
Disdayne mee not, allthoughe I bee not fayre,
Who ys an heyre, of many hundred sheepe
Dothe beutyes kepe, whiche never sone can burne,
Nor stormes do turne, fayrenes serves ofte to wealthe.
Yet, all my healthe, I place in youre good will.

idem. *Whiche, yf yow will, (O Doo) bestowe on mee,*
Suche as yow see, suche still yow shall mee fynde,
Constant, and kynde, my sheepe youre foode shall breede,
Theyre woolle youre weede, I will yo^w musick yeelde,
In flowery fielde, and as the day beginnes,
With Twenty ginnes, wee will the smalle Byrdes take,
And pastymes make, as Nature thinges hathe made,
But when in shade, wee meete of Mirtle bowes,
Then Love allowes, Oure pleasures to enriche,
The thoughte of whiche, dothe pass all worldly pelf.

Dorus. *Lady youre self, whome neyther name I dare,*
And tytles are, but spottes to suche a worthe,
Her playntes come forthe, from Dongeon of my mynde,
The Noblest kynde, rejectes not others woes,
I have no shewes of welthe, my Wealthe ys yow,
My Beutyes hew, youre beames, my healthe youre Deedes,
My mynde for weedes, youre vertuous Livery weares,
My foode ys teares, my Tunes Weymenting yeelde.

Idem. *Dispayre my feelde, the flowers, Spirittes, Warres*
   My day newe Cares, my ginnes my daily sighte,
 In whiche do lighte, smalle Byrdes of thoughtes overthrown
   My Pastymes none, Tyme passeth on my falle,
 Nature made all, But mee of Doloures made
   I fynde no shade, But where my sunne dothe burne,
 No place to turne, Withowte, Within yt fryes,
   Nor help by lyfe, or Deathe who living dyes.

Lalus. *But yf my Kala, this my suite denyes,*
   Whiche so muche reason beares:
 Let Crowes pick owte myne eyes,
   Whiche to muche sawe,
 Yf shee still hate loves Lawe, my earthy moulde dothe melt
   in watery teares.

Dorus. *My earthy moulde do melt in watery teares,*
   And they ageane resolve, to ayer of sighes,
 Sighes to the hartes fyer turne, wch dothe to Asshes burne,
   Thus dothe my lyfe within yt self dissolve.

Lalus. *Thus dothe my Lyfe within yt self Dissolve,*
   That I growe like the Beaste,
 Whiche beares the Bitt:
   A weyker force dothe guyde:
 Yet pacyence must abyde.
 Suche weight yt hathe, whiche once ys full possest.

Dorus. *Suche weighte yt hathe, whiche once ys full possest,*
   That I became a Vision,
 Whiche hathe in others hed his onely beeyng,
   And lives in Francyes seeyng,
   O wretched state of man, in self Division?

Lalus. *O wretched state of man in self Division?*
   O, well thow sayest, a feeling declaracion?
 Thy tongue hathe made of Cupides deepe incision,
   But now hoârse voyce dothe fayle this occupacyon.
 And others longe to tell theyre Loves Condicion,
 Of singing, thow haste gott the Reputacyon.

59

Dorus. *Of singing, thow haste gott the Reputacyon,*
    Good Lalus *myne, I yeelde to thy habillity*
    My harte dothe seeke an other estimacyon,
      But, Ah (my Muse) *I woulde thow hadst facility?*
    To worcke my Goddess so by thy Invention;
    On mee to cast those eyes, where shyne Nobility,
    Seene & knowne, hearde, but, withoute attention.

The Eglogue betuixt *Lalus* and *Dorus* of every one of the Beholders receyved greate Commendacyon, savinge onely of the twoo grave Shepeardes *Geron*, and *Dicus* : who bothe playnely protested yt was pity witt shoulde bee employde aboute so very a Toye, as that (they called *Love*) was. *Geron* thereto the more enclyned, as that Age having taken from him, bothe the thoughtes, and the fruites of that passyon, wisshed all the worlde proportioned to him self: But, *Dicus*, whether for certeyne mischaunces of his owne, (or oute of a better judgment whiche sawe the bottome of thinges) did more detest and hate love, then the moste Envyous man dothe in him self cherysh and love, hate. Whiche as hee did at all tymes publiquely profess, so nowe hee came (as a man should say) Armed, to shewe his Malice, for in the one hand hee bare a whipp, in the other, a naked *Cupide*, suche as wee comonly sett him forthe: But, on his Brest hee ware, a paynted Table, wherein hee had given *Cupide* a quite newe forme, making him sitt upon a payre of gallows like a Hangman, aboute whiche there was a Rope very handsomely provyded; hee him self paynted all ragged and torne so that his Skinne was bare in moste places, where a man mighte perceyve his body full of eyes, his heade horned with the hornes of a Bull, with longe eares, accordingly, his face oulde and wrinckled & his feete Cloven. In his Right hand hee was paynted holdinge a Crowne of Lawrell, in his lefte a purse of money, and oute of his mouthe hange a lase, whiche helde the pictures of a goodly man and an excellent fayre woman : And with suche a Countenaunce he was drawne, as yf hee had perswaded every man by those Intisementes, to come and bee hanged there. The *Duke* laughed when hee sawe *Dicus* come oute, in suche maner, and asked him what hee meant, by suche transforming the gentle *Cupid*: But, *Dicus* as yf yt had beene no jeasting matter, toulde him playnely, y^t longe they had done the heavens greate wronge, to make *Cupide* a god, and muche more to the fayre *Venus*, to calle him her sonne, in deede the Basterd of false *Argus*, who having the charge of the Deflowered Io, (what tyme shee was a Cowe) had trayterusly in that shape begott him of her, and that the Naughtynes of mens Lust had given him so highe a Tytle: Every one (except olde *Geron*) began to stamp with theyre feete, and hisse at him, as thinckinge, that hee had spoken an unpardonable blasphemy. But, *Geron* well backing him in yt, *Dicus* bouldly stept forthe, and after having Rayled at the name of *Cupid* as spitefully, as hee coulde devyse, calling to *Pan*, to help his songe in revenge of Losing the fayre Syren,: Hee thus tuning his voyce to a Rebeck, sange ageanst him.

Pore Paynters ofte, with silly Poettes *joyne,*
　To fill the worlde wth straunge but vayne Conceyptes:
One bringes the Stuff, the other stampes the Coyne,
　Whiche breedes nought else but glosses of Deceiptes:
　　Thus Paynters Cupid *paynte, thus* Poettes *doo,*
　　A naked god, blynde, younge, with Arrowes twoo.

Is hee a God, that ever flies the Lighte?
　Or naked hee disguysd' in all untruthe:
Yf hee bee blynde how hitteth hee so righte,
　Or ys hee younge, that tamed oulde Phebus *youthe.*
　　But, Arrowes twoo and tipt wth golde or leade,
　　Some hurt accuse a thirde with horned heade.

No, no thinge so; an oulde false knave hee ys,
　By Argus *gott on* Io, *then a Cowe:*
What tyme for her Juno *her* Jove *did misse,*
　And charge of her to Argus *did allowe.*
　　Mercury *killed his false* Syre *for this Acte:*
　　His Damme a Beast was pardoned beastly facte.

With fathers Deathe, and Mothers guilty shame,
　With Joves *disdayne, at suche a Rivalls seede,*
The wretche compelde, a Rouneagate became;
　And learned what evell a miser state dothe breede,
　　To lye, to steale, to prye and to accuse,
　　Nought in him self eche other to abuse.

Yet, beares hee still his Parentes stately giftes,
  A horned head Cloven feete, and thowsand eyes,
Some gasing still some winckinge wyly shiftes,
   With longe large eares where never Rumor dyes,
      His horned heade dothe seeme the heaven to spighte:
      His Cloven feete dothe never treade arighte,

Thus half a Man, with many easily hauntes,
  Clothde in the shape wch soonest may deceyve,
Thus half a Beast, eche beastly vyce hee plantes,
   In those weyke hartes, that his advyce receyve.
      Hee proulles eche place, still in newe Coloures deckt,
      Sucking ones evill, an other to infect.

To narrow brestes hee comes all wrapte in gayne,
  To swelling hartes hee shynes in honors fyer,
To open eyes all Beutyes hee dothe Rayne,
   Creeping to eche, with flatering of Desyer,
      But, for that Love ys worste wch Rules the eyes,
      Thereon his Name, there his cheef tryumphe lyes.

Millions of yeares this oulde Drivell Cupid *lives,*
   While still more wretche, more wicked hee dothe prove;
Till nowe at lengthe, that Jove *him office gives,*
   At Junos *sute, who muche did* Argus *love:*
      In this oure worlde, a hangman for to bee:
      Of all those fooles, that will have all they see.

Hee had not fully ended his last wordes of his Invective
songe, when, a younge Shepearde named *Histor*, who, (while
Dicus was singing sometymes with his eyes up to heaven, sometymes seeming to stopp his eares, did shew a fearefull myslike of
suche unreverent reproches) with great vehemency desyered all
the heavens to take heede, howe they seemed to allowe any
parte of his speeche, ageanst so Revengefull a God, as *Cupid*
was: who had even in his first Magistracy shewed ageanst
Apollo ye heate of his anger. But, (saide hee) yf yo^w had hearde
or seene suche vyolence of his wrathe, as I even yesterday, and
the other day, have, yow woulde tremble at the recitall of his
name: The *Duke* & all the rest, streighte desyered him to tell,
what that was; And hee (seeming Loathe, lest his wordes
mighte disgrace the Matter) toulde them y^t as hee was twoo

dayes before sitting in the shade of a Busshe, hee did heare the moste wailefull Lamentation of an *Iberian* Nobleman called *Plangus*, (uttered to the wyse Shepearde *Boulon*) that ever hee thoughte any wordes coulde express, and all tuching a pityfull adventure, the grounde and mayntenance wherof was onely *Cupid*: And y^t songe sayde hee (for in a songe I gathered yt) woulde I let yo^w heare, but that for the better understanding I must first repeate ye subject therof. This *Plangus* when no perswasion of the wyse *Boulon* coulde kepe him from the pity-full Complayning of his sorowes, (yet yeelded so muche at my Request) as to harber with mee these last dayes in my simple Caban : where with muche intreatyng hee toulde mee this pity-full Story. That of late there Raigned a *Kinge* of *Lidia* who for the blessing of his mariage had his onely Daughter *Erona*, a Princess worthy for her beuty, asmuche prayse, as beuty may bee praysed. This *Erona* beeyng fourteene yeares olde, seeynge the Contrye of *Lidia* so muche devoted to *Cupid*, as that in eche place, his naked pictures and Images were supersticiously adored, procured so muche of her Father and eyther moved thereunto by the hate of that god, or the shamefast Consideracyon of suche nakednes, utterly to deface and pull downe all those pictures of him : whiche howe terribly hee punisshed, quickly after, appeared, for, shee had not lived a yeare longer, when shee was stricken with moste obstinate Love, to a younge man, but of meane parentage, in her fathers Courte, named, *Anthi-philus*, so meane, as y^t hee was but the sonne of her Nurse, and by y^t meanes came knowne to her. And so evell coulde shee conceale this fyer, and so willfully persevered shee in yt that her Father offering her the Mariage of the greate *Otaves* kinge of *Percia*, (who desyered her more then the Joyes of heaven) shee for *Anthiphilus* sake, refused him : Many wayes her Father did seeke to with drawe her from yt, sometymes perswasions, sometymes threateninges; sometymes hyding *Antiphilus*, and giving her to understand hee was fledd the Contrey, lastly making a solempne execution to bee done of an other, under the name of *Antiphilus*, whome hee kept in prison. But shee neyther liked perswasions nor feared threatninges nor chaunged for absence, and when shee thoughte him deade yt was mani-festly seene, shee saughte all meanes aswell by poyson, as knyfe to followe him : This so brake the Fathers harte with greef, that, leaving thinges as hee founde them, hee shortly after dyed. Then forthewith *Erona*, (beeyng seized of the Crowne) sought to satisfy her mynde with *Antiphilus* mariage, but, before shee coulde accomplish yt shee was overtaken with a crewell warr, the kinge *Otanes* made uppon her; onely for her person: Towardes whome for her Ruyn Love had kindled his crewell harte, in deede crewell & tyrannous, for beeyng farr to stronge in the fielde, hee spared not man, woman nor Chylde, but with miserable tortures slewe them. Allthough his fayre sister *Artaxia* (who accompaned him in the Army) sought all meanes to mollify his Rage: Till lastly hee besieged *Erona* in her best City, vowynge hee woulde have her, eyther by force or otherwyse. And to the extremity hee had brought her, when there had landed in *Lidia* (driven thether by tempest) twoo excellent younge *Princes*, as *Plangus* named them, *Pyrocles* Prince of *Macedon*, and *Musidorus*, Duke of *Thessalia*; At these wordes a man mighte easily have perceyved a starting and blusshing bothe in *Cleophila*, and *Dorus*, but beeyng utterly unsuspected to bee suche they were unmarcked. Those twoo Princes, aswell to helppe the weyker, as for the naturall hate the *Grecyans* bare the *Persyans*, did so muche with theyre incomparable valure, as that they gatt into ye City, and by theyre presence muche repelled *Otanes* assautes: wch hee understanding to bee occasyoned by them, made a Chalenge of three Princes in his Retinewe, ageanst those twoo *Princes* & *Antiphilus*. And that thereuppon, the matter shoulde bee decyded, with Compact, that neyther shoulde help his fellowes, but of whose syde the more overcame, with him the victory shoulde remayne: Of his syde was *Barzanes*, Lorde of *Hircania*, ageanst *Pyrocles*, *Nardes*, satrapas of *Mesopotamia*, to feighte with *Musidorus*, and ageanst *Antiphilus* hee plased the same *Plangus*, second sonne, to the Kinge of *Iberia*, who served him with dere estimacyon. And so yt fell owte, that *Pyrocles* & *Musidorus* overcame bothe theyre Adversaryes, but, of the other syde *Plangus* tooke *Antiphilus* prisoner: under whiche Coloure, as thoughe ye matter had bene equall, thoughe in deede yt was not, *Otanes* continewed his Warr, and to bring *Erona*, to a compelled yeelding, sent her one day worde, that, the next morrowe, hee woulde before the walles of ye Towne stryke of *Antiphilus* heade, yf shee yeelded not to his Desyer. Then loe, was *Cupids* worcke well seene, for hee had brought this miserable Princess to suche a Case, as shee had Love ageanst Love: For, yf shee loved him, (as unmeasurably shee did) then coulde shee Condiscend to no other, Ageane, yf shee loved him, then muste shee save his lyfe, whiche twoo thinges were impossible to bee joyned together. But the Matcheles Corage of those Twoo Princes prevented him, & preserved her, for the same nighte with a desperate *Camisada*, they pearsed into the midst of his Army, where *Otanes* valyantly defending him self was by *Pyrocles* slayne, and *Antiphilus* by *Musidorus* rescewed: *Plangus* seeyng no other Remedy, conveyed in safty, to her Contry, the fayre *Artaxia*, nowe Queene of *Persia*, who with the extremest Lamentacyons coulde issue oute of a womans mowthe, testifyed to ye worlde, her newe greatenes, did no way comfort her, in respect of her Brothers Losse: whome shee studyed all meanes possible to revenge uppon every one of the Occasyoners. But thus was *Antiphilus* redeemed, and (thoughe ageanst the Consent of y^e *Lydian* Nobility) marryed to *Erona*: In whiche Case, the twoo *Greeke* Princes lefte them, beeyng called away, by one of the noblest Adventures of the worlde. But the vindicatif *Cupid*, who had given *Erona* onely somuche tyme of sweetenes, as to make the myseryes more crewell, that shoulde falle upon her, had turned *Antiphilus* harte, while hee was *Otanes* prisener, quyte from her to the Queene *Artaxia*: Insomuche, that longing to have ye great crowne of *Persia*, on his heade, and like a base man, sodeynly advaunced, having no scoape of his Insolency, made *Artaxia* secretly understand, who (hee knewe) mortally hated *Erona*, that yf shee woulde rewarde his vehement Loving of her with mariage, hee woulde eyther with poyson or otherwyse make away the buetyfull *Erona*; And so with the mighte of *Persia* easely joyne those twoo Kyngdomes together. The wyse *Artaxia*, that had nowe a good enterance to her desyers, fynely handled the vyle *Antiphilus* and broughte his harte to suche a wicked paradyse, that one day, under coloure of hunting, hee entyced abroade the excellent *Erona*: To a place where hee had layde some of *Artaxias* men in ambushm^t, and there delivered bothe him self and her into theyre handes. Who conveying them to theyre Mistriss, *Antiphilus* was justly rewarded, of his expected Mariage; For, shee presently gave him into the handes of Fowre valyant gentlemen (who dearely

65

had loved theyre Master *Otanes*) to bee slayne wth as many Deathes, as theyre witt and hate coulde fynde oute: whiche accordingly was done, and hee helde a whole moneth together in continuall wretchednes, till at last his lyfe lefte him rather with continuance of ye miserable payne, then any vyolent stroke added to him. As for *Erona*, shee putt her in prison, swearing, that yf by that tyme twoo yeare, shee did not bringe *Pyrocles* and *Musidorus* to feighte with those fower (who woulde prove uppon them, they had trayterusly killed her Brother *Otanes*) shee shoulde bee publiquely burned at a stake: whiche likewyse shee shoulde bee, yf *Pyrocles* and his fellowe were overcome. But, yf they woulde take the matter uppon them, then shoulde they have a free Campe graunted them to trye the matter, in the Courte of the Kinge of *Parthia*, bycause, they mighte holde hers for suspected: This did shee hoping that the Corage of the Twoo younge *Princes* woulde leade them to so unequall a Matche, (wherein shee rested assured) theyre deathe and so Consequently her Revenge shoulde bee fully performed. But *Erona*, because shee mighte exceede even misery, with misery, did not, for all the Treachery, of *Antiphilus* (able to make any love a mortall hatred), nor yet for his deathe (the breaker of all worldly fancyes) leve to love *Antiphilus*, and to hate her self, since shee had loste him: And in respect of his revenge uppon those fower his Murderers (not for her owne lyfe whiche shee was weary of) shee desyered, that *Pyrocles* and *Musidorus* mighte ageanst the daye bee broughte thether, having suche Confidence in the notable prooffes shee had seene of theyre vertue, that those fowre shoulde not bee able to withstand them, but, suffer deathe, for killing her, (in spighte of hate) beloved *Antiphilus*. But, whome to sende for theyre searche, shee knewe not, when *Cupid* (I thinke for some greater myscheef) offered this *Plangus* unto her: who from the day of her first imprisonment, was so extremely enamoured of her, that, hee had soughte all meanes how to delyver her, but that beeyng impossible, for the narrow watche was of her, hee had, (as well hee mighte) beeyng greatly trusted of *Artaxia* Conference wth *Erona*. And allthoughe shee woulde promyse no affection (in Rewarde) whiche was finished absolutely in *Antiphilus*, yet hee tooke upon him the Quest of those twoo Heroicall Princes, who in this meane tyme had done suche famous actes, that all *Asia*

ARCADIA

was full of theyre historyes: But hee having traveyled a whole yeare after them, and still hearing theyre Doynges notably recoumpted; yet, coulde never (beeyng stayed by many mysadventures) fully overtake them. But, was newly come into *Egipt*, after they had shipped them selves thence for *Greece*, and into *Greece* lykewyse followed, taking this Contry in his waye: Bycause Maryners had toulde him, suche a Shippe had tuched uppon yᵉ southe parte of *Peloponesus*, where yt was my happe to heare him to make yᵉ pittyfullest Lamentacyon, that ever before came into my eares. Neyther coulde the wyse *Boulon*, (who had founde him making the like Dolefull Compleyntes as his mynde otherwyse occupyed ledd him contrary in those wordes) any thing mitigate his agonyes: But as hee toulde us (having like wyse at oure request recoumpted the full story of those twoo rare *Princes*) his purpose was to goo into *Thessalia* and *Macedon*: where yf hee can not heare of them, hee will returne into *Persia*, and eyther fynde some waye, to preserve *Erona*, or burne at the stake with her. Great was the Compassyon *Cleophila* and *Dorus* conceyved of the Queene *Eronas* daunger, whiche was the first enterpryse they had even entred into, and therefore, besydes theyre Noble humanity, they were loathe theyre owne worke shoulde bee spoyled: Therefore, considering, they had yet, allmoste a yeare, of tyme to succor her, they resolved, assoone, as this theyre present action (whiche had taken full possession of all theyre desyers) were wrought to any good poynte, they woulde forthewith take in hande that Journey. Neither shoulde they neede, in the meane tyme anything reveyle them selves to *Plangus*, who thoughe unwittingly had done his arrant: To wᶜʰ they thoughte them selves in honor bounde, since *Artaxia* layde treason to theyre Charge, But, howe that fancy was stopped, shall bee after toulde. Now *Dorus* desyered *Histor* to repeate the Lamentable songe hee first spake of, and *Histor* was redy to doo yt, and owte startes oulde *Geron* and sayde, yt was very undecent a younge manns tongue shoulde possess somuche, tyme, and that Age shoulde become an Auditor: And therefore bending him self to an other younge Shepeard, named *Philisides* who neyther had daunced, nor songe with them, & had all this tyme layen uppon the grounde, at the foote of a *Cypres* tree, (leaning uppon his ellbowe with so deepe a Melancholy, that his sences carryed to his mynde no

67

delighte from any of theire objectes) hee strake hym uppon the shoulder, with a righte olde mannes grace, that will seeme lyvelyer, then his Age will afforde him: And thus began his Eglogue unto him.

Geron.   Philisides.   Histor.

Geron.

Upp, upp Philisides, *Let sorowes goo,*
  Who yeeldes to woo, dothe but encrease his smarte.
Doo not thy hart, to playntfull Custome bringe,
  But, let us singe, sweete tunes doo passyons ease,
  And olde man heare, who woulde thy fancyes rayse.

Philisides.

Who myndes to please the mynde drownde in Annoyes?
  With outeward Joyes, whiche inlie can not sincke,
As well may thinck, with Oyle to coole the fyer,
  Or with desyer, to make suche foe a frende,
  Who dothe his sowle to endles mallice bend.

Geron.

Yet sure, an ende, to eche thing tyme dothe give,
  Thoughe woes now live, at length thy woes must dye,
Then vertue trye, yf shee can worcke in thee,
  That whiche wee see, in many tyme hathe wroughte
  And weykest hartes to Constant temper broughte.

Philisides.

Who ever taughte a skilless man to teache,
  Or stopp a breache, that never Canon sawe,
Sweete vertues Lawe, barres not a Causefull moane,
  Tyme shall in one, my lyfe and sorowes ende,
  And mee perchaunce youre Constant temper lende.

Geron.

What can amend, where Phisick *ys refused,*
  The wittes abusde, with will, no Counsell take,
Yet, for my sake, Discover us thy greef
  Ofte comes Releef when moste wee seeme in trapp,
  The starres thy state, fortune may chaunge thy happ.

Philisides.

Yf fortunes Lapp became my duelling place,
  And all the starres conspired to my good
Still were I one, this still shoulde bee my Case,
  Ruyns Relique, Cares webb, and sorowes foode,
  Synce shee faire fierce to suche estate mee Galles
  Whose witt the starres, whose fortune fortune thralles.

Geron. Alas what falles are fallen unto thy mynde,
    That there where thow confest thy mischeef lyes,
Thy witt doste use still, still more harmes to fynde,
    Whome witt makes vayne or blynded with his eyes,
What Counsell can preveyle, or Lighte give lighte,
    Synce all his force ageanst him self hee tryes,

Then eche Conceypt that enters in by sighte,
    Ys made forsoothe a Jurate of his woes,
Earthe, sea, Aire, heaven, hell and gastly spirit,
    Then cryes to senceles thinges wch neither knowes,
What eyleth thee, and yf they know thy mynde
    Woulde scorne (in man) theyre kinge, suche feeble
      shewes.

Rebell, rebell in golden fetters bynde,
    This tyrant Love or rather do suppress,
Those rebell thoughtes wch are thy slaves by kynde,
    Let not a glittering name thy fancy dresse,
In paynted Clothes because they calle yt love
    There ys no hate that can thee more oppresse.

Begin, and half the worcke ys done, to proove,
    By raysing up, uppon thy self to stande,
And thincke shee ys a Shee that dothe thee moove
    Hee water plowes, and soweth in the sande,
And hopes the flickering wynde with nett to holde
    Who hathe his hopes layde up in womans hande.

What man ys hee that hathe his freedome soulde?
    Ys hee a manlike man, that dothe not knowe a Man?
Hathe power that sexe with brydle to withholde,
    A ficle sex and true in trust to no man.
A servant sex, soone prowde yf they bee coyde
    And to Conclude, thy Mistris ys a woman.

Those wordes did once the Lovelyest Shepearde use,
    That erste I knewe and with moste playnefull Muse
Yet not of woemen Judging, as hee sayde,
    But forste with rage, his Rage on them obrayde.

Philisides. *O Godds how longe this oulde foole hathe anoyde?*
   My wearyed eares, O gods yet graunte mee this,
That, soone the worlde of his false tongue bee voyde,
   O Noble aige who past theyre onely blisse
In beeyng hearde, untill the hearer dye,
   Uttering a Serpentes mynde, with Serpentes hisse.

Then, who will heare a well authorized lye?
   And patience hathe, let him go learne of him,
What swarmes of vertues did in his youthe flie
   Suche hartes of brass, wyse heddes, and garmentes
     trym͂,
Were in his dayes, whiche hearde, one no thing heares,
   Yf from his wordes the falsehoodes hee do skym.

And here in moste theyre folly vayne appeares,
   That since they still alledge when they were younge,
Yt shewes they fetche theyre witt from yowthfull yeares,
   Lyke beaste for sacrifice, where (save the tongue,
And Belly) noughte ys lefte, suche sure ys hee,
   This lyfe Deade man in this oulde Dongeon flonge.

Oulde howses are throwne Downe, for newe wee see,
   The Ouldest Rammes are called from the flock,
No man dothe wishe his Horse shoulde aged bee,
   The Auncyent Oke well makes a fyered block,
Olde men them selves do love younge wyves to choose,
   Onely fond youthe admires a Rotten stock.

Who once a white long bearde well handle Doose,
   (As his bearde him, not hee his bearde did beare)
Thoughe Cradle witted must not honor loose,
   O, when will men leave of to judge by heare,
And thinck them Oulde, that have the Ouldest mynde,
   With vertue fraughte, and full of holy feare.

[Geron.] *Yf that thy face were hidd, or I were blynde,*
   I yet shoulde knowe, a young man speaketh now?
Suche wandering reasons in thy speeche I fynde,
   Hee ys a Beaste, that Beastes use will allowe,
For proof of man, who spronge of heavenly fyer
   Hathe strongest sowle, when moste his Raynes do bowe.

But fondlinges fonde knowe not youre owne desyer,
   Loathe to dye younge, and then yo^w must bee oulde,
Fondly blame that to whiche youre selves aspier,
   But, this lighte Choler, that dothe make yow bolde,
Rather to wronge, then unto just Defence,
   Ys past with mee, my blood ys waxen colde.

Thy wordes, though full of malapert offence,
   I weyghe them not, but still will thee advise,
How thow from foolish Love mayste purge thy sence,
   First, thincke they err, that thinck them gayly wyse,
Who well can sett a passion oute to shewe,
   Suche sighte have they that see with gogling eyes,

Passyon beares hye, when puffing witt dothe blowe,
   But ys in deede a Toye, yf not a Toye,
Trewe Cause of evills, and Cause of Causeles woe,
   Yf once thow mayste that fancyes glosse destroy,
Within thy self thow soone wilt bee asshamed,
   To bee a Player of thyne owne Anoy.

Then let thy mynde with better Bookes bee tamed,
   Seeke to espye her faultes aswell as prayse,
And let thy eyes to other sportes bee framed,
   In hunting Fearefull Beastes, do spende some dayes,
Or catche the Byrdes with Pittfoldes, or with Lyme,
   Or trayne the foxe, that traynes so Crafty layes.

Lye but to sleepe, and in the earthly Prime,
   Seeke skill of herbes in hilles, haunte brookes nere
      nighte,
And trye with bayte, howe fish will byte some tyme,
   Go grafte ageane, and seeke to grafte them righte,
Those pleasant plantes, those sweete and fruitfull trees,
   Whiche bothe the Pallat, and the eyes delighte,

Cherish the hyves of wysely paynfull Bees,
   Let speciall Care uppon thy flock bee stayde,
Suche Active mynde, but sildome passyon sees.

Philisides. Hathe any man hearde, what this Oulde man sayde ?
   Truely not, I, who did my thoughtes engage?
Where all my paynes, one Looke of hers hathe payde.

Histor.
Thus may yow see howe youthe esteemeth aige,
And never hathe therof a rightly deemde
While hott desyers do raigne in fancyes rage,
Till Age yt self do make yt self esteemed.

Geron was eeven oute of Countenaunce, fynding the wordes
(hee thought were so wyse) wonne so litle reputacyon, at this
young mans handes. And therefore, looking uppon an olde acqueyntance of his named *Mastix*, one of the Repyningest fellowes
in the worlde, And that hee beheld no body but with a mynde
of mislike (saying still the worlde was amyss but, howe yt shoulde
bee amended hee knewe not) sometymes casting his eyes to the
grounde, even ashamed to see his gray hayres despysed. At last hee
espyed his twoo Dogges, wherof the elder was called *Melampus*,
and the younger *Lelanx*, (in Deede the Jewells hee ever had with
him) one brawling with the other; whiche occasion hee tooke to
restore him self to his Countenaunce, and Rating *Melampus*, hee
began to speake to his Dogges, As yf in them a man shoulde fynde
more obaydience, then in unbrydeled younge men.

Geron. Mastix.

Geron.
Downe, Downe Melampus, *what? youre fellowe byte?*
I sett yow ore the Flock I dearely Love,
Them to Defend, not with youre selves to feighte,
Do yow not thinck this will the wolves remove?
From former feare they had of youre good myndes?
When they shall suche devyded weykenes prove?

What yf Lelanx *a better morsell fyndes?*
Then thow erste knowe, rather take parte wth him,
Then jarle, Loo, Loo, even these how envy blyndes?
And thow Lelanx, *let not pryde make thee brym,*
Bycause thow haste thy fellowe overgoñ,
But thanck the Cause thow seest, when hee ys Dym̃.

Here Lelanx *here, in deede ageanst thy foen,*
Of my good sheepe, thow never truce tyme tooke,
Bee as thow arte, but bee with myne at one,
For thoughe Melampus *though a wolfe do looke,*
(For Age dothe make him of a wolvish hewe)
Yet have I seene, when well a wolfe hee shooke.

Foole, that I am, that with my Dogges speake grewe,
  Come nere good Mastix *tis now full tway score,*
Of yeares alas, synce I good Mastix *knewe,*
  Thow heardest even now a young man snebb mee sore,
Bycause I redd him, as I woulde my sone.
  Yowthe will have will, Aige must to age therefore.

Mastix.   *What merveyle yf in youthe suche faultes bee done?*
  Synce that wee see oure saddest Shepeardes oute,
Who have theyre Lesson so longe tyme begun,
  Quickly secure, and easily in doubte.
Eyther a sleepe bee all, yf noughte assayle,
  Or all abroade, yf but a Cubb start oute.

Wee Shepeardes are like them that under sayle,
  Do speake hye wordes, when all the Coaste ys clere,
Yet, to a Passinger, will Bonett vayle,
  I Con thee thanck to whome, thy Dogges bee dere,
But comonly like Curres wee do them intreate,
  Save, when great neede of them perforce appeare.

Then him wee kiss, whome late before wee beate,
  With suche Intemperance, that eche way growes,
Hate of the first, Contempt of Later feate.
  And suche discord tuixt greatest Shepeardes flowes
That, sporte yt ys, to see, with how greate Arte,
  By Justice worcke they, theyre owne faultes disclose.

Like buysy boyes to wynn theyre Tutors harte,
  One saythe hee mockes, the other saythe hee playes,
The Thirde his lesson myst, till all doo smart,
  As for the rest, how Shepeardes spend theyre dayes
At Blow-poynte, Hott Cockles, or Keles
  (Whyle let us pass oure tyme, eche Shepeheardes sayes)

So smalle accoumpte of tyme, the Shepearde feeles,
  And dothe not feele, that lyfe ys noughte but tyme,
And when that tyme ys past, dethe holde his heeles,
  To age, thus do they drawe theyre youthfull pryme
Knowyng no more, then what pore Tryall showes,
  As fish sure tryall hathe of muddy slyme.

73

COUNTESS OF PEMBROOKES

This Pattern good unto oure Children goes,
   For, what they see, theyre Parentes love or hate,
Theyre first taughte sence preferrs to Teachers blowes,
   These Cocklinges cokered, wee bewayle too late,
When that wee see oure ofspring gayly bent,
   Woemen, Manwood, and men effeminate.

[Geron.]   Fye Man, Fye man what wordes hathe thy toungue lent?
   Yet, thow arte mickle worse, than ere was I,
Thy too muche zeale, I feare thy Brayne hathe spent,
   Wee ofte are angryer with the feeble flie,
For buysynes, where yt perteynes him not,
   Then with the poysonous toades, that quyett lye.

I pray thee, what hathe ere the Parrett gott,
   And yet (, they say) hee talkes in great mens bowers,
A Cage, (Gylded perchance) ys all his Lott,
   Who, of his toungue the licoure gladly powers,
A good foole calde, with payne perhaps may bee,
   But even for that shall suffer mighty Lowers.

Let Swanns example, siker serve for thee,
   Who once all Byrdes in sweetly singing past,
But, now to scylence turnde his Minstrelsy,
   For, hee woulde singe, that others were defaste,
The Peacockes pryde, The Pyes pilde flatery,
   Cormorauntes glutt, Kytes spoile, Kinges fishers waste,

The faulcons fiercenes, Sparowes lechery,
   The Cocowes shame, the gooses good intent,
Even Turtle toughte hee with hypocrisy,
   And worse of other more, till by assent,
Of all the Byrdes, but namely these were greeved:
   Of Fowles there called was a Parlement.

There, was the swañ of dignity deprived,
   And statutes made, hee never shoulde have voyce,
Synce, when I thinck, hee hathe in sylence lived,
   I warne thee therefore, synce thow mayste have choyse,
Let not thy toungue become a fyery matche?
   No sworde so bytes, as that evill Toole anoyes.

> *Let oure unparciall eyes, a litle watche,*
>   *Oure owne Demeane, and soone wee wonder shall,*
> *That, hunting faultes, oure selves wee did not Catche,*
>   *Into oure myndes, let us a litle falle,*
> *And wee shall fynde more faultes then Leoperdes skynñ,*
>   *Then who makes us suche Judges over all,*
> *But, farewell nowe, thy faulte ys no greate sinne,*
> *Come, Come, my Curres, tis late, I will goo in.*

And away with his Dogges streyghte hee went, as yf hee went, as yf hee woulde bee sure to have the last worde, All the Assembly laughing at yᵉ lustynes of the oulde fellowe, who Departing muttering to him self, hee had seene more in his dayes then Twenty of them: But as hee went oute *Dorus* seeyng a Lute, lying under the Princess *Pamelas* feete, glad to have suche an Arraunt to approche her, hee Came, but came with a dismayed grace, all his blood stirred betuixte feare and Desyer, and playing uppon yt with suche sweetenes, as every body wondered, to see suche skill in a Shepearde, hee sange wᵗʰ a sorowyng voyce, these *Elegian* verses.

$$- - - - \smile \smile - \smile \smile - \smile \smile - -$$
$$- - - \smile \smile - - \smile \smile - \smile \smile -$$

Dorus.

Fortune, Nature, Love, longe hathe contended aboute mee,
   Whiche shoulde moste misery Cast on A worme yᵗ I am;
Fortune thus can say, Misery & misfortune ys al one,
   And of mysfortune, Fortune hathe onely the gifte,
With stronge Foes on Lande, on Seas wᵗʰ contrary tempestes
   Still doo I Crosse this wretche, what so hee taketh in hand.

Tush, Tush, saide Nature, this ys all but a Tryfle, a mans lyfe
   Gives happes or Misshapps, eeven as hee ordereth his harte,
But, so his humor I frame in a Molde of Choler adusted,
   That the Delightes of lyfe shall bee to him dolorus.

Love smyled, and thus sayde, want, joyned to desyer ys unhappy,
   But yf hee noughte doo desyer, what can Heraclitus *ayle?*
None, but I worckes by desyer, by desyer have I kindled in his sowle,
   Infernall Agonyes unto a Bewty Devyne.

COUNTESS OF PEMBROOKES

Where thow pore Nature lefte all thy due glory to fortune,
Her vertue ys Soveraigne, Fortune a vassall of hers,
Nature abasht went back, Fortune blusht, yet, shee replyed thus,
And even in that Love shall I reserve him a spyte,
Thus, Thus alas wofull in Nature, *happy by* Fortune,
But moste wretched I am nowe Love *wakes my desyer.*

Dorus, when hee had sunge this, having had all the while a free beholding, of the fayre *Pamela,* (who coulde well have spared suche honor, and defended the assault hee gave unto her face, wth bringing a fayre stayne of shamefastnes unto yt,) let falle his Armes, and remayned so fastned in his thoughtes, as yf *Pamela* had graffed him there, to growe in continuall imaginacyon: But, *Cleophila* espying yt, and, fearing, hee shoulde too muche forgett him self, shee came to him, and tooke oute of his hande the Lute, and laying fast holde of *Philocleas* face, with her eyes, hee sange these Sapphistes, speaking as yt were, to her owne hope.

$$- \cup - - - \cup \cup - \cup - -$$
$$- \cup - - - \cup \cup - \cup - -$$
$$- \cup - - - \cup \cup - \cup - -$$
$$\qquad\qquad - \cup \cup - -$$

Cleophila. *Yf myne eyes can speake to doo harty Arrant,*
Or myne eyes Language, shee doo happ to judge of,
So that eyes Message bee of her receyved,
Hope, wee do live yet?

But, yf eyes fayle then, when I moste do neede them,
Or yf eyes language bee not unto her knowne,
So that eyes Message do returne rejected,
Hope, wee do bothe dye.

Yet, Dying, and Deade, do wee singe her Honor,
So become oure Tombes, Monumentes of her prayse,
So becomes oure Losse the Tryumph of her game,
Hers bee the glory.

Yf the senceles Spheares do yet holde a Musick,
Yf the Swanns *sweete voyce bee not hearde, but at deathe,*
Yf Mute Tymber when yt hathe the lyfe loste,
Yeeldeth a Lutes tune.

Are then humane myndes priviledged so meanely?
As that hatefull Deathe can abridge them of power,
With the voyce of Truthe, to recorde to all worldes,
                    That wee bee her spoyles.

Thus not ending endes the due prayse of her prayse,
Fleshly vaile Consumes, but a Sowle hathe his lyfe,
Whiche ys helde in Love, Love yt ys that hathe joynde,
                    Lyfe to this oure sowle.

But yf eyes can speake to doo harty Arraunt,
Or myne eyes Language shee dothe happ to judge of,
So that eyes Message bee of her receyved,
                    Hope, wee do live yet.

Greate was the pleasure of *Basilius* and greater woulde have
bene *Ginecias*, but, that shee founde, to well, yt was intended to
her Daughter : As for *Philoclea*, shee was sweetly ravished withall,
when *Dorus*, desyering in a secrett maner, to speake of theyre
Cases, as perchaunce the party intended mighte take some lighte
of yt.

Making lowe reverence to *Cleophila*, hee began this provoking
songe, in Exameter verse, unto her; whereunto, shee soone
fynding, whether his wordes were directed (in like tune and verse)
answered as followeth.

Dorus.   Cleophila.

Dorus.   *Lady reserved by the heavens to doo* Pastors *Company,*
              honor?
              Joyning youre sweete voyce to the Rurall Muse of a
              Dezart,
          Here, yow fully do fynde this straunge operacyon of
              Love,
              Howe, to the woodes Love ronnes, aswell, as ryde to
              the Pallace,
          Neyther hee beares reverence to a Prince, nor pity to a
              Begger.
              But like a poynte in mydst of a Circle, ys still of a
              nerenes,
          All, to a Lesson hee drawes, Nor hilles, nor Caves can
              avoyde him.

77

Cleophila. *Worthy Shepearde, by my Songe, to my self all favoure ys hapned,*

That to the sacred Muse, my anoyes somewhat bee reveiled,

Sacred Muse, who, in one conteynes, what Nyne doo in all them?

But, O happy bee yow, whiche safe from fyery reflection,

Of Phebus *vyolence, in shade of stately* Cypres *tree,*

Or pleasant Mirtle *may teache the unfortunate* Eccho,

In these woodes to resounde the renoumed Name of a Goddess.

Happy bee yow that may to the Sainte youre onely Idea,

Allthough (simply attyrde) youre manly affections utter.

Happy bee those mysshapps, whiche justly proportion holding,

Give righte sounde to the eares, and enter arighte to ye judgment.

But wretched bee the sowles whiche vaylde in a Contrary subject,

Howe muche more wee do Love, so the less oure Loves bee beleeved.

What skill serveth a Sore, of a wrong infirmity judged,

What can Justice availe to a Man that telles not his owne Case?

Yow, thoughe feares do abashe, in youre still possible hopes, bee,

Nature ageanst, wee do seeme to rebell, seeme fooles in a vayne sute,

But, (so unhearde) Condempnd, kept thence, wee doo seeke to abyde in,

Self lost, and wandering, banisshed that place wee do come from.

What meane ys there, alas, wee can hope oure Losse to recover.

What place ys there lefte, wee may hope oure Woes to recomfort?

Unto the heavens, oure winges bee to shorte; The earthe
    thinckes us a burden.
    Ayer wee do still with sighes encrease to the fyer, wee
    do want none,
And yet, his outeward heate oure teares woulde quenche,
    but an inward,
    Fyer, no Liquor allwayes, Neptunes *seate woulde bee*
    dryed up there.
Happy Shepeardes with thanckes to the Goddes, still
    thinck to bee thanckfull
    That to thy advauncement, theyre wisdomes have
    thee abased.

Dorus. *Unto the Godds, with a thanckfull harte, all thanckes*
    I do render,
    That to my advauncement, theyre wisdomes have
    mee abased,
But, yet alas, O, but yet alas, Oure happes bee but
    hardd happs,
    Whiche must frame Contempt to the highest purchase
    of honor,
Well may a Pastor *playne, but, alas his playntes bee not*
    esteemed,
    Silly shepeardes, pore pype, where his harshe sounde
    testifyes oure woes,
Into the fayre Looker on, pastyme, not passyon enters,
    And to the woodes or brookes, who do make suche
    dreary recitall,
What bee the panges they beare, and whence those
    panges bee deryved,
    Pleasde to receyve that name by rebounding answer
    of Echo,
And hope thereby to ease theyre inward horrible
    anguish,
    Then shall those thinges ease, theyre inward horrible
    anguish,
When Trees daunce to the pype, and swifte streames
    stay by Musick,
    Or when an Echo *unmooved begins to singe them*
    a love songe,

Say then what vauntage do wee gett by the trade of a Pastor ?

Synce no estates bee so base, but love vouchsafeth his Arrowe,

Synce no Refuge dothe serve from woundes wee do carry aboute us,

Synce owteward pleasures bee but halting helps to decayed sowles,

Synce that dayly wee may discerne, what fyer wee do burne in,

Farre more happy bee yo^w, whose greatnes gettes a free Access,

Whose fayre bodily giftes are framed moste Lovely to eche eye,

Vertue yow have, of vertue yo^w have lefte proof to ye whole worlde,

And vertue ys gratefull with beuty and Richenes adurned,

Neyther Doubt yow a whitt, Tyme will youre passion utter,

Hardly remaynes fyer hidd, where skill ys bent to the hyding,

But in a mynde, that woulde his flames shoulde not bee expressed

Nature worcketh ynoughe with a small help, for the Reveiling,

Give therefore to the Muse greate prayse, in whose very likenes,

Yow do aproache to the fruite, youre onely Desyers bee, to gather.

Cleophila. *First shall fertile groundes not yeelde increase of a good seede,*

First the Rivers shall Cease to repay theyre Floodes to the Occean,

Firste may a Trusty grayhound transforme him self to a Tyger,

First shall vertue bee vice, and Beuty bee coumpted a Blemish,

Ere that I leave with songe of prayse, her prayse to solempnish,

Her prayse, whence to the worlde all prayse had his
    beginning,
But, yet, well I do fynde eche man moste wyse in his
    owne Case,
    None can speake of a wounde with skill, yf hee have
      not a wound felt,
Greate to thee, my estate faynes, thy estate ys blest by my
    judgment,
    And yet neyther of us are blest, deemeth his owne
      self,
For yet, weighe this, alas, greate ys not greate, to the
    greater,
    What, (Judge yow) dothe a hillock shewe, by the lofty
    Olympus
Suche this smalle greatenes dothe seeme comparde to the
    greatest,
    When Cædars to the grounde bee opprest by the
    weighte of an Emmott
Or when a Riche Rubyes just pryce, by the worthe of a
    Wallnutt,
    Or to the Sunne for wonders seeme smalle sparckes of
    a Candle,
Then by my highe Cædar, Riche Ruby, and onely
    shyning Sunne,
Vertue, Riches, Beautyes of myne shall greate bee
    reputed,
    Oh no, no hardy Shepearde, Worthe can never enter
    a Tytle,
Where proofes justly do teache (thus machte) suche worthe
    to bee nought worthe
    Lett not a puppitt abuse thy spirit, Kinges Crownes
    do not help them,
From the Cruell heade ache, nor shooes of golde, do the
    goute heale,
And precyous Cowches full ofte are shakte with a
    fever.
    Yf then a bodily evell in a bodily glose bee not
    hidden,
Shall suche morning Dewes bee an ease to the heate of a
    Loves fyer.

COUNTESS OF PEMBROOKES

Dorus.
O glittering miseryes of Man, yf this bee the fortune,
    Of those fortune lulles, so smalle rest restes in a
        Kyngdome,
What Merveyle thoughe a Prince *transforme him self*
    to a Pastor?
    Come from Marble bowers, many tymes the gay
        harber of anguish,
Unto a silly Cabban, thoughe weyke, yet stronger
    ageanst wooes,
    Now, by thy wordes, I begin (moste famous Lady) to
        gather,
Comforte into my sowle I do fynde, I do fynde, what a
    blessing,
    Ys chaunced to my lyfe, that from suche muddy
        abundance,
Of Carcking Agonyes, (wch still to estates bee adherent,)
    Desteny keepes mee aloof, for, yf all this estate to thy
        vertue,
Joynde by thy beuty adournd, bee no meanes this greef to
    abolish
    Yf neyther by that help thow canst clyme up to thy
        fancy,
Nor yet fancy so drest, do receyve a plausible hearing,
    Then, doo I thincke in deede, that better yt ys, to bee
        private,
In sorowes tormentes then tyed to the pompes of a
    Pallace,
    Nurse inwarde Maladyes, wch have not scope, to bee
        breathed oute,
But perforce disgest all bitter Joyces of horror,
    In sylence, from a Mans owne self, with Company
        robbed,
Better yet do I live, that thoughe by my thoughtes I bee
    plunged,
    Into my Lyves bondage, yet may disburden a
        passyon,
(Opprest with Ruynous Conceiptes) by the help of an oute
    Crye,
    Not limitted to a whispering note, the Lament of a
        Courtyer,

But, *some tymes to the woodes, some tymes to the heavens*
   do decypher,
      With boulde Clamoure, unhearde, unmarckte what I
      seeke, what I suffer,
And *when I meete these Trees in the earthes fayre*
   Livery cloathed,
      Ease I do feele, (suche ease as falles to one wholly
      diseazed)
For, *that I fynde in them parte of my estate repre-*
   sented,
      Lawrell *shewes what I seeke, by the* Myrhe *ys*
      shewed how I seeke yt,
Ollyve *payntes mee the peace, that I must aspire to the*
   Conquest
      Myrtle *makes my Request, my Request ys crowned*
      wth a Willowe,
Cyprus *promyseth help, but a help, where comes no*
   recomfort,
      Sweet Jenuper *saith thys, though I burne, I burne in*
      a sweete fyer,
Ewe *dothe make mee bethinck, what kynde of Bowe the*
   Boy holdeth,
      Whiche shootes strongly withoute any Noyse, & deadly
      withoute smarte,
Firre *trees greate and greene, fixte on a hye hill but a*
   barren,
      Like to my Noble thoughtes still newe well plaste, too mee
      fruitless,
Figg *that yeeldes moste pleasaunt fruite, his shadowe ys*
   hurtfull,
      Thus bee her giftes moste sweete, thus more daunger to
      bee nere her,
But *in a* Palme, *when I marcke, howe hee dothe ryse*
   under a burden,
      And may not I (say I then) gett up, thoughe greefes bee
      so weighty;
Pyne *ys a* Mast *to a Shipp, to my shipp, shall hope for*
   a Mast serve,
      Pyne *ys hye,* Hope *ys as hye, sharpe leavde, sharp yt*
      bee my hopes buddes.

Elme *embraste by a* Vyne, *embracyng fancy revyveth,*
  Popler *chaungeth his hewe from a rysing* Sunne *to a
  setting,*
*Thus to my sonne do I yeelde, suche beames her lookes do
  aforde mee,*
  Oulde aged Oke *cutt downe, of newe worcke serves
  to ye buylding,*
So my Desyers *by my feare cutt downe, bee the frames
  of her* Honor,
  Asshe *makes speares whiche· shieldes do resist, her
  force no Repulse takes,*
Palmes *do rejoyce to bee joynde by the Matche of a Male
  to a female,*
  *And shall sensive thinges bee so senceles, as to resist
  sence?*
*Thus bee my thoughtes dispearst, thus thincking nurseth
  a thincking,*
  *Thus bothe Trees and eche thing else bee the Bookes
  of a fancy.*
But to the Cedar, *Queene of Woodes, when I lifte my
  beteared eyes,*
  *Then do I shape to my self, that forme whiche
  raignes so w^{th}in mee,*
*And thincke there shee do dwell, and here what playntes
  I do utter,*
  *When that Noble Topp dothe nodd, I beleeve shee
  salutes mee,*
*When by the Wynde yt maketh a Noyse, I do thinck
  shee dothe answer,*
  *Then kneeling to the grounde ofte thus do I speake
  to y^t Image,*
Onely Jewell, O onely Jewell, whiche onely deservest,
  *That Mens hartes bee thy seate, and endles fame bee
  thy servaunt*
*O descend for a while from this greate heighte, to
  beholde mee,*
  *But noughte else do beholde, else ys nought worthe the
  beholding*
*Save what a worck by thy self ys wraughte, and since
  I am altered*

Thus by thy worck disdayne not that, whiche ys by thy self done,

In meane Caves ofte tresure abydes, to an Hostry a Kinge comes,

And so behynde foule Cloudes full ofte fayre starres do lye hidden.

Cleophila. *Hardy Shepeard, suche as thy merites, suche may bee her Insighte,*

Justly to graunte thy rewarde, suche envy I beare to thy fortune,

But to my self, what wishe can I make for a salve to my sorowes,

Whome bothe Nature seemes to debarr from meanes to bee helped,

And yf a meane were founde, fortune ye whole Course of yt hinders,

Thus plagued how can I frame to my sore, any hope of amendement?

Whence may I shewe to my mynde, any lighte of a possible escape,

Bounde and bounde by so noble bandes, as lothe to bee unbounde,

Jaylor I am to my self, Prison and Prisoner to my owne self,

Yet bee my hopes thus plaste, here fixed lives all my recomforte,

That that dere Dyamond where wisdome holdeth a sure seate,

(Whose force had suche force so to transforme, nay to reforme mee,)

Will at lengthe perceyve these flames by her beames to bee kyndled,

And will pity the wounde festered so straungely within mee,

O bee yt so, graunte suche an event O goddes that event give.

And for a sure sacrifice I doo dayly oblation offer,

Of my owne harte, where thoughtes bee the Temple, sight ys an Alter,

> *But, Cease worthy Shepearde, now Cease, wee do*
> *weary the hearers,*
> *With Monefull melodyes, for ynoughe oure greeves bee*
> *reveiled,*
> *Yf by the partyes meant, oure meaninges rightly bee*
> *marcked,*
> *And sorowes do require some respite unto the sences.*

What exclaming Prayses *Basilius* gave first to *Cleophilas* songes, & now to this *Eglogue*, any man may guess, y^t knowes Love ys better then a payre of spectacles to make every thinge seeme greater wch ys seene throughe yt; And then ys yt never toungue tyed, where fitt Comendacyon (wherof woemen kynde ys to likerous) ys offered unto yt. But the wasting of Torches served for a watche unto them to make them knowe ye Nightes waste: And therefore *Basilius* remembring *Cleophilas* hurte, thoughe unwilling, rase up from his seate wch hee thought of the one syde excellently seated, and perswaded her, to take her Rest, ye like rest of y^t nighte, & so of all sydes they went to recomend them selves to the elder brother of Deathe.

Here endes ye first Eglogues of ye Countess of Pembrookes Arcadia.

The Second Booke or Acte

IN these Pastorall pastymes a great Nomber of dayes were
spent to followe theyre flying Predecessors, while the Cupp
of poyson wch was deepely tasted of all this Noble Company
had lefte no synew of theyres, withoute mortally searching into
yt: yet never manifesting his venemous worck, till once that
having drawne oute his eevening to his longest lyne, No sooner
had the nighte given place to ye morninges lighte, and the sunne
bestowed his beames uppon the Toppes of the Mountaynes, but
that the wofull *Ginecia*, (to whome Rest was no ease) had lefte
her loathed lodging, and gotten her self into the Solitary places,
those dezartes [were] full of, goyng up and downe, with suche
unquyet motyons, as the greeved and hopeles mynde ys wonte
to bringe forthe. There appeared unto the eyes of her judgment
the evills shee was like to ronne into, with ougly infamy wayting uppon them, shee sawe the Terrors of her owne Conscience,
shee was witnes of her longe exercysed vertue, whiche made this
vyce the fuller of deformity; The uttermoste of the good shee
coulde aspyre unto, was but a fountayne of daunger, and the
leste of her dangers was a mortall wounde to her vexed spirites,
and lastly no smalle parte of her evills was that shee was wyse to
see her evills. In somuche that having a great while cast her
Countenaunce, gastly aboute her, as yf shee had called all the
powers of the whole worlde to bee witnes of her wretched
state, at lengthe, casting up her watery eyes to heaven: O *Sunne*
saide shee whose unspotted lighte directes the stepps of mortall
Mankynde, arte thow not ashamed to imparte the Clearenes of
thy presence to suche an overthrowne worme as I am? O yee
heavens, wch continually keepe the Course allotted unto yo^w,
can none of youre Influences preveyle somuche uppon the
miserable *Ginecia*, as to make her preserve a Course so long
embrased by her? O Desartes Dezartes how fitt a guest am
I for yo^w, synce my hart ys fuller of wylde Ravenous beastes
then ever yow were, O vertue, how well I see, thow werte never
but a vayne name, and no essentiall thinge wch haste thus lefte
thy professed Servaunt when shee had moste neede of thy lovely

presence; O Imperfect proportion of Reason, whiche can to muche foresee, and so litle prevent, Alas, alas saide shee, yf there were but one hope for all my paynes, or but one excuse for all my faultynes: But wretche that I am, my torment ys beyonde all succor, and my evill deserving dothe exceede my evell fortune. For no thinge else did my husband take this strange Resolution to live so solitarily, For no thing else did the wyndes delyver this straunge guest to my Contry, For no thing else have the Destinyes reserved my lyfe to this tyme: But that I onely, moste wretched I shoulde become a plague to my self and a shame to woman kynde; yet yf my desyer how unjust soever yt bee, mighte take effect, thoughe a Thowsande Deathes followed yt, and every deathe were followed wth a thousand shames, yet, shoulde not my Sepulchre receyve mee withoute some Contentment: But alas, sure I am not that *Cleophila* ys suche, as can answer my Love, And yf shee bee, how can I thinck shee will synce this mysguysing must come needes for some foretaken Conceipte, And eyther way, wretched *Ginecia*, where canst thow fynde, any small ground plott for hope to dwell uppon? No, no yt ys *Philoclea* his hart ys sett uppon, yf hee bee a hee, yt ys my Daughter whiche I have borne to supplant mee; But, yf yt bee so, the lyfe I have given the ungratefull *Philoclea*, I will sooner with these handes bereve thee of then my Byrthe shall glory shee hathe bereved me of my desyers? In shame there ys no Comforte, but, to bee beyonde all bondes of shame? Having spoken this, shee began, to make pityous warr with her fayre hayer, when shee might heare not farr from her, a pityous Dolefull voyce; But, so suppressed with a kynde of whispering Note, that shee coulde not conceyve the wordes distinctly, but as a Lamentable Tune ys the sweetest Musick to a wofull mynde, shee drue thither nere away in hope to fynde some Companyon of her mysery. And as shee passed, on, shee was stopped with a nomber of Trees, so thickly placed, together, y^t shee was afrayde shee shoulde with russhing throughe stopp the speeche of ye Lamentable party whiche shee was so desyerus to understand: And therefore sitting her downe as softly as shee coulde (for shee was now in distance to heare) shee mighte first perceyve a Lute excellently well playde uppon, and then the same dolefull voyce accompanying yt, with these fewe verses.

In vayne, myne eyes yow Laboure to amend,
  With flowing Teares youre fainte of Hasty sighte?
Synce to my harte her shape yo^w so did sende,
  That her I see, though yo^w did lose youre sighte.

In vayne my harte, now yo^w wth sighte are burnde
  With sighes yow seeke to coole youre whott desyer;
Synce sighes into myne inwarde furnace turnde,
  For Bellowes serve to kindell more the fyer.

Reason, in vayne, now yo^w have lost my harte,
  My heade yo^w seeke, as to youre strongest forte:
Synce there myne eyes have playde so false a parte,
  That to youre strengthe youre foes have suche resorte?
    And since in vayne (I fynde) were all my stryfe,
    To this straunge deathe I vaynely yeelde my lyfe.

The ending of the Songe served but for a beginning of newe
Playntes as yf the Mynd oppressed with the hevy burden of
Cares, was fayne to discharge yt self in all manners, and as yt
were, paynte oute the sharpenes of the payne in all sortes of
Coloures: For, the wofull person (as yf the Lute had evell
joyned with the voyce) threwe yt downe to the grounde wth
suche like wordes. Alas pore Lute, how muche, thow arte deceyved, to thinck that in my miseryes, thow couldest ease my
woes, as in my Careles tunes thow werte wonte to please my
fancyes? The tyme ys chaunged, my Lute, the tyme ys
Chaunged, and no more did my Joyfull mynde, then, receyve
every thinge, to a joyfull Consideracyon, then my Carefull mynde
now makes eche thinge taste like the bitter Joyce of Care. The
evill ys inward, my Lute, the evell ys inwarde whiche all tho^w
doest serve, but to make mee thincke more freely of, and the
more I thincke, the more Cause I fynde of thincking, but less
of hoping: The Discorde of my thoughtes, my Lute, dothe
yll agree to the Concorde of thy sweete stringes, therefore bee
not asshamed to leave thy Master, synce hee ys not afrayde to
forsake him self. And thus muche spoken in steade of a Conclusyon was Closed up, with so harty a groaning y^t *Ginecia* coulde
not refrayne to shewe her self, thincking suche greefes coulde
serve fitly for no thinge, but her owne fortune; But as shee
came into the Litle Arboure of this sorowfull musick, her eyes
mett wth the eyes of *Cleophila*, whiche was the party that thus

had witnessed her sorowe. So that eyther of them remayned Confused with a sodeyne astonishment, *Cleophila* fearing lest shee had hearde some parte of those sorowes, whiche shee had risne up earely that morning of purpose, to breathe oute in secrett to her self: But *Ginecia* a while stoode still with a kynde of dull amasement, looking stedfastly uppon her, at lengthe returning to some use of her self shee began to say to *Cleophila* that shee was sory shee woulde venture her self to leave her Rest, beeyng not alltogether healed of her hurt. But as yf the opening of her Mouthe to *Cleophila* had opened some great Flood gapp of sorowe, wherof her harte coulde not beare the vyolent Issue, shee sanck to the grounde, wth her handes over her face: Crying vehemently *Cleophila* help mee, O *Cleophila*, have pitty on mee? *Cleophila* rañ to her, merveiling what sodeyne sicknes had thus possessed her. And beginning to aske her the Cause of her sorowe and offering her service to bee employed by her, *Ginecia* opening her eyes wyldely uppon her, pricked wth the flames of love and the Tormentes of her owne Conscyence: O *Cleophila*, *Cleophila* sayde shee doest thow offer me phisick, whiche arte my onely poyson? or wilte thow doo mee service, whiche haste allredy broughte mee into eternall slavery? *Cleophila* yet, more merveyling and thinckling some extreme payne did make her rave, Moste excellent Lady (sayde shee) yow were best retyer youre self into youre Lodging, that, yow the better may passe this sodeyne fitt. Retyre my self saide *Ginecia*? yf I had retyered my self into my self, when thow (to mee) unfortunate Guest came to drawe mee from my self, blessed had I beene and no neede had I had of thy Counseyle: But now (alas) I am forced to flee to thee for sorrowe, whome I accuse of all my hurte, and make thee Judge of my Cause, who arte the onely Auctor of my myscheef? *Cleophila* yet more astonisshed, Madame saide shee, wherof doo yo^w accuse mee, y^t I will not Cleare my self, or wherein may I stede yo^w, that yo^w may not comaund mee? Alas answered *Ginecia*, what shall I say more, take pity of mee O *Cleophila*, but not as *Cleophila*, and disguyse not with mee in wordes, as I knowe thow doest in apparell? *Cleophila* was striken even Deade with that worde, fynding her self discovered: But as shee was amased, thinckling what to aunswer her, they mighte see olde *Basilius* passe by them, withoute ever seeyng them: Complayning likewyse of Love very freshly, and

ending his Compleynt with this songe, Love having renewed
bothe his Invention and voyce.

> *Lett not Oulde age disgrace my hye desyer,*
>   *O heavenly sowle in humane shape conteynde?*
> *Oulde wood inflamde dothe yeelde the bravest fyer,*
>   *When younger dothe in smoake his vertue spende.*
>
> *Ne let white hayers, (whiche on my face dothe growe,)*
>   *Seeme to youre eyes, of a Disgracefull hewe,*
> *Synce Whitenes dothe present the sweetest showe,*
>   *Whiche makes, all eyes do honor unto yow.*
>
> *Oulde age ys wyse and full of Constant truthe,*
>   *Oulde age well stayde, from raunging Honor lives,*
> *Oulde age hathe knowne what ever was in youthe,*
>   *Oulde age orecome the greater Honor gives.*
>   *And to oulde age, since yo^w youre self aspyer,*
>   *Let not Oulde age disgrace my hye desyer?*

Whiche beeyng done, hee looked very Curyously upon him
self, some tymes fetching a litle skipp, as yf hee had sayde his
strengthe had not yet forsaken him : But, *Cleophila* having in
this tyme gotten some Leysure, to thinke for her answer, Looking
uppon *Ginecia*, as yf shee thoughte shee did her some wronge.
Madame (sayde shee) I am not acquaynted with these wordes of
disguysing, neyther ys yt the profession of an *Amazon*, neyther
are yo^w a party, with whome yt ys to bee used? Yf my service
may please yow, employ yt so longe as yow do mee no wronge
in mysjudging of mee: Alas, *Cleophila*, saide *Ginecia*, I perceyve
yow knowe full litle, howe pearsing the eyes are of a true Lover,
there ys no one beame of those thoughtes yow have planted in
mee, but ys able to discerne a greater Cloude then yow do go in :
Seeke not to conceale youre self further from mee, nor force not
the passyon of Love into vyolent extremityes. Now was *Cleophila*
broughte to an *Exigent*, when the *Duke* turning his eye that way
throughe the Trees, perceyvid his Wyfe, and Mistris, together,
so that, framing the most lovelyest Countenaunce hee coulde,
hee came streight way towardes them, and at the first worde,
thancking his wyfe, for having interteyned *Cleophila* desyered her
shee woulde now returne into the Lodge, bycause, hee had
certeyne matters of estate to imparte to the Lady *Cleophila*: The
Duchess beeyng no thing trubled with jealosy in that poynte,

obeyde the *Dukes* Comaundement full of raging agonyes, and determinately bent that, as shee woulde seeke all meanes to wynne *Cleophila*, so shee woulde stirr up terrible trajedyes rather then faile of her intent. But assoone as *Basilius* was ridd of his wyves presence, falling downe on his knees, O Lady sayde hee, whiche have onely had the power to stirr up ageane those flames which had so long layen deade in mee : See in mee ye power of youre Beauty, whiche can make oulde age, to aske Counseill of yowthe? And a Prince unconquered to become a Slave to a straunger? And when yow see that power of youres Love, that at leste in mee since yt ys youres (allthoughe in mee yow see no thing to bee loved). Worthy Prince answered *Cleophila*, (taking him up from his kneeling) bothe youre maner, and youre speeche are so straunge unto mee, as I knowe not how to answer yt better then with sylence : yf sylence please yo^w (saide the *Duke*) yt shall never displease mee, since my harte ys wholy pledged to obay yow, otherwyse yf yow woulde vouchesafe myne eares suche happynes, as to heare yow, they shall but Convey youre wordes to suche a mynde, whiche ys with the humblest degree of reverence to receyve them. I Disdeyne not to speake to yow mighty Prince (sayde *Cleophila*) but, I disdayne to speake to any matter wch may bring myne Honor into questyon : And therewith, with a brave Counterfected scorne, shee departed from the *Duke*, Leaving him not so sory for his short answer as prowde in him self, that hee had broken ye matter. And thus did the *Duke* feeding the mynde with these thoughtes, pass great tyme in wryting of verses, and making more of him self then hee was wonte to doo, that with a litle help hee woulde have growne into a prity kynde of Dotage : But *Cleophila* beeyng ridd of this Loving, but litle loved Company, Alas (sayde shee,) pore *Pyrocles* was ever one, but, I y^t had receyved wronge, and coulde blame no body, that having more then I woulde desyer, am still in wante of that I woulde. Truly, Love, I must needes say thus muche on thy behalf, thow haste employed my Love there, where all Love ys deserved, and for recompence hathe sent mee more Love, then ever I desyered : yet, a Chylde in deede thow shewest thy self that thinckest to glutt mee with quantity, as thoughe therein tho^w didest satisfy the harte, an other way dedicated. But what wilt thow doo *Pyrocles*, whiche way canst thow fynde to ridd thee of these intricate trubles? To her whome I woulde bee knowne to I live in darkenes, and to her am reveiled, from whome I wolde bee moste secrett, what shielde shall I fynde ageanst the doting Love of *Basilius*? and the vyolent passyon of *Ginecia*? And yf that bee done, yet how am I ye nearer to quenche the fyer that Consumes mee? Well Well, *Philoclea*, my whole Confidence must bee buylded in thy devyne spirite, whiche can not bee ignorant of the Crewell wounde I have receyved by yow. Thus did *Cleophila* wade betuixt smalle hopes and huge dispayers, whilest in the meane tyme, the sweete *Philoclea* founde straunge unwonted motions in her self: And yet, the pore sowle coulde neyther descerne what yt was, nor whether the vehemency of yt tended. Shee founde a burning affection towardes *Cleophila*, an unquyet desyer to bee with her, and yet shee founde that the very presence kyndled her desyer; And examening in her self the same desyer, yet coulde shee not knowe to what the desyer enclyned, sometyme shee woulde compare the Love she bare to *Cleophila*, with the naturall good will shee bare to her sister, but shee perceyved yt had an other kynde of worcking: Sometyme shee woulde wish *Cleophila* had bene a Man, and her Brother, and yet in truthe yt was no Brotherly Love shee desyered of her. But, thus like a sweete mynde, not muche traversed in the Cumbers of these greeffes shee woulde eeven yeelde to the burthen, rather suffering sorowe, to take a full possession, then exercysing any way her mynde, how to redress yt? Thus in one Lodge, was Lodged eche sorte of greevous passyons, while in the other, the worthy *Dorus* was no less tormented, even, with the extreamest Anguyshe, that Love at any tyme can plague the mynde with all: Hee omitted no occasion, whereby hee mighte make *Pamela*, see, howe muche extraordinary devotion hee bare to her service, and dayly withall strave to make him self seeme more worthy in her sighte, That, desert beeyng joyned to affection might preveyle some thinge in the wyse Princess. But, to well he founde, that a Shepeardes eyther service or affection was but Considered of, as from a Shepearde, and the liking limited to that proportion: For, in deede *Pamela*, having had no smalle sturring of her mynde towardes him, aswell for the goodlynes of his shape, as for the excellent tryall of his Corage had not-withstanding with a true tempered vertue, sought all this while to overcome yt, and a greate Mastery, (allthoughe not withoute

payne) shee had wroughte with her self. When *Dorus* sawe of
the one syde, that the highest poynte this service coulde bring
him to, shoulde bee but to bee accoumpted a good servaunt:
And of the other, that for the suspicyousnes of *Dametas*, and
Miso, with his younge Mistris *Mopsa*, hee coulde never gett any
peece of tyme, to give *Pamela* to understand the estate eyther
of him self, or affection. For *Dametas* according to the righte
Constitution of a Dull heade, thoughte no better way to shewe
him self wyse, then by suspecting every thinge in his way:
whiche suspicion, *Miso* for ye shrewdenes of her brayne, and
Mopsa, for a certeyne unlike envy shee had caughte ageanst
Pamelas beuty were very glad to execute. In somuche, y^t *Dorus*
was ever kept of, and the fayre *Pamela* restrayned to a very
unworthy servitude: *Dorus* fynding his service by this meanes
lightly regarded, his affection despysed, and him self unknowne,
was a greate while like them, that in the midste of theyre Leape
knowe not where to lighte. Whiche in Dolefull maner hee
woulde often tymes utter, and make those Dezart places of
Counsell in his miseryes, but, in the ende, seeyng that no thinge
ys atcheeved before yt bee attempted, and, that lyinge still dothe
never goo forwarde: Hee resolved, to take this meane, for the
manifesting of his mynde, allthoughe yt shoulde have seemed to
have bene the way, ye more to have darckened yt. Hee began to
Counterfeit the extremest Love towardes *Mopsa*, that mighte bee,
and as for the Love, so lyvely in deede yt was in hym (althoughe
to an other Subject) that litle hee needed, to counterfeit any
notable Demonstration of yt: Hee woulde besily employ him
self aboute her, giving dayly some Contrey Tokens, and makinge
store of Love songes unto her. Whereby as hee wann *Dametas*
harte who had before borne him a certeyne rude envye for the
favour the *Duke* had lately shewed unto him, so likewyse, did the
same make *Pamela* begin to have the more Consideracion of him:
(For in deede, so falles yt often in the Excellent woemen) that
eeven that wch they disdayne to them selves, yet, like they not
that others shoulde wynn yt from them. But the more shee
marcked the expressing of *Dorus* affection towardes *Mopsa*, the
more shee founde suche phrases applyed to *Mopsa*, as must needes
argue eyther great ignorance or a second meaning in *Dorus*, and
so to this scanning of him was shee now content to falle, whome
before shee was resolved to banish from her thoughtes: As one

94

tyme among the rest, *Mopsa* beeyng alone with *Pamela*, *Dorus* with a face full of Clowdy fancyes, came sodenly unto them, and taking a Harpe, sunge this passyonate songe.

> *Synce so myne Eyes are subject to her sighte,*
> *That, in youre sighte they fixed have my brayne,*
> *Since so my harte ys filled with my Lighte,*
> *That onely Lighte dothe all my lyfe meynteyne.*
>
> *Synce in sweete yoᵂ all goods so richely raigne,*
> *That, where yow are, no wisshed good can want,*
> *Synce so youre Living Image lives in mee;*
> *That in my self youre self true Love dothe plant*
> *Howe can yow him unworthy then decree?*
> *In whose cheef parte, youre worthes implanted bee?*

The songe beeyng ended, whiche had often tymes broken of in yᵉ mydste with greevous sighes, whiche overtooke every verse hee sange, hee lett falle his Harp from him, and Casting his eye sometymes upon *Mopsa*, but settling his sighte principally uppon *Pamela*: And ys yt onely the fortune, (moste beutyfull *Mopsa*) sayde hee of wretched *Dorus*, that, fortune must bee the measure of his mynde? Am I onely hee, yᵗ bycause I am in mysery, more mysery must bee layde uppon mee? Must that, whiche shoulde bee Cause of Compassyon, become an Argumẽt of Cruelty ageanst mee?: Alas excellent *Mopsa* consider, that a vertuous Prince requyres the Lyfe of his meanest Subject & the Heavenly sonne disdaynes not to give lighte to the smallest worme? O *Mopsa*, yf my harte coulde bee as manifest to yoᵂ as yt ys uncomfortable to mee, I Doubt not the heighte of my thoughtes shoulde well counterveyle the Lowlynes of my quality. Who hathe not hearde of the greatnes of youre estate? who sees not that youre estate ys muche excelled wᵗʰ that sweete uniting of all Beutyes wᶜʰ remayneth & dwelleth with yoᵂ: who knowes, not, that all these are but Ornamentes, of that devyne sparck within yow, whiche beeyng descended from heaven, coulde not else where pick owte so sweete a Mansyon? But, yf yoᵂ will knowe what ys yᵉ Bonde that oughte to knitt all these excellencyes together, yt ys a kynde of mercyfullnes, to suche a one, as ys in sowle devoted to those perfections: *Mopsa*, who allredy had had a certeyne smackering towardes *Dorus*, stoode all this while with her hande some tyme before her face, but Comonly (wᵗʰ a certeyne speciall grace, of her owne) wagging her Lippes, and grenning, in stede of smyling: But all the wordes hee coulde gett of her was (wrying her waste) in faythe yow Jeste with mee, yo^w are a mery man, in deede? But *Pamela* did not somuche attend *Mopsas* interteynement as shee markd bothe the matter *Dorus* spake, and the maner hee used in uttering yt, and shee sawe in them bothe a very unlikely proportion to Mistris *Mopsa*; So that, shee was contented to urge a litle farther of him. Master *Dorus* (sayde the fayre *Pamela*) mee thinckes yo^w blame youre fortune very wrongfully since the faulte ys not in fortune, but in yo^w that can not frame youre self to youre fortune?: And as wrongfully yow do requyer *Mopsa*, to so greate a Dispargement, as to her Fathers Servaunte, since shee ys not worthy to bee loved, that hathe not some feeling of her owne worthynes. *Dorus* stayde a good while after her wordes, in hope shee woulde have continewed her speeche, so greate a delighte hee receyved in hearing of her: But seeyng her say no further, with a quaking all over his body, hee thus answered her. Lady, moste worthy of all Duety, how falles yt oute, that yow in whome all vertue shynes will take the patrony of fortune ye onely Rebellyous hande mayde ageanst vertue: Especyally, since before youre eyes, yo^w have a pityfull spectackle of her wickednes, a forlorne Creature, wch must remayne, not suche as I am but, suche as shee makes mee, synce shee must bee the Ballance of worthynes or dispargement. Yet alas, yf the Condempned man may even at his deathe have leave to speake, Lett my mortall wounde purchase thus muche Consideracyon, since the perfections are suche in the party I Love, as the feeling of them can not come into any unnoble harte; Shall that harte whiche dothe not onely feele them, but hathe all the worckinges of his lyfe placed in them, shall that hart (I say) lifted up to suche a heighte, bee counted base? O lett not an excellent Spirite do yt self suche wronge, as to thincke where yt ys placed, embraced and loved, there can bee any unworthynes, synce the weykest Myst ys not easlyer driven away by the Sunne, then that ys chased away with so highe Thoughtes. I will not deny (answered the Gracyous *Pamela*) but that the Love yow beare to *Mopsa*, hathe broughte yo^w to the Consideracyon of her vertues, and the Consideracyon may have made yo^w the more vertuous, and so the more worthy: But even that then yow must Confess yo^w have receyved of her, and so are rather gratefully to thancke her, then to press any further, till yo^w bringe some thing of youre owne, by wch to Clayme yt. And truly *Dorus*, I must in *Mopsas* behalf say thus muche to yo^w, that yf her beuty have so overtaken yow, yt becomes a true Love to have her harte more sett uppon her good, then youre owne, and to beare a tenderer respect to her Honor, then to youre affection: Nowe by my Hallydam, (Madame saide *Mopsa*) (throwyng a great nomber of sheepes eyes uppon *Dorus*) yow have even tuched myne owne mynde to the quick forsoothe. *Dorus* fynding that the pollicy, hee had used had at lestewyse procured thus muche happynes unto hym, as that hee mighte even in his Ladyes presence discover the sore, whiche had deepely festered within hym: And that shee woulde better conceyve his reasons applyed to *Mopsa*, then shee woulde have vouchesafed them, (whilest her self was a party) thoughte good to pursue on his good beginning, using this fitt occasyon of *Pamelas* witt, and *Mopsas* ignorance. Therefore, with an humble persing eye, (Looking upon *Pamela*, as yf hee had rather bene condepned by her mouthe, then highly exalted by the other) turning him self to *Mopsa*, but keeping his eye where yt was: Fayre *Mopsa* (sayde hee) well doo I fynde, by the wyse knitting together of youre answer, that, any Disputacyon I can use ys as muche to weyke, as I unworthy. I fynde my Love shall bee prooved in Love, withoute I leave to love, beeyng too unfitt a vessell, in whome so highe thoughtes shoulde bee engraved: yet, since ye Love I beare yow, hathe so joyned yt self to the best parte of my lyfe, as the one can not departe, but that the other will followe, before I seeke to obay yow in my last passage, Lett mee knowe, whiche ys my unworthynes, eyther of mynde, estate or bothe? *Mopsa*, was aboute to say, in neyther for her hart did eeven quake, with over muche kyndenes, when *Pamela*, with a more favourable Countenaunce then beefore, (fynding how apte hee was to falle into despayre) toulde him, hee mighte therein have answered him self: For, besydes that, yt was graunted hym y^t the inwarde feeling of *Mopsas* perfections had greately beutyfyed his mynde, there was none coulde deny, but, that his mynde, and body (of themselves) deserved greate allowance. But *Dorus* (sayde shee) yow muste so farr bee Master of youre Love, as to Consider, that synce ye Judgm^t of the worlde standes uppon matter of fortune, and that the Sexe of woman kynde of all other ys moste bounde to have regardefull eye to mens Judgementes: yt ys not

97

for us to play the *Philosophers* in seeking oute youre hidden vertues, since that, whiche in a wyse Prince woulde bee coumpted wysdome, in us woulde bee taken for a lighte grounded affection, so ys not one thinge One, done by dyvers persons. There ys no man in a burning feyver, feeles so greate Contentment in colde water, greedely receyved, whiche assoone as ye Drincke ceasseth, the Rage reneweth: As pore *Dorus* founde his sowle refresshed with her sweetely pronounced wordes, and newly and more vyolently ageane inflamed, assoone as shee had closed up her delightfull speeche, with no less well graced sylence. But, remembring in hym self, that aswell the Souldyor dyes wch standes still, as hee that gives the bravest onsett, and seeyng y^t to the making up of his fortune, there wanted no thinge so muche as the making knowne of his estate, with a face well witnessing howe deepely his sowle was possessed, and with the moste submissive behaviour, that a thralled harte coulde express, even as yf his wordes had bene to thick for his mouthe, at lengthe spake to this purpose.

Alas moste worthy Princess, and do not then (saide hee) youre owne sweete wordes sufficyently testify, that there was never man coulde have a juster accyon ageanst filthy fortune, then I synce all other thinges beeyng graunted mee her blyndenes ys myne onely lett: O heavenly God, I woulde eyther shee had suche eyes as were able to descerne my Desertes or I were blynde not to see the daily Cause of my mysfortune. But yet (saide hee) moste Honoured Lady, yf my miserable speeches have not all redy cloyed yow, and that the very presence of suche a wretche become not hatefull in youre eyes, Let mee replye thus muche further ageanst my mortall sentence, by telling yow a story, which hapned in this same Contry longe synce (for woes make the shortest tyme seeme longe) whereby yow shall see that myne estate ys not so Contemptible but that a Prince hathe bene content to take the like uppon hym, and by that onely hathe aspyred to enjoy a mighty Princess: *Pamela* gracyously harckened, and hee toulde his tale in this sorte. In the Contry of *Thessalia*, (alas why name I that accursed Contry whiche bringes forthe no thinge but matters of tragedyes) but name yt I must, In *Thessalia* (I say) there was, (well may I say there was) a Prince? no, no Prince, whome bondage wholly possessed, but yet, accoumpted a Prince, and named *Musidorus*: O *Musidorus*, *Musidorus*, but to what serve

98

exclamacions, where there are no eares, to receyve the sounde? This *Musidorus* beeyng yet in the tenderest aige his aged Father payde up to *Nature* her last duetyes, leaving his Chylde to the faithe of Frendes and proof of tyme: Deathe gave hym not suche panges as the foresightfull Care hee had of his silly successor, and yet, yf in his foresighte, hee coulde have seene somuche, happy was that good Prince in his tymely departure, whiche barred hym from ye knowledge of his Sonnes myseryes, whiche his knowledge coulde neyther [have] prevented nor releeved. The younge *Musidorus* beeyng thus (as for the first pledge of Destenyes good will) deprived of his Principall stay, was yet for some yeares after, (as yf the starres woulde breathe them selffes for a greater myscheef) lulled up in asmuche good Luck, as the heedefull Love of his Dolefull mother, and the florisshing estate of his Contry coulde breede unto him. But when the tyme now came, that misery seemed to bee rype for hym bycause hee had age to knowe mysery, I thincke there was a Conspiracy in all heavenly and earthely thinges to frame fitt occasions to leade hym unto yt: His people (to whome all foreyne matters in fore-tyme were odyous) began now to wish in theyre beloved Prince experyence by travell. His dere Mother whose eyes were helde open onely with the Joyes of looking uppon him, did now dis-pence with the Comfort of her wydowhood lyfe desyering the same her Subjectes did for her sones worthynes: And hereto did *Musidorus* owne vertue (see how vertue can bee a Minister to myscheef) sufficyently provoke him. For in deede thus muche must I say for hym (allthoughe the likenes of my myshappes makes mee presume to patterne my self unto him) That well-doynge was at that tyme his scope from whiche no faynte pleasures coulde withholde him: But the present occasion wch did knitt all these together was his unckle, the Kinge of *Macedon*, who having lately before gotten suche victoryes, as were beyonde expectation did at this tyme sende bothe for ye Prince his Sonne broughte up together (to avoyde the Warres) with *Musidorus* and *Musidorus* hym self, that his joy mighte bee the more full having suche partakers of yt. But alas, to what a Sea of myseryes my playntfull tongue dothe leade mee? and thus oute of breath rather with that hee thought, then with that hee sayde, *Dorus* stayed his speeche: Till *Pamela* shewyng by Countenaunce, that suche was her plesure hee thus continewed yt. These twoo younge

Princes (to satisfy the Kinge) tooke theyre way by Sea towardes
Bizantium, where at that tyme his Courte was, but when the
Conspired heavens had gotten this subject of theyre wrath (uppon
so fitt a place as the Sea was) they streight began to breathe oute
in boysterus wyndes some parte of theyre mallice ageanst hym,
so that with the Losse of all his Navy hee onely with the Prince
his Cossen were cast a land farr of from the place whether theyre
desyers woulde have guyded them: O crewell wyndes in youre
unconsiderate rages, whye eyther began yow this furye or why
did yow not ende yt in his ende? but youre Crewelty was suche
as yow woulde spare his lyfe for many deathfull Tormentes? To
tell yow what pityfull myshappes fell to the younge Prince of
Macedon his Cossen, I shoulde too muche fill youre eares w^th
strange horrors: Neyther will I stay upon those Laboursome
adventures nor loathsome mysadventures to whiche and throughe
wch his fortune and corage conducted hym, my speeche hasteth
ytself to come to ye full poynte of all *Musidorus* infortunes. For
as wee fynde the moste pestilent dezeases do gather into them
selves all the infirmityes with whiche the body before was anoyed,
so did his last misery embrase in the extremity of yt self all his
former myscheef: *Arcadia, Arcadia* was the place prepared to
bee stage of his endles overthrowe *Arcadia*, was, (alas well might
I say yt ys) the Charmed Circle where all his spirites shoulde
for ever bee enchaunted. For, here, and no where ellse did his
infected eyes make his mynde knowe what power heavenly
Beuty hathe; to throwe yt downe to hellish agonyes: Here here
did hee see the *Arcadian* Dukes eldest Daughter, in whome hee
forthe with placed so all his hopes of joy and joyfull partes of his
harte that, hee lefte in hym self no thinge but a mase of Longing
and a Dongeon of sorrowe. But, alas, what can sayinge make
them beleve whome seeyng can not perswade those paynes must
bee felt before they bee understood, no owtewarde utterance can
comaunde Conceypte: Suche was as then the estate of the *Duke*,
as yt was no tyme by direct meanes to seeke her, and suche was
the estate of his Captyved will, as hee coulde delay no tyme of
seeking her. In this entangled Case hee cloathed hym self in a
Shepeardes weede, that under ye basenes of that forme hee might
at least have free access to feede his eyes wth that whiche shoulde
at lengthe eate up his hart: In wch doynge thus muche withoute
Doubte hee hathe manifested, that this estate ys not allwayes to

bee rejected, since under that vaile there may bee hidden thinges to bee esteemed. And that yf hee might wth taking on a She-peardes looke cast up his eyes to the fayrest *Princess* nature in that tyme created: The like may the same desyer of myne neede no more to bee disdayned or helde for disgracefull, but, now alas myne eyes waxe dymme, my tounge begyns to faulter, and my harte to want force to help eyther with the feeling remembrance I have in what heape of myseryes the Caytive Prince lay at this tyme buryed. Pardon therefore, (moste excellent Princess) yf I cutt of the Course of my Dolorous tale, synce yf I bee understood I have sayde ynoughe for the defence of my basenes: And for that whiche after mighte befalle to that Patterne of yll fortune, the matters are to monsterus for my Capacity, his hatefull destenyes must best declare theyre owne worckmanship. Hee ended thus his speeche, but withall began to renewe his accustomed playntes & humble Intercessyons to *Mopsa*, who having no greate Battell in her Spirit, was allmoste broughte asleepe with the sweete delivery of his Lamentacyons. But *Pamela* (whome liking had made willing to conceyve and naturall wysdome able to judge) lett no worde slipp withoute his due pondering, even Love began to revyve his flames wch the opinyon shee had of his meanes, had before covered in her: Shee well founde hee meante the Taile by hym self, and that hee did under that Covert maner make her knowe ye greate Noblenes of her byrthe, but, no Musick coulde with righter accordes possesse her sences, then every hee expressed, had his mutuall worcking in her. Full well shee founde the Lyvely Image of a vehement desyer in her self, which ever ys apte to receyve beleef, but hard to grounde beleef, for as desyer ys glad to embrase the first shewe of hope, so by ye same nature, ys desyer desyerus of perfect assurance: Shee did ymediately catche holde of his signifying hym self to bee a Prince, and did glad her harte with having reasonable grounde to buylde her Love uppon, but streighte the longing for assurance made suspicyons aryse and say unto her self. *Pamela* take heede, the synewes of wysdome ys to bee hard of beleef, who dare place his harte in so hye places, dare frame his heade, to as greate fayninges: *Dorus*, that founde his speeches had given *Alarum* to her Imaginacyons to holde her the longer in them, and bringe her to a dull yeelding over her forces, (as the nature of musick ys to doo) hee tooke up his Harp, & sange these fewe verses.

COUNTESS OF PEMBROOKES

My Sheepe are Thoughtes wch I bothe guyde & serve,
Theyre Pasture ys fayre Hilles of fruteles Love;
In barreyn sweetes they feede, and feeding sterve,
I wayle theyre Lott but will not other proove.

My Sheepehooke ys Wanhope, wch all upholdes:
My weedes Desyer, cutt oute in endles Foldes;
What wolle my Sheepe shalle beare, while thus they live?
In yow yt ys, yow must the judgment give.

The Musick added to the Tale, and bothe fitted to suche
motions in her, (as nowe began ageane to bee awaked) did steale
oute of the fayre eyes of *Pamela*, some droppes of Teares, allthoughe with great Constancy shee woulde fayne have overmastered at least the shewe of any suche weykenes: At lengthe
with a sighe came even up to her mowthe & there stopped. But,
Lorde (sayde shee) yf suche were the Princes burning affection
what coulde hee hope by living here, yf yt were not to growe
purer in ye fyer like the *Sallamander*: And even so too (answered
Dorus) but with all perchaunce (for what can not love hope) hee
hoped to carry away the fyer with him. With hym (sayde shee)?
now what coulde induce a Princess to goo away with the Shepearde? Principally (saide hee) the vertuous gratefullnes for his
affection, then knowyng hym to bee a Prince, and lastly seeyng
her self in unworthy bondage. *Pamela* founde in her Conscyence
suche an accusing of a secrett Consent thereto, that shee thought
yt safest way to direct the speeche, leste in Parley, the Castell
mighte bee given upp: And therefore with a gracyous closing
up of her Countenaunce towardes *Dorus*, shee willed *Mopsa*, to
take good heede to her self, for her Shepearde coulde speake well,
but, truly *Mopsa* (sayde shee) yf hee can proove him self suche
as hee saythe, (I meane the honest Shepearde *Menalcas* brother
and heyre) I knowe no reason why, a better then yo^w need thinck
scorne of his affectionate suite? *Mopsa* did not love Comparisons,
yet beeyng farr spent towardes *Dorus*, shee answered *Pamela*, that
for all his quaynt speches shee woulde keepe her honesty close
ynoughe: And that as for ye hye way of Matrimony, shee woulde
go never a furlong furder, till my Master her Father did speake
the whole worde hym self. But ever and anon turning her self
towardes *Dorus* shee threwe suche a prospect uppon hym, as
mighte well have given a surfeit to any lighte Lovers stomack:

But, *Dorus* (full of inwarde joy that hee had wroughte his matters to suche a towardnes) tooke out of his bagg a very riche Jewell kept among other of his precyous thinges, whiche bycause of the Devyse, hee thought fittest to give. It was an Alter of golde very full of the moste esteemed stones, dedicated to *Pollux*, who bycause hee was made a God for his Brother *Castors* vertue, all the honoure men did to him, seemed to have theyre finall intent to the greater God *Castor*: Aboute yt was written in Romane wordes, *Sic vos non vobis*; And kneeling downe to the fayre Princess *Pamela*, hee desyered her shee woulde in his behalf, bestowe yt upon the crewell harted *Mopsa*, who was as then benomde with Joy, seeyng so fayre a present: *Pamela* gave yt to her, having receyved into her owne mynde a greate Testimony of the givers worthynes. But alas sweete *Philoclea*, how hathe my penn forgotten thee? synce to thy memory principally all this longe matter ys intended, Pardon the slacknes to come to those woes whiche thow didest acuse in others, and feele in thy self: The sweete mynded *Philoclea* was in theyre degree of well doynge to whome the not knowyng of evell serveth for a grounde of vertue, and holde theyre inwarde powers in better Temper with an unspotted simplicity, then many, who, rather cunningly seeke to knowe, what goodnes ys, then willingly to take unto them selves the followyng of yt. True yt ys, that that sweete and symple breathe of heavenly goodnes ys the easyer to falle, bycause yt hathe not passed throughe the worldly wickednes, nor feeling founde the evill that evell carryeth with yt: As now the Amiable *Philoclea*, whose eyes and sences had receyved no thinge, but according as the naturall Course of eche thinge requyred, whose tender youthe had obeydyently lived under her Parentes behestes, withoute the framing (owte of her owne will) the fore-chosing of any thinge, was sodenly (pore sowle) surprysed, before shee was aware; that any matter layde holde of her, Neyther did shee consider that the least gapp a Sea wynnes ys enoughe withoute ageanst stryving industry, to overflowe a whole Contry. But fynding a Mounteyne of burning desyer to have over whellmed her harte, and that the fruites therof having wonne the place, began to manifest them selves wth horrible terrors of Danger, Dishonor and dispayre, shee did suffer her sweete Spirites to languish under the heavy weighte: Thinckyng yt impossible to resist, as shee founde yt deadly to yeelde. Thus ignorant of her owne disease, allthoughe (full well) shee founde her self dizeazed, her greatest pleasure was, to putt her self into some Lonely place, where shee might freely feede ye humor wch did tyrannize w^thin her. As one Nighte, that the Moone beeyng full, did shewe her self in her moste perfect beuty, the unmatched *Philoclea* secretly steale from her Parentes whose eyes were now so bent upon an other Subject, that ye easyer shee mighte gett her desyered advauntage: And goyng with uncerteyne paces to a litle woode, where many tymes before, shee had delighted to walke, her rowling eye lighted upon a Tufte of Trees, so cloasely sett together, (as with the shade the Moone gave throughe yt) yt bredd a fearefull Devotion to looke uppon yt. But, well did shee re-member the place, for there had shee often defended her face from the Sunnes rage, there had shee enjoyed her self often, while shee was Mistris of her self, and had no other thoughte but suche, as mighte aryse oute of quyett sences: But the Principall Cause that made her remember yt was a fayre white Marble stone, that shoulde seeme had bene dedicated in auncyent tyme, to the *Sylvan* goddes: whiche shee fynding there (a fewe dayes before *Cleophilas* comyng) had written these wordes uppon yt, as a Testimony of her mynde ageanst the suspicion shee thoughte shee lived in. The wryting was this.

> *Yee Living Powers enclosde in stately shryne,*
> *Of growyng Trees, yee Rurall goddes that weelde,*
> *Youre scepters here, yf to youre eares devyne,*
> *A voyce may come wch trubled sowle dothe yeelde.*
> *This vowe receyve, this vowe O goddes meyntayne,*
> *My virgyn Lyfe no spotted thoughte shall stayne.*
>
> *Thow purest stone, whose purenes dothe present,*
> *My purest mynde, whose Temper, hardd dothe shewe:*
> *My Tempered hart, by thee my promyse sent*
> *Unto my self; Lett after Livers knowe;*
> *No fancy myne, nor others wronge suspect,*
> *Make mee (O vertuous shame,) thy Lawes neglect.*
>
> *O Chastity the cheef of Heavenly Lightes,*
> *Whiche makes us moste Immortall shape to beare,*
> *Holde thow my Harte, establish thow my Spirites*
> *To onely thee, my Constant Course I beare,*
> *Till spottles sowle unto thy bosome flye,*
> *Suche lyfe to leade, suche Deathe I vowe to dye.*

ARCADIA

But now that her Memory served as an accuser of her Change, and that her owne hande wryting was there to beare Testimony of her falle shee went in amonge the fewe Trees so closed in the Topp together, as they seemed a litle Chappell: And there mighte shee by the Moone lighte perceyve the goodly stone whiche served as an Alter in that wooddy Devotion, but neyther the Lighte was ynoughe to reade the wordes, and the Incke was all redy forworne, and in many places blotted. Wch as shee perceyved, Alas, sayde shee fayre Marble, whiche never receyved Spott, but by my wryting, well do these blottes become a blotted wryter: But pardon her whiche did not dissemble then, allthough shee have chaunged synce? Enjoy and spare not the glory of thy Nature, whiche can so constantly beare the Marckes of my Inconstancy. And herewith (hyding her eyes a while with her softe handes) there came into her heade certeyne verses, whiche yf the Lighte had suffered, shee woulde fayne presently have adjoyned, as a retraction to the other: the verses were to this effect.

> My wordes, in hope to blase my stedfast mynde,
> This Marble chose, as of like Temper knowne:
> But, Lo, (my wordes defaced) my fancyes blynde,
> Blottes to the stone, shame to my self I fynde.
> And witnes am, how yll agree in one,
> A womans hand with constant Marble stone.
>
> My wordes full weyke, the Marble full of mighte,
> My wordes in store, the Marble all alone,
> My wordes black Inck, the Marble kyndly white,
> My wordes unseene, The Marble still in sighte
> May witnes beare how yll agree in one,
> A womans hande with constant Marble stone.

But, seeyng shee coulde not see perfectly to joyne this Recantation to the former vowe, laying all her fayre lengthe under one of the Trees for a while, the pore sowle did nothing but turne up and downe, and hyde her face, as yf shee had hoped to turne away the fancy, that mastered her, or coulde have hidden her self from her owne thoughtes: At lengthe, with a whispering voyce to her self, O mee unfortunate wretche (saide shee) what poysonous heates bee these that thus possess mee,

how hathe the sighte of this Straunge guest invaded my sowle?
Alas what entrance founde this desyer, or what strength had yt,
thus to conquer mee? Then looking to the starres, wch had
perfectly as then butyfyed the clere skye, My Parentes (sayd
shee) have tolde mee, that in these fayre heavenly bodyes, there
are great hidden Deityes, whiche have theyre worcking in the
ebbing and flowyng of oure estates. Yf yt bee so, then, O yee
starres judge rightly of mee: And yf I have willingly made my
self a pray to fancy, or yf by any idle lustes I framed my hart
fitt for suche an Impression, then let this plaigue daily increase
in mee, till my name bee made odyous in womankynde. But,
yf extreme and unresistable vyolence have oppressed mee, who
will ever doo any of yow sacrifice O, yee starres, yf yee doo not
succour mee? No, no, yow can not help mee, my Desyer must
needes bee wayted on with shame, and my Attempt with
daunger: And yet are these but chyldish objections. Yt ys the
Impossibility that dothe torment mee for unlawfull Desyers are
punisshed after the effect of enjoying, But impossible desyers are
plagued in the desyer yt self: Then woulde shee wish to her
self (for even to her self shee was asshamed to speake yt oute in
wordes) that *Cleophila* might become a younge transformed
Ceneus. For, saide shee, yf shee were a Man I might eyther
obteyne my desyer, or have Cause to hate for refusall, besydes
the many Duetyes *Cleophila* did to her, assured her, *Cleophila*
might well want power, but not will to please her : In this
depth of her Muses there passed a Cloude betuixt her sighte and
the Moone, whiche tooke away the present beholding of yt.
O Diana, saide *Philoclea*, I woulde either the Cloude that now
hydes the lighte of my vertue woulde as easely passe away, as
yow will quickly overcome this lett, or ellse that yow were for
ever thus darckened, to serve for a better excuse of my outeragyous
folly? In this dyvers sorte of straunge discourses woulde shee
ravingly have remayned, but that shee perceyved by the highe
Clyming of the Moone, the Night was farr spent and therefore
with stealing stepps shee returned to ye Lodge. Where, for all
the latenes shee founde her father and Mother giving a Tedyous
interteynem^t to *Cleophila*, oppressed wth beeyng loved allmoste
as muche as with loving : *Basilius* not so wyse in covering his
passyon woulde falle to those imoderate prayses wch the foolish
Lover ever thinckes shorte of his Mistris allthough they reche

farr beyond ye heavens. But, *Ginecia*, whome womanly modesty did more owtewardly brydle, yet did many tymes use the advantage of her sexe in kissing *Cleophila*, whiche did but in deede encrease but the rage of her Inwarde fury, bothe Imoderately feeding theyre eyes with one intention though by contrary meanes: But once *Cleophila* coulde not sturr, but that as yf they had bene Puppettes (whose motyons stoode onely upon her pleasure) they woulde with forced stepps and gasing lookes follow her. *Basilius* mynde *Ginecia* well perceyved, and coulde well have founde in her harte to laughe at yf her fortune coulde have endured myrthe: But all *Ginecias* actions were by *Basilius* interpreted, as proceeding from Jelosy. *Cleophila* betwixt bothe, like the pore Chylde, whose Father (while hee beates hym) will make him beleeve yt ys for Love: Or as the sick man to whome the Phisicion sweares, the medicyn hee profers ys of a good taste theyre Love was hatefull, theyre Curtesy trublesome, theyre presence Cause of her absence: Thence where her harte lived, *Philoclea* comming among them, made them all perceyve, yt was tyme to rest theyre bodyes, how litle parte soever theyre myndes tooke of yt. And therefore bringing *Cleophila* to her Chamber, *Basilius* and *Ginecia* retyred them to theyres: Where *Basilius* now a sleepe, and all the Lightes wch naturally kept a chearefullnes in the mynde, putt oute, *Ginecia* kneeling up in her bedd, began with a softe voyce, and swolne harte, to renewe the Curses of her Byrthe. And then (in a manner) embrasing her bedd Ah Chastest bedd of myne saide shee, wch never heretofore couldest accuse mee of one defyled thoughte, howe canst thow now receyve this Desastered Chaungeling? Happy happy bee onely they wch bee not, and thy blessednes onely in this respect thow mayste feele, that thow haste no feeling. With that shee furiously tare of a great parte of her fayre hayer. Take here O Forgotten vertue (saide shee) this miserable sacrifice. More shee woulde have sayde, but that *Basilius* awaked wth the noyse, tooke her in his armes, and began to Comfort her. The good man thinking yt was all for love of hym, whiche humor yf shee woulde a litle have meynteyned, perchaunce yt might have weykened his new conceyved heates. But hee fynding her answers wandering from ye purpose lefte her to her self, glad the next day to take the advauntage of her deade sleepe (whiche her overwatched sorrow had layde uppon her) to have the more

Conference with the afflicted *Cleophila*: Who (bayted on this fashion by these twoo Lovers, and ever kepte from any meanes to declare her self to *Philoclea*) was in farr harder estate, then the Pastor *Dorus*: For hee had to doo in his pursute with sheperdish folkes who trubled him with a litle envyous care and affected diligence, But *Cleophila* was wayted on by Princes, & watched by the twoo wakefull eyes of Love and Jelosy: But this morning of *Ginecias* sleepe, *Basilius* gave her occasion to goo beyonde hym in this sorte. *Cleophila* thus at one instant bothe beseged and banished, founde in her self a dayly encrease of her vyolent desyers, wch as a River (his current beeyng stopped), dothe the more swell, so did her hart the more impedimentes shee mett, the more vehemently stryve, to over pass them: The onely Recreation shee coulde fynde in all her anguish was, to visitt some tymes that place, where, first shee was so happy as to see the Cause of her unhapp, there woulde shee kiss the grounde and thancke the Trees, bless the ayer, and doo dutyfull reverence to every thing that shee thought did accompany her at theyre first meeting. But as Love, thoughe yt be a passyon, hathe in yt self a very active maner of working, so had shee in her brayne all sortes of Inventyon, by whiche shee might come to some satisfaction of yt: But still the combersome Company of her twoo yll matched Lovers was a crewell barr unto yt, till this morning, that *Basilius* having Cõmde and trickt him self (more curyously then any tyme xl^ti winters before) did fynde her given over to her Muses, wch shee did express in this songe, to the greate pleasure of the good oulde *Basilius*, who retyered hym self behynde a Tree, whilest shee with a moste sweete voyce did utter these passionate verses.

> *Loved I am, and yet Complayne of Love,*
> *As Loving not, accusde, in Love I dye,*
> *When pitty moste I Crave, I Cruell proove,*
> *Still seeking Love, Love founde, as muche I dye.*
>
> *Burnde in my self, I muse at others fyer,*
> *What I calle wronge, I do the same and more,*
> *Barrd of my will, I doo beyonde desyer.*
> *I wayle for want, and yet am chookt with store,*

This ys thy worcke, thow God for ever blynde :
Thoughe thousandes olde a Boy entiteled still ;
Thus Children do the silly byrdes they fynde,
With stroking, hurte, and too muche Cramming kyll.
Yet thus muche Love, (O Love) I crave of thee?
Let mee bee Loved, or els not Loved bee?

Basilius made no greate haste from behynde the Tree, till hee
perceyved shee had fully ended her Musick, but then lothe to
loose the precyous fruite of tyme hee presented hym self unto
her, falling downe uppon bothe his knees, and holding upp his
handes, as the oulde Governess of *Danae* ys paynted, when shee
sodenly sawe the golden shower: O Heavenly woman, or
earthely goddess (saide hee) let not my presence bee odyous unto
yow, nor my humble sute seeme of smalle weighte in youre
eares. Vouchesafe youre eyes to descend uppon this miserable
oulde Man, whose lyfe hathe hetherto beene mayntayned, but to
serve for an increase of youre beutyfull Tryumphes: yow onely
have over throwne mee, and in my Bondage consistes my glory.
Suffer not youre owne worcke to bee despysed of yo^w, but Looke
upon hym wth pity whose lyfe serves for youre prayse? *Cleophila*
keeping a Countenaunce, ascanses, shee understood hym not,
toulde hym yt became her evill to suffer suche excessive reverence
of hym, but that, yt worse became her to correct hym to whome
shee owed Duety: That the opinyon, shee had of his wysdome
was suche, as made her esteeme gratefully of his wordes, But
that the wordes them selves sounded so, as shee coulde not
ymagyn what they mighte intend. Intend sayde *Basilius* (allmoste
prowde with beeying askte ye question) Alas, (saide hee) what
may they intend, but a refresshing of my sowle, an asswaging
of my heate, and enjoying those youre excellencyes, wherein
my lyfe ys uphelde, and my Deathe ys threatened: *Cleophila*
lifting up her face, as yf shee had receyved a mortall injury of
hym, And ys this the Devotion youre Ceremonyes (saide shee)
have beene bent unto? Ys yt the Disdayne of my estate, or the
opinion of my lightnes y^t have emboldened suche base fancyes
towardes mee? Enjoyng (quoth yo^w) now litle joy come to them,
that yeelde to suche enjoying. Pore *Basilius* was so appaled,
that his legges bowed under hym, his eyes waxed staring Deade,
and (his oulde blood goyng to his hart) a generall shaking all

over his body possessed hym: At lengthe, with a wañ mouthe
hee was aboute to give a stamering answer, When *Cleophila*
seeying yt was now tyme to make her proffett of his folly, with
somewhat a Relented Countenaunce sayde unto hym. Youre
wordes, (Mighty Prince) were unfitt eyther for yow to speake,
or mee to heare, but yet the large Testimony I see of youre
affection, makes mee willing to suppress a great nomber of
Errors: Onely thus muche I thincke good to say, that the same
wordes in my Lady *Philocleas* mouthe, as from one woeman to
an other, mighte have had a better grace, and perchaunce have
founde a gentler receypte, Desyer holdes the Sences open, and
Lovers Conceyptes ys very quick. *Basilius*, no sooner receyved
this answer, but that as yf speedy flighte might save his lyfe,
hee turnde withoute any ceremony, away, from *Cleophila*, and
ranne with all speede his body woulde suffer hym, towardes his
fayre Daughter *Philoclea* : whome hee founde at that tyme
watching her Mother *Ginecia*, taking suche Restes as unquyett
sleepes & fearefull Dreames woulde yeelde her. *Basilius* delayed
no tyme, but, with all those Conjuring prayers whiche a Fathers
authority may lay uppon an humble Chylde, besought her shee
woulde preserve his lyfe, in whome her lyfe was begun, shee
woulde save his gray hayers from Rebuke, and his aged mynde
frome despayer. That yf shee were not cloyed with his Company,
and that shee thoughte the earthe overburdened with hym, shee
woulde coole his fyery plaigue, whiche was to bee done but by
her breathe. That in fyne, what soever hee was, hee was no
thing, but, what yt pleased *Cleophila*, hee lived in her and all
the powers of his Spirites depended of her: That, yf shee continewed Crewell, hee coulde no more susteyne hym self, then
the Earthe remayne fruitfull in the sonnes continuall absence.
Hee concluded shee shoulde in one payment requyte all his
desertes, and that shee needed not disdayne any service thoughe
never so base, whiche was warraunted by the sacred name of a
Father: *Philoclea*, more glad, then ever shee had knowne her
self, that shee mighte by this occasyon enjoy ye private Conference of *Cleophila*, yet had so sweete a feeling of vertue in her
mynde, that shee woulde not suffer a vyle Coloure to bee cast
over her highe thoughtes. But with an humble looke, and
obeydyent hart answered her Father, that there needed neyther
promyse nor perswasion unto her to make her doo her uttermoste

110

for her Fathers service: That, for *Cleophilaes* favoure in all vertuous sorte, shee woulde seeke yt towardes hym, and that, as shee woulde not perce further into his meaning, then hym self shoulde declare, so woulde shee interpret all his Doynges to bee accomplisshed in goodnes. And therefore, desyered, yf otherwyse yt shoulde bee, hee woulde not imparte yt unto her, who then shoulde bee forced to begynn by true obeydyence a shewe of Disobeydyence: Rather performing his generall Comaundem^t, whiche had ever bene to embrace vertue, then any new perticuler spronge oute of passyon, and contrary to the Former. *Basilius* y^t did but desyer by her meanes to have the beginning of a more free access unto *Cleophila*, allowed her reasons, and accepted her service, desyering but a speedy returne of Comfort: Away departed the moste Excellent *Philoclea*, with a newe fielde of fancyes in her traveyled mynde. For well she sawe her Father was now growne her adverse party, and her owne Fortune suche, as shee must needes favoure her Ryvall, who mighte have shewe of hope, where her self was oute of possibility of help: As shee walked a litle on, shee sawe at a Ryvers syde a fayre Lady, whose face was so bent over the River, that her flowyng teares continually fell into the water. Muche like as wee see in some pleasant gardens, costly Images are sett for founteynes, whiche yeelde abundance of waters, to the delightfull streames that ronne under them: Newly was *Philoclea* departed oute of the Chamber, when *Ginecia* trubled with a fearefull Dreame, frightfullye awaked. The Dreame was this, It seemed unto her to bee in a place full of thornes, whiche so molested her, as shee coulde neyther abyde standing still, nor treade safely goyng forward: In this Case, shee thoughte, *Cleophila*, (beeyng uppon a fayre Hill delightfull to the eye, and easy in apparance) called her thether. But, thether with much Anguish beeyng come, *Cleophila* was vanysshed, and shee founde no thing but a Deade body, whiche seeming at the first with a straunge smell so to infect her, as shee was redy to dye: Lykewyse, within a whyle, the Dead body shee thoughte tooke her in his Armes, and sayde, *Ginecia*, here ys thy onely Rest, with that shee awaked crying very lowde; *Cleophila. Cleophila.* But, remembring her self, and seeyng her husband by (as a guilty Conscyence dothe more suspect then ys suspected) shee turned her Calle, and called for *Philoclea*: *Basilius* (that God knowes knewe no reason whye hee mighte spare to tell yt) tolde her *Philoclea* was goñ to enterteyne the Lady *Cleophila* who had longe remayned in solitary Muses. *Ginecia,* as yf shee had heard her last Doñe pronounced ageanst her with a syde looke and chaunged face, O my Lorde (sayde shee) what meane yow to suffer those younge folckes together? *Basilius* smyling tooke her in his Armes, sweete wyfe (saide hee) I thanck yow for youre Care of youre Chylde, but they must bee youthes of other mettell then *Cleophila,* that can endaunger her: O but, (Cryed oute *Ginecia*) and therewith shee stopped, for then in deede did her spirite suffer a greate Conflict, betwixt the force of Love, and the rage of Jelosy. Many tymes was shee aboute to satisfye the spyte of her mynde, and tell *Basilius,* what, and upon what reasons shee thoughte *Cleophila,* to bee farr other then the owtewarde apparance: But these many tymes were all putt back by the manifolde forces of her vehement Love, fayne shee woulde have barred her Daughters happ, but lothe shee was to cutt of her owne hope; Often shee offered to have risen, to have broken, that which her Jelosy made her Imagyn, muche more, then so stollen a Leysure could suffer. But *Basilius,* who had no less desyer to taste of his Daughters laboure, woulde never suffer yt, swearing hee sawe sicknes in his wyves face, and therefore woulde not the Ayer shoulde have his power over her: Thus did *Ginecia* eate of her jealosy, pyne in her Love, and receyve, kyndenes, no where but from the founteyne of unkyndenes. In the meane tyme *Philoclea* sawe the Dolefull Lady and hearde her playnte, whiche was uttered in this sorte.

Fayre streames saide shee, that do vouchsafe in youre kyndenes, Clerenes, to represent unto mee my bloubered face, stay a litle youre Course, and receyve knouledg of my unfortunate fortune: Or yf ye vyolence of youre springe comaunde yo^w to haste away, to pay youre Duetyes, to youre great Mother the sea yet, Carry with yow these fewe wordes and Let the uttermoste ende of the worlde knowe them. *A Love as cleare as youre selves, employde to a Love (I feare) as Collde as youre selves, makes mee encrease youre flood with my teares, & continew my teares in youre presence.* With that shee tooke a Willow stick and wrote in a Sandy Bancke these verses.

Over these Brookes trusting to ease myne eyes,
(Myne eyes even greate in laboure with theyre teares)
I layed my face, my face wherein there lyes,
Clusters of Cloudes wch no Sunne ever cleares,
In watery glass my watery eyes I see:
Sorrowes yll easde, where Sorrowes paynted bee.

My thoughtes imprisond, in my secrett woes,
With flamy breath dothe issue ofte in sounde:
The sounde to this straunge Ayer no sooner goes,
But that yt dothe with Echos force rebounde,
And makes mee heare, the playntes I wolde refrayne
Thus owteward helps my inward greef menteyne.

Now in this Sande, I woulde discharge my mynde,
And Cast from mee parte of my Burdenous Cares:
But in the Sandes my paynes foretolde I fynde,
And see therein, howe well the wryter fares.
Synce streame, ayer, sand, myne eyes & eares conspire
What hope to quenche, where eche thing blowes ye fyer?

Philoclea, at the first sighte well knewe this was *Cleophila*, (for
so in deede yt was) but as there ys no thinge more agreeable then
a beloved voyce, shee was well content to heare her wordes,
whiche shee thought, mighte with more Cause have bene spoken
by her owne mowthe: But, when *Cleophila* did bothe cease to
speake and had ended her wryting, Philoclea gave her self to bee
seene of her, with suche a meeting of bothe theyre eyes together,
with suche a mutuall astonishment to them bothe, as yt well
shewed eche party had ynoughe to doo to meynteyne theyre
vitall powers in theyre due worcking. At lengthe, *Philoclea* having
a while mused, how to wade betwixt her owne hopeles affection,
and her Fathers unbrydled hope, with blusshing Cheekes, and
eyes cast downe to the grounde shee began to say: My Father,
to whome I owe my self, and therefore must performe all Duetyes
unto. When *Cleophila* streight embracing her, (and warranted by
a womanly habite ofte kissing her) Desyered her to stay her sweete
speeche, (For well shee knewe her Fathers arraunt, and should
receyve a sufficyent answer): But, now shee demaunded leave,
not to loose this longe soughte for Comodity of tyme, to ease her
hart thus farr, that yf in her Agonyes her Desteny was, to bee
condempned by *Philocleas* mouthe, at least *Philoclea* might knowe,

whome shee had Condempned. *Philoclea* easily yeelded to this Request, and therefore, sitting downe together uppon the greene banck hard by the ryver, longe in a deepe doubte howe to begyñ, thoughe shee had often before thoughte of yt, with panting harte brought yt forthe on this maner: Moste beloved Lady, the incomparable Worthynes of youre self joyned to the greatenes of youre estate, and the Importance of the thinge whereon my lyfe consisteth dothe requyre, bothe lengthe of tyme in the beginning and many Ceremonyes in yᵉ uttering my enforced speeche. But the smalle oportunity of envyous occasyon with the malicyous eye hatefull Love dothe cast uppon mee, and the extreme bent of my affection, whiche will eyther breake oute in wordes or breake my hart, compell mee not onely to embrace yᵉ smallest tyme, I may obteyne, but, to lay asyde all respectes due to youre self in respect of my owne lyfe, whiche ys nowe or never to bee preserved: I do therefore vowe to yow hereafter, never more to omitt all dutyfull formes, Doo yow now onely vouchsafe, to heare the matters of a moste perplexed mynde, yf ever the sounde of Love have come to youre eares, or yf ever yow have understood what force yt hathe had, to Conquer the strongest hartes, and chaunge the moste setled estates. Receyve here not onely an Example of those straunge Tragedyes, but one, that in hym self hathe conteyned all the particularityes of theyre mysfortune: And from henceforthe beleeve yt may bee, synce yoʷ shall see yt ys, yow shall see I say, a Living Image and a present Story of the best Paterñ, Love hathe ever shewed of his worckmanship. But, alas, whether goest thow my toungue, or how dothe my harte consent to adventure the reveyling my nerest tuching Secrettes, but, spare not my speeche, here ys the Author of my harmes, the witnes of thy wordes, and the Judge of thy lyfe: Therefore ageane I say, I say, O onely Princes attend here a myserable mirackle of affection, beholde here before youre eyes *Pyrocles* Prince of *Macedon*, whome onely yow have broughte to this falle of fortune, and unused *Metamorphoses* whome yow onely have made neglect his Contry, forgett his Father, and lastly forsake hym self. My sute ys to serve yow, and my ende ys to doo yow Honor, youre fayre face hathe many marckes in yt of amasement at my wordes: Thinke then what his amasement ys, from whence they come, synce no wordes can carry with them the lyfe of the Inward feeling. Yf the highest love in no base person may beare place in youre judgement then may I hope, youre beuty will not bee withoute pity: yf other wyse yow bee (alas but let yt never bee so) resolved, yet shall not my deathe bee withoute Comfort, receyving yt by youre sentence. The Joy whiche wroughte into *Pygmalyons* mynde whilest hee founde his beloved Image, waxe by litle and litle bothe softer and warmer in his folded armes, till at length yt accomplished his gladnes with a perfect womans shape still butyfyed with the former perfections, was even suche as by eche degree of *Cleophilas* wordes stealing entered into *Philocleas* sowle: Till her pleasure was fully made up with the manifesting of his beeyng, whiche was suche as in hope did overcome hope, yet did a certeyne sparcke of Honor aryse in her well disposid mynde whiche bredd a starting feare, to bee nowe in secrett with hym, in whose presence notwithstanding consisted her Comfort: (Suche Contradictions there must needes growe in those myndes whiche neyther absolutely embrace goodnes, nor frely yeelde to evell). But that sparcke soone gave place, or at least gave no more light in her mynde, then Candle dothe in the Sunnes presence, but even astonished with a surfett of Joy, and fearefull of shee knewe not what (as hee whiche newly fyndes muche treasure ys moste subject to Doubtes) with a shrugging kynde of Tremor throwe all her principall partes, shee gave these affectionate wordes for answer: Alas, how paynefull a thinge yt ys to a devyded mynde to make a well joyned answer. How harde ys yt to bringe shame to owteward Confessyon, and how foolish trowe yee must that answer bee, whiche ys made one knowes not to whome? Shall I say, O *Cleophila*, alas youre wordes bee ageanst yt? shall I say Prince *Pyrocles*, (wretch y^t I am) youre shewe ys manifest ageanst yt? But this this I may well say yf I had continued, as I oughte, *Philoclea*, yow had eyther never bene, or ever bene, *Cleophila* yow had eyther never attempted this Chaunge fed with hope, or never discovered yt, stopt wth dispayre. But I feare mee my behavyour yll governed gave yo^w ye first Comfort I feare mee my affection yll hidd hathe given yow this last assurance: yf my Castle had not seemed weyke, yow woulde never have broughte these disguysed forces? No, No, I have betrayed my self, yt was well seene I was glad to yeelde, before I was assaulted. Alas then what shall I doo, shall I seeke farr fetched inventions? Shall I laboure to lay Coloures over my galled thoughtes, or rather, thoughe the purenes of my virgyn mynde bee stayned, Let mee keepe the true simplicity of my worde. True yt ys alas too true yt ys O *Cleophila* (for so I do love to calle thee) synce in that Name my Love first began, and in ye shade of that name my Love shall best bee hidden, that even whyle so thow werte (what eye bewitched mee I knowe not) my passyons were farr fitter to desyer then to bee desyered: Shall I say then I am sory, or that my Love must bee turned to hate, synce thow arte turned to *Pyrocles*? How may that well bee, since when thow werte *Cleophila*, the Dispayre, thow mightest not bee thus did moste torment mee? Thow haste then the victory, use yt now with vertue, synce from the steppes of vertue my sowle ys witness to yt self yt never hathe, and pledge to yt self yt never shall declyne no way to make mee leave to Love the, but by making mee thincke thy Love unworthy of mee. *Pyrocles* so carryed away with Joy that hee did not envy the goddes felicity presented her with some Jewells of inestimable pryce, as tokens bothe of his Love and quality: And for Conclusion of proof shewed her Letters from his Father Kinge *Evarchus* unto hym, whiche hande shee happily knewe, as having kept dyvers wch passed betuixt her Father and hym. There, with many suche embrasinges (as yt seemed theyre sowles desyered to meete, and theyre hartes to kisse as theyre mowthes did) they passed the promys of mariage: But *Ginecias* restles affection & furyous Jelosy had by this tyme preveyled somuche with her husband as to come to seperate them. O Jelosy the fransy of wyse folkes, the well wisshing spirit & unkynde Carefullnes, the self punishment for others faulte and self misery in others happynes: The sister of Envy, Daughter of Love & Mother of hate, howe couldest thow so quickly gett a seate in ye unquyet hart of *Ginecia*, a Lady very fayre, in her strongest aige, knowne, wyse and esteemed vertuous. Yt was thy breeders power that planted ye there, yt was the inflaming Agonyes of affection, that drue on ye feyver, of thy sicknes in suche sorte that Nature gave place: The growing of her Daughter seemed the decay of her self, the blessinges of a Mother turned to the Curses of a Competitor, and the fayre face of *Philoclea* appeared more horrible in her sighte, then the Image of deathe. Possest with these Devills of Love and Jelosy, the greater and wretched Lady *Ginecia* had ridd her self from her tedyus Husband (who thoughte now hee mighte freely give her leave to goo hoping his Daughter by that tyme had performed his

116

message) and as soone as shee was alone, with Lookes straungely
cast aboute her, shee began to denounce Warr to all the worckes
of earthe & powers of heaven: But the invenymed heate wch lay
within her gave her not scope for many wordes, but with as muche
rage as the *Troyan* woman went to burne *Æneas* shippes shee
rann headlongly towardes the place, where shee guessed her
Daughter and *Cleophila* might bee together: yet by the way there
came into her mynde, an oulde songe, whiche shee thoughte did
well figure her fortune, The songe was this, thoughe her leysure
served her not as then to singe yt.

> *With twoo straunge fyers of equall heate possest,*
> *The one of Love, the other Jelosy,*
> *Bothe still doo worcke, in neyther fynde I rest:*
> *For, bothe, alas theyre strengthes together lye,*
> *The one alofte dothe holde the other hye,*
> *Love wakes the Jelous eye leste thence yt mooves,*
> *The Jelous eye, the more yt lookes, yt loves*
>
> *These fyers increase, in these I dayly burne,*
> *They feede on mee, and with my wynges do flye,*
> *My Lyvely Joyes to dolefull asshes turne,*
> *Theyre flames mount up, my powers prostrate lye:*
> *They live in force, I quyte consumed dye.*
> *One wonder yet farr passeth my Conceipt?*
> *The fewell smalle, howe bee the fyers so greate?*

Beeyng come where they were, to the greate astonishment of
the sweete *Philoclea*, (whose Conscyence now began to knowe
Cause of blusshing) for first salutation, shee gave an eye to her
Daughter, full of the same disdaynefull scorne, w^ch *Pallas* shewed
to ye pore *Arachne*, that durst contend with her for the pryce of
well weaving: yet, see the force of Love did somuche rule her
that thoughe for *Cleophilas* sake shee did detest her, yet for *Cleophilas* sake, shee used no harder wordes to her, then to bidd her
goo home, and accompany her solitary father. Then began shee
to display to *Cleophila* the storehowse of her Deadly desyers, when
sodenly the Confused Rumor of a mutinus multitude gave just
occasion to *Cleophila*, to breake of any suche Conference: For,
well shee founde they were no frendly voyces they hearde, and
to retyre with as muche diligence as Conveyniently they coulde
towardes the lodge. Yet before they coulde wynn the Lodge by

Twenty paces, they were overtaken by an unruly sorte of Clownes whiche lyke a vyolent flood were carryed, they them selves knewe not whether: But assoone, as they came within the Compas of blowes, like enraged beastes withoute respect of theyre estates or pitty of theyre sexe, They rann uppon these fayre Ladyes, to shewe the righte nature of a villeyn, never thinckyng his estate happy, but when hee ys able to doo hurte. Yet so many as they were, so many allmoste were theyre myndes, all knitt together onely in madnes, some cryed, take, some kill, some save; But, even they that cryed save, rañ for Company with them that mente to kill, every one Commaunded none obeyed, hee onely seemed to have moste preheminence, that was moste ragefull. *Cleophila*, whose vertuous Corage was ever awake in her, drawyng oute her sworde kepte a while ye villaynes at a Bay, while the Ladyes gott them selves into the Lodge: Owte of whiche the good oulde *Basilius* having putt on an Armoure longe before untryed, came to proove his aucthoritye among his Subjectes, or at least to adventure his lyfe with his dere Mistrys. The Ladyes in the meane tyme tremblingly attended the Issue of this daungerus adventure, but, *Cleophila*, did quickly make them perceyve, that one Eagle ys worthe a greate nomber of kytes: No blowe shee strake that did not suffyce for a full rewarde of hym that receyved yt, yet at length the many handes woulde have preveyled ageanst these twoo, had not the noble Shepearde *Dorus* hearde this noyse, and come to theyre succoure. *Dorus* had bene uppon a fyne litle hill not farr of in the Company of some other Shepeardes, defending hym from the sunnes heate, with the shade of a fewe myrtle Trees feeding his Masters sheepe, practizing his newe learned shepeardes pype; And singing with greate joy for the longe pursewed victory hee had lately gotten of the gracyous *Pamelas* favoure, victory, so farr as the promysed affection came unto, hee having lately (keeping still his disguysed maner) opened more playnely bothe his mynde and estate; his songe (as the Shepeardes after recoumpted yt) was this.

Feede on my sheepe, my Charge, my Comforte, feede?
    With Sunnes approche, youre pasture fertile growes,
O, onely Sunne, that, suche a frute can breede,
    Feede on my sheepe youre fayre sweete feeding flowes
    Eche flower, eche herbe dothe to youre service yeelde
O blessed Sunne, whence all this blessing goes,

Feede on my sheepe, possess youre fruitfull fielde,
*   No Wolves dare howle, no murrayne can prevayle,*
And from the stormes oure sweetest Sunne will sheelde,
*   Feede on my Sheepe, sorrowe hathe stricken sayle.*

Enjoy my Joyes as yow did taste my payne,
While oure sonne shynes, no Cloudy greeves assayle.
Feede on my Sheepe, youre Native Joyes meynteyne,
Youre wolle ys riche, no toungue can tell my gayne.

His Songe beeyng ended, the younge Shepeheard *Philisides* at
that tyme in his Company, as yf *Dorus* Joy had beene a Remembraunce to his sorowe, Tuning his voyce in Dolefull manner,
thus made answer unto hym, using the burden of his owne wordes.

Leave of my sheepe, yt ys no tyme to feede,
*   My Sunne ys goñ, youre pasture bareyn growes,*
O Crewell Sunne thy hate this harme dothe breede,
*   Leave of my Sheepe, my shower of Teres oreflowes*
*   Youre sweetest flowers youre herbes no service yeelde*
My Sunne, alas, from mee for ever gooes.

Leave of my Sheepe my sighes burne up youre feelde,
*   My Playntes calle wolves, my plagues in yo^w prevayle,*
My Sunne ys gonñ, from stormes that shoulde us shielde:
*   Leave of my Sheepe, sorowe hathe hoysed saile.*

Wayle in my woes, taste of youre Masters payne,
My sunne ys gonne, now Cloudy greeves assayle;
Leave Leaving not my mourning to meyntayne,
Yow beare no wolle, and losse ys all my gayne.

Before *Philisides* had finisshed the last accent of his songe, the
horrible Cryes of the madd multitude gave an untymely Conclusyon to his passionate Musick: But *Dorus* had streighte represented before the eyes of his Carefull Love, the Perrill wherein
his other sowle mighte bee. Therefore taking no other weapen
then his sheepehooke whiche hee thought sufficyẽt (bycause yt
had suffyced to bringe hym in a Towardnes of his moste redoubted request) hee gave example to *Philisides*, and some other
of the best mynded Shepeards to followe hym: First hee went
to *Pamelas* Lodge, where fynding her allredy Close in a stronge
Cave, a litle from the Lodge, (not possible to bee entred into by
force), with *Miso*, *Mopsa* and *Dametas*, who woulde not that

tyme of the day have opened the entrie to his father. Hee ledd his litle Troupe to the other Lodge, where hee sawe *Cleophila*, having Three of that rustick Route deade at her feete, and bathed in the blood of a greate nomber other: But bothe shee and the Duke so wearyed with the excessive nomber of them, y^t they were bothe resolved to sell theyre lyves at a deare pryce. When *Dorus* comĩng in, and Cryinge, Corage, here ys *Dorus* to his dere frende *Cleophila*, felled one of them with his sheepe hooke, and taking his bill from hym, valyantly seconded by *Philisides*, and the other honest Shepeherdes, made so fayre way among them, that hee wañn tyme for them all to recover the Lodge, and to give the Rebells a face of wood on the owtesyde: The Joy *Ginecia* and *Philoclea* felt in seeyng them safely come in, whome bothe they loved, and in whome theyre lyves consisted woulde have bene unspeakeable, had yt not beene muche kept downe with the savage howling the Rascalls made wthoute, who, now begañ to seeke fyer to burne the gates, seeynge other wyse they were unlikely to prevayle. But, before I tell yow what became therof, mee thinckes yt reason yo^w knowe what raging motion was the beginning of this Tumulte: *Bacchus* (they say) was begotten with Thunder, I thinck that made hym ever synce so full of sturr, and debate, *Bacchus* in deede yt was wch sounded the first Trompett of this rude Allarum, a Maner the *Arcadians* had, to solempnize the Princes byrthe dayes with banquetting together: As largely as the quality of ye Company coulde suffer a barbarus opinyon to thincke, with vyce, to doo honor, or with activity in beastlynes to shewe abundance of Love. This Custome beeyng generall, was particulerly this tyme of *Basilius* nativity observed by a village, nere the Dezarte of the twoo Lodges, called *Phagona* ; there beeyng chafed with wyne, and emboldened with the Dukes absented maner of Living: There was no matter theyre eares had ever hearde of, that grewe not to bee a Subject of theyre wyny Conference, publique afares were mingled with private grudge, neyther was any man thought of witt, that did not pretend some Cause of myslyke, Raylinge was coumpted the fruite of freedome, and saying no thing had his uttermoste prayse in ignorance. At the lengthe the Princes person fell to bee theyre Table talke, and to speake lycencyously of that, was a tickling poynte of Corage to them, a proude worde did swell in theyre stomackes, and disdaynefull reproches to great persons had putt on a shadowe

of greatenes in theyre litle myndes: Till at lengthe the very
unbrydeled use of wordes having increased fyer to theyre myndes
(whiche thoughte theyre knouledg notable bycause they had at
all no knouledg, to Condempne theyre owne wante of knowledge) they discended to a direct myslyke of ye Dukes living from
among them. Whereuppon yt were tedyous to wryte theyre farr
fetched Constructions, but the Some was hee Disdayned them,
and what were the shewes of his estate yf theyre Armes meynteyned hym not? who woulde calle hym *Duke* yf hee had not a
people? When certeyne of them of wretched estates, and worse
myndes (whose fortunes, chaunge coulde not empayre) began to
say, a Straunge Woman had now possest theyre Prince and
government. *Arcadians* were too playne headed to give the Prince
Counseyll, what neede from henceforward to feare forreyne
enimyes, synce they were conquered withoute stroke stryking,
theyre secrettes opened, theyre tresures abused, them selves
tryumphed over, and never overthrowen. Yf *Arcadia* grewe
Loathsome in the *Dukes* sighte, why did hee not ridd hym self
of the truble, there would not want those shoulde take so fayre
a Comber in good parte, since the Contry was theyres and that
the governement was an adherent to the Contry: whye shoulde
they that needed not to bee partakers of the daunger, bee partakers with the Cause of the Daunger. Nay rather (sayde they)
let us begyn that, whiche all *Arcadia* will followe, lett us deliver
oure Prince from forreyne handes, and oure selves from ye wante
of a Prince? Lett us bee the first to doo that whiche all the Rest
thincke? Lett yt bee sayde the *Phagonians* are they wch are not
astonished with vayne Tytles, that have theyre force, but in oure
forces? Lastly, to have saide and hearde somuche was as punish-
able, as to have attempted, and to attempt they had the gloryous
shewe of Comon Wealthe with them. These wordes beyng
spoken, like a furyous storme tooke holde presently of theyre
well enclyned braynes, there needed no Drum, where eche man
cryed, eche spake to other, that spake as fast to hym, and the
Disagreeing sounde of so many voyces was the onely token of
theyre unmeete agreement: Thus was theyre Banquett turned
into a Battell, theyre wyny myrthes to bloody rages and ye happy
prayers for the *Duke* to monstrous threatninges his estate, the
solempnizing his byrthe day tended to the Cause of his funeralles.
But as Rage hathe, besydes his wickednes, that folly, that the

more yt seekes to hurte, the less yt considers howe to bee able
to hurt: They never weyed howe to arme them selves but tooke
up every thinge for a weapon, that fury offered to theyre handes,
some swordes and Billes, there were other that tooke pitche
forckes and Rakes converting husbandry to Souldyery. Some
caughte holde of Spittes, thinges servisable for ye lyves of men,
to bee the Instrumentes of theyre Deathes, and there wanted
not suche, whiche helde the same pottes wherein they had
Droncke to the *Dukes* healthe, to use them (as they coulde) to
his myschief: Thus Armed, thus governed, adding fury to fury,
and encreasing rage with ronning, they went headlonge towardes
the Dukes lodge, no man in his owne hart resolved, what was
the uttermoste hee woulde doo when hee came thether. But,
as myscheef ys of suche nature, that yt can not stande but with
strengthening one evill by an other, and so multiply in yt self
till yt come to the hyghest and then falle with his owne weighte:
So to theyre myndes once passed the bondes of obeydyence, more
and more wickednes opened yt self, And they whiche first pretended to succoure hym then, to reforme hym now thoughte
no safety to them selves, withoute killing hym in this madd
moode. *Cleophilas* excellent valoure joyned to *Basilius* and suc-
cored by the worthy *Dorus*, and his fellow Shepeheardes made
them feele the Smarte, of theyre folly, till for last extremity they
soughte for unmercyfull fyer to bee theyre foregoer: Then did
ye Ladyes with pityfull shrikes shewe the Deadly feare they had
of a present Massacre, especially the sweete *Philoclea*, who ever
caughte holde of *Cleophila*, So by the folly of Love hindering the
succoure, whiche succoure shee desyered. But *Cleophila* seeyng
no way of defence, nor tyme to deliberate, thoughte the onely
meane with extraordenary bouldenes to overcome bouldnes, and
with Daunger to avoyde Daunger: And therefore, when they
were even redy to putt fyer, shee caused the gate to bee opened
by *Dorus*, whoo stoode there, redy to doo his uttermoste for her
Defence. For all the rest cryed to her, shee shoulde not so adventure her lyfe, and so with her sworde by her syde redy but
not drawne, shee issewed amonge them: The blowes shee had
dealte before (thoughe all in generall were hasty) made eche or
them take breathe, before they broughte them selves sodenly
over nere her. So that shee had tyme to gett up to the Judgment seate, of the *Duke*, wch according to the guyse of that

122

Contry was hard before the Courte gate: There shee paused,
a while, making signe with her hande unto them that shee had
some thing to say woulde please them. Truely owtewarde graces
are not with oute theyre efficacyes, the goodlynes of her shape,
with that quyet Magnanimity representid in her face in this
outter moste perill, did even fixe the eyes of this barbarus people
with thadmiration uppon her: And the nature of man ys suche,
that as they leave no ragefull vyolence unattempted whyle theyre
Choler ys nurrished with resistance, so when the very Subject
of theyre wrothe ys unlooked for, offered to theyre handes, yt
makes them at leste take a pause, before they determeyn Cruelty.
Cleophila whose wittes were not dismayed quickly espyed her
Comming had bredd an alteracyon, and therefore meaning to
use the advantage of tyme, and to speake determinately while
shee mighte bee hearde, with a brave unbasshed Countenance
thus sayde: An unadvysed thinge yt ys, and I thincke, not
heretofore seene, O *Arcadians*, that a woman shoulde give
Counsell to men, a Straunger to the Contrey people, and that
lastly in suche a presence a private person as I am shoulde possess
the Regall throne? But the strangenes of youre action makes
that used for vertue, whiche youre vyolent necessity imposeth,
for certeynly a woman may well speake to suche men, who have
forgotten all manly governement: A Straunger may with reason
instruct suche subjectes as neglect due poyntes of subjection.
And ys yt merveyle this place ys entred into by an other, synce
youre owne *Duke*, after xxx yeares government, dare not shewe
his face to his faythfull people? Heare therefore O *Arcadians*,
and bee asshamed, ageanst whome hathe this zealous rage bene
styrred? whether have yow bent those manfull weapons of youres
in this quyet harmeles Lodge? There are harboured no *Troianes*
youre auncyent Enimyes, nor *Persians*, whome yow have in
present feare? Here lodge none but suche, as eyther yow have
greate Cause to love, or no Cause to hate? But, none other moste
sure can yt bee, ys yt I? O *Arcadians* ageanst whome youre
anger ys armed? Am I the marck of youre vehement quarrell?
yf yt bee so, that Innocency shall not bee a stopp for furye? yf
yt bee so, the Lawe of hospitallity may not Defend a Straunger
fled to your Armes for succour: Yf lastly yt bee so, that so many
valyant mens Corages can bee enflamed to the myscheef of one
hurtles woman, I refuse not to make my lyfe a sacrifice to youre

wrathe. Exercyse in mee youre indignation, so yt goo no furder,
I am content to pay the great favoures I have receyved among
yow, with the usury of my well deserving lyfe: I present yt to
yo^w here, O *Arcadians* yf that may suffyse yo^w, rather then yo^w
(called over the worlde the wyse and quyett *Arcadians*) shoulde
bee so vayne as to attempt that alone, (wch all youre Contry will
abhorr) then yow shoulde shewe youre selves so ungratefull, as
to forgett the fruite of so many yeares peaceable government, or
so unmercyfull as not to have any fury over mastered wth the
holy name of youre Naturall *Duke*. For, suche a hellish madnes
(I knowe) will never enter into youre hartes, as to attempt any
thing ageanst his person, wch no Successor (thoughe never so
hatefull to hym) will for his owne sake leave unpunished: Neyther
can youre wonted valure bee turned to suche a basenes, as instede
of a *Duke* delyvered unto yo^w by so many Royall Auncestors, to
take the Tyrannous yoke of youre fellow subject, in whome the
[innate] meanes will bringe forthe Ravenous Covetusnes, and
the newnes of his estate suspectfull Cruelty. Imagyn what coulde
youre enimyes more wishe unto yo^w, then to see yow with youre
owne handes overthrowe youre estate: O what woulde the first
Arcadians youre worthy predecessors saye, yf they lived at this
tyme, and sawe theyre ofspring defacyng suche an excellent
Monarchy? whiche they with muche laboure and bloode wysely
establisshed? No no, youre honest hartes will never so gratify
youre hatefull Neighboures, nor so degenerate from youre famous
Auncesters. I see in youre Countenaunces now vertuously settled
no thing but Love and Duty to hym, (who onely, for youre
sakes dothe embrace the government) the uncerteynty of his
estate made yo^w take Armes: Now yow see hym well with the
same Love lay them down. Yf now yow ende, (as I knowe yow
will) hee will take no other accoumpte of yow, but, as of a
vehement, I must confess over vehemẽt affection, the onely
Countenaunce shoulde proove a wickednes, But yt ys not so,
I see very well, yow begañ with zeale, and will ende with
reverence. The Action *Cleophila* used wth a sweete magnanimity
and stately myldenes, did so perse into theyre hartes, whome the
taking of breathe had Cooled, and leysure had taughte Doubtes,
that in steade of roaring Cryes, there was nowe hard no thinge,
butt a Confused muttering: whether her sayinge was to bee
followed betuixt Doubte to pursue, and feare to leave. Glad

124

every one woulde have bene, yt had never bene beguñ, but how
to end yt (eche afrayed of his Companyon) they knew not: So
muche easyer yt ys to enflame then to quenche, to tye, then to
loose knottes. But, *Cleophila*, (to take an assured possession of
theyre myndes, wch shee founde began to waver) Loyall *Arcadians* (sayde shee) now do I offer unto yo^w the manifesting of
youre Duttyes All those that have taken Armes for the *Dukes*
safety, lett them turne theyre backes to the gate, with theyre
weapons bent ageanst suche as woulde hurt the sacred person of
the *Duke*: O weyke trust of the many headed multitude, whome
inconstancy onely dothe guyde at any tyme, to well dooyng.
Let no man lay confidence there where Company taketh away
shame, and eche may lay, the faulte in his fellowe, the worde no
sooner came from *Cleophila* but that there were showtes of Joy
w^th *God save the Duke*: And they with muche Jolity growne
to bee the *Dukes* garde, that but then before meant to bee his
Murderers. And in deede no yll way yt ys in suche mutinyes
to give them some occasyon of suche service as they may thincke
in theyre owne judgmentes may Counterveyle theyre trespas:
yet was not this done with suche an unity of hartes but that
theyre faces well shewed yt was but a sheepes Draught and no
thirst of good will. Namely some of them who, as they were
forwardest in the myscheef, coulde leste perswade a pardon to
them selves woulde fayne have made a resistance to the Rest;
But theyre fellowes that were moste glad to have suche a meane
to shewe theyre Loyalty dispatched moste of them with a good
Rule, that to bee Leaders in Disobeydience, teacheth ever dis-
obedyence to the same Leaders. So was this ungracyous motion
converted in to theyre owne bowells, and they by a true Judgment
growne theyre owne punysshers, Till the *Duke*, promysing a
generall pardon, moste parte with Marckes of theyre folly returned home: Saving a fewe to the nomber of a Dossen (in
whome theyre owne Naughtynes coulde suffer no assurance)
fledd to certeyn woodes not farr of, where they kept them selves,
to see how the pardon should bee observed, Where feeding
wyldely with grass and suche other foode, Drincking onely
water, they were well disciplyned from the Dronken ryottes.
To describe unto yo^w the miserable feare *Cleophilas* Lovers lived
in, while shee stoode at the discressyon of those undiscreet rebells
(howe at every angery Countenaunce any of them made they

thoughte a knyfe was layde uppon theyre owne throate) would requyer as many wordes, as to make yow knowe, howe full they were now of unspeakeable joy : That they sawe, besydes the savety of theyre owne estates, the same wroughte, and safely wroughte by her meane, in whome they had placed all theyre delightes. There wanted no embracem^{tes} no prayses of her vertue, no owte-ward signes of theyre inward affection : But, as they were in the mydst of those unfayned Ceremonyes a Gitterne yll played on, accompanyed with a hoarse voyce, (who seemed to singe maugre the Muses & to bee mery in spite of fortune) made them looke the way of the yll noysed songe, but the song was this

> *A Hatefull Cry, with hate to heale,*
> *A bloody help, with blood to save,*
> *A foolish thinge, with fooles to deale :*
>   *Let hym bee boulde, that Bobbes will have.*
>   *But, who by meanes of wysdome hye :*
>   *Hathe saved his Charge? yt ys even I.*
>
> *Lett other deck theyre pryde with scarres,*
>   *And of theyre woundes make brave lame showes,*
> *First lett them dye, then passe the starres,*
>   *When rotten fame will tell theyre Blowes.*
>   *But eye from blood, and eare frome Crye,*
>   *Who hathe saved all? It ys even I.*

They had soone perceyved yt was Master *Dametas*, who came with no less lifted up Countenaunce, then yf hee had passed over the bellyes of all his enemyes : So wyse a poynte hee thoughte hee had performed in using the naturall strength of his Cave, but never was yt his dooyng to come so soone thence, till the Coastes were more assuredly cleare. For yt was a Rule with hym, yt after great stormes there ever fell fewe Droppes before they bee fully finisshed : But *Pamela*, who had now experyenced (howe muche Care dothe sollicite a Lovers harte) used this occasyon of goyng to her Parentes in deed unquyett, till her eye mighte bee assured howe her Shepeheard had goñ throwe the daunger. *Basilius*, with the sighte of *Pamela*, of whome his heade (otherwyse occupyed) had lost the wonted remembrance, was sodenly stricken into a devoute kynde of admiracyon. And therefore presently commaunded his wyfe and Daughters to assist hym in a sacrifice hee woulde make to

126

Apollo, for even now (saide hee) doo I fynde the force of his Oracle. Hee woulde not, for all that, reveyle the secrett therof for, that, no man ever knewe of hym, but his best trusted frend *Philanax*, but, in his mynde, thus hee construed yt : That where the Oracle sayde (*His Elder care shoulde by Princely meane bee stollen awaye from hym And yet, not Loste*), yt was now performed, since *Cleophila* had as yt were robde from hym, the Care of his first begotten Chylde, yet was yt not lost since in his harte the grounde of yt remayned. *His younger shoulde with natures bliss embrace the Love*—of *Cleophila*, bycause hee had so commaunded her, for his service, so to doo, yet, shoulde yt bee wth as muche hate of nature) for beeyng so hatefull an opposite to the Jelosy hee thought her mother had of hym. The thirde was yt wch moste rejoyced hym, for now hee interpreted the meaning therof, that hee *Shoulde accomplish hys unlawfull desyer, with—Cleophila* : And that (after the *Deathe of Ginecia*) *shee shoulde become hys wyffe*. And no less Comforte receyved hee of the last poynte, for that hee thoughte *The threatning Influence to his estate* was in this passed, in respect *Cleophila* had (as yow have hearde) possest his Regall throne. Thus the fawning Honoure of false hope made hym take every thing to his owne best. And suche ys the selfnes of affection, that (bycause hys mynde ranne wholy upon *Cleophila*) hee thoughte the *Godds* in theyre Oracles did mynde no thing but her. These many good Successes aswell essentiall, as Imaginative, made hym gratefull to *Apollo*, and therefore excluding all the rest, saving his wyfe and Daughters (as theyre maner was) when they privately made Oblations to theyre howseholde *Godds*, after sacrifice done, they sange together this theyre yearely used *Hymne*.

Apollo *greate, whose beames the greater worlde do lighte,*
   And in oure litle worlde doste clere oure inwarde sighte :
Whiche ever shynes, thoughe hidd from earthe, by earthly shade,
   Whose Lightes do ever live, but in oure Darcknes fade.
Thow God whose youth was deckt with spoyle of Pithons *skynn*
   So humble knowledge can throwe downe the Snakish synn
Latonas *sonne, whose byrthe in paynes and travell longe,*
   Dothe teache to learne the good, which Travells doo belonge.
In travell of oure lyfe, a short, but tedyous space,
   Whyle brickle Hower glass ronnes, guyde thow oure panting Race,

127

Give us foresightfull myndes, give us myndes to obaye,
  What foresight telles oure thoughtes uppon thy knowledg stay,
Lett so oure fruites growe up, that nature bee meyntaynde,
  But so oure hartes keepe downe, wth vyce they bee not staynde.
Lett this assured Holde, oure Judgementes ever take,
  That, no thinge wynnes the heaven, but what dothe earthe for-
  sake.

Assoone as hee had ended his Devotion, the Coming thether together of a greate nomber of Shepeheardes (whiche had followed *Dorus,* to succoure hym) remembred *Basilius,* to calle ageane for the Pastoralles, wch in this sorte was handled.

Here endes the Second Booke or Acte.

HERE BEGIN THE SECOND EGLOGUES.

The Rude tumulte of the *Phagonians* gave occasyon to the honest Shepeheardes, to bringe theyre Pastoralles this day with a Daunce whiche they called *The Skirmish betuixt Reason and Passyon.* For, Seaven Shepeardes whiche were named the *Reasonable* Shepeheardes joyned them selves, fowre of them making a square and the other twoo goyng a litle wyde of eyther syde, like winges of the Mayne battell, and the seaventh Man foremoste lyke the forlorne hope, to begyn the skirmish. In like order came oute the Seaven *Passionate* Shepeheardes, all keeping the pace of theyre foote by theyre voyce, and sondry Consorted instrumentes they helde in theyre Armes: And first the foremoste of the *Reasonable* syde begañ to singe.

Reason. *Thow Rebell vyle, come, to thy Master yeelde;*

       (And the other that mett with him answered)

Passion. *No Tyrant, no, myne, myne shall bee the feelde.*
R.   *Can Reason, then a Tyrant coumpted bee?*
P.   *Yf Reason will that Passyons bee not free.*
R.   *But Reason will, that Reason governe moste :*
P.   *And Passyon will that passyon rule the Roste.*
R.   *Youre will ys will but Reason, Reason ys :*
P.   *Will hathe his will, when Reasons will dothe mysse.*
R.   *Whome passyon leades unto his deathe, ys bent :*
P.   *And lett hym dye, so that bee dye content.*
R.   *By Nature yow, to Reason faythe hathe sworne:*
P.   *Not so ; but Fellowlike together borne.*
R.   *Who passyon dothe ensewe lives in anoye;*
P.   *Who passyon dothe forsake, lives voyde of Joye.*
R.   *Passyon ys blynde, and treades an unknowne trace:*
P.   *Reason hathe eyes, to see his owne evell Case.*

      Then (as they approched nearer) Twoo of *Reasons*
      syde (as yf they shott att the other) thus sange.

Reason. *Dare passyons then abyde in Reasons lighte?*
Passyon. *And ys not Reason dyñed with passyons mighte?*
R.   *O Foolish thinge, whiche glory doest destroy.*
P.   *O gloryous Tytle of a Foolish Toye.*

R.   *Weykenes yow are, dare yo^w with oure strengthe feighte?*
P.   *Bycause, oure Weykenes weykeneth all youre mighte.*
R.   *O sacred Reason helpp oure vertuous Toyles?*
P.   *O passyon pass, on feeble Reasons spoylles.*
R.   *Wee with oure selves abyde a dayly stryfe:*
P.   *Wee gladly use the sweetenes of oure Lyfe.*
R.   *But, yet oure stryfe sure peace in ende dothe breede?*
P.   *Wee now have peace, youre peace wee doo not neede.*

Then did the twoo Square Battells meete, and (in
steade of feighting) embrace one an other, singing thus.

R.   *Wee are too stronge, but, reason, seekes not blood;*
P.   *Whoo bee too weyke, do fayne they bee too good.*
R.   *Thoughe wee can not orecome, oure Cause ys Just:*
P.   *Lett us orecome, and lett us bee unjust.*
R.   *Yet, passyon yeelde, at lengthe to Reasons strooke:*
P.   *What shall wee wynn by taking Reasons yooke.*
R.   *The Joyes yow have shall bee made permanent:*
P.   *And so wee shall with greef Learne to repent.*
R.   *Repent in Deede, but, that shall bee youre Blisse:*
P.   *Howe knowe wee that, synce present Joyes wee misse.*
R.   *Yow knowe yt not, of Reason, therefore knowe yt:*
P.   *No Reason yet, had ever skill to showe yt.*

Then Let us bothe to Heavenly Rules give place:
Whiche Reasons *skill, and* Passyons *doo deface.*

Then embraced they one an other, and came to the *Duke*,
who framed his prasyes of them, according to *Cleophilas* liking
that satt at y^t tyme betwixt the *Duke* and the *Duchess*: As yf
shee had had her choyse of drowninge or burning: but, her
twoo unrestrayned partes the mynde and eye, had theyre free
Convoy to the dilicate *Philoclea*, whose Looke was not shorte
in well requyting yt: Allthoughe shee knewe yt was a hatefull
sighte to the marcking eye of her Jelous Moother: But *Dicus*,
that had in this tyme taken a greate lyking of *Dorus* for the
good partes hee founde above his age in hym, had delighte to
taste the fruites of his wittes: Thoughe in a Subject, whiche
hee hym self moste of all other despysed, and so entered into
speeche with hym in ye maner of this followyng Eglogue.

130

Dicus.   Dorus.

Dicus. Dorus *tell mee, where ys thy wonted Motyon?*
> *To make these woodes resound thy Lamentacyon:*
> *Thy Sainte ys Deade, or Deade ys thy Devotyon,*
> *For, who dothe holde his Love in estimatyon,*
> *(To witnes that hee thinckes his thoughtes Delicious)*
> *Seekes to make eche thing Badge of his sweet passyon.*

Dorus. *But what dothe make thee* Dicus, *so suspicyous?*
> *Of my due faythe whiche needes must bee Immutable,*
> *Who others vertue doubtes, them selves are vicyous?*
> *Not so, allthoughe my mettle were moste mutable,*
> *Her Beames hathe wroughte therein moste sure impressyon.*
> *To suche a force, soone Chaunge were nothing sutable.*

Dicus. *The hart well sett, dothe never shonne Confessyon,*
> *Yf Noble bee thy Bandes, make them Notoryous,*
> *Sylence dothe seeme the Maske of base oppressyon.*
> *Who gloryes in his Love dothe make Love gloryous,*
> *But who dothe beare, or hydes mute willfully,*
> *Shewes guylty hart dothe deeme his state opprobrious.*
> *Then thow that framest bothe wordes and voyce moste skillfully*
> *Yeelde to oure eares a sweete & sounde Relacyon,*
> *Yf Love tooke thee by force, or caughte thee guylefully:*

Dorus. *Yf Sunnye Beames shame Heavenly habitatyon,*
> *Yf Three leaved grasse seeme to the Sheepe unsavery,*
> *Then base and sowre ys Loves moste hye vocatyon,*
> *Or yf sheepes Cryes can help the Sunnes owne bravery,*
> *Then may I hope, my pype may have abillity,*
> *To help her prayes, who deckes mee in her slavery.*
> *No, No, No wordes enoble self Nobility.*
> *As for youre Doubtes, her voyce was yt deceyved mee,*
> *Her eyes the force beyonde my possibility.*

Dicus. *Thy wordes, well voyste, well graste, had allmoste heaved mee,*
> *Quite from my self to Love Loves Contemplacyon,*
> *Till of these thoughtes thy soeden end bereved mee,*
> *Go on therefore, and tell us by what fashyon,*
> *In thy owne proof hee gettes so straunge possession,*
> *And howe possest, hee strengthens the Invasyon?*

Dorus. *Sighte ys his Roote, in thoughte ys his progressyon,*
  His Chyldehood wonder, Prentiship, attention,
 His youthe Delighte, his Age the sowles oppressyon.
  Doubt ys his sleepe, hee waketh in Inventyon,
 Fancy ys his foode, his Cloathing all of Carefullnes,
  Beuty his Booke, his play Lovers Discention,
 His eyes are curyous searche, but wylde with warefullnes.
  His wynges Desyer ofte Clipte with Desperatyon,
 Largess his handes coulde never skill of sparefullnes,
  But howe hee dothe by mighte, or by perswasyon,
 To Conquer and his Conquest howe to ratify,
  Experyence Doubtes, and Schooles holde Disputatyon.

Dicus. *But so thy Sheepe may thy good wisshes satisfy,*
  With large encrease, and woolle of fyne perfection,
 So shee thy Love, her eyes, thy eyes may gratify,
  As thow wilte give oure sowles a dere refection,
 By telling how shee was, howe nowe shee framed ys,
  To help oure hurte in thee her owne infection.

Dorus. *Blessed bee the Name, wherewith my Mistris named ys,*
  Whose woundes are salves, whose yokes please more then
   plesure dothe
  Her staynes are beames vertue the faulte shee blamed ys,
  The harte, eye, eare, here onely fynde his treasures
   dothe
  All Nombring Artes her endles graces nomber not,
  Tyme, Place, lyfe witt scarcely her rare giftes mesure
   dothe,
  Ys shee in rage? So ys the Sunne in Somer hott,
  Yet harvest bringes, Dothe shee (alas) absent her self?
 The Sunñ ys hidd his kyndely shadowe Combers nott.

 But when to give some grace shee dothe content her self,
  O then yt shynes, then are the heavens distributed,
 And Venus *seemes to make up her, shee spent her self,*
  Thus then I say, my myscheefes have contributed,
 A greater good by her devyne Reflection,
  My harmes to mee my Bliss to her attributed,
 Thus shee ys framed, her eyes are my direction,
  Her Love my Lyfe, her Anger my Instruction,
 Lastly what so shee bee ys my protection.

ARCADIA

Dicus. *Thy saftye sure ys wrapped in Destruction,*
    For that Construction thy owne wordes do beare,
    A Man to feare a Womans muddy eye,
    Or Reason lye, a slave to servyle sence,
    There seeke defence, where weykenes ys the force,
    Ys Late Remorse, in folly dearely boughte,

Dorus. *If I had thoughte, to heare Blaspheymous wordes,*
    My Brest to swordes, My sowle to hell have soulde,
    I sooner woulde, then thus my eares defyle,
    With wordes too vyle, whiche vyler breath dothe brede.

    O Hearde, take heede, for I a wolffe have founde,
    Who hunting rounde the strongest for to kill,
    His Chest dothe fill with earthe of others woe,
    And Loden so, pulles downe, pulde downe destroyes.

    O Shepeheardes boyes, eschewe these toungues of venym
    Whiche doo envenym, bothe the Sowle and senses,
    Oure best Defences, are to flee theyre adders,
    O tungues, even Ladders, made to clyme Dishonour.
    Who judge that Honor, whiche hathe scoape to slaunder?

Dicus. *Dorus, yow wander, farr in greate Reproches,*
    So Love encroaches, in youre charmed reason,
    But yt ys season, for to ende oure singinge,
    Suche Anger bringing, as for my fancy
    In sicke mans franzy, rather takes Compassyon,
    Then Rage for Rage, rather my wish I send to thee,
    Thow soone may have some help, or chaunge of passyon,
    Shee ofte her Lookes the starres theyre favoure bend to thee,
    Fortune, store, Nature, healthe, Love graunte perswasyon,
    A Quyet mynde, none but thy self can lend to thee,
    Thus I commend all oure Former Love.

Dorus. *Well doo I prove, error lyes ofte in zeale,*
    Yet ys yt zeale, thoughe error of true harte,
    Noughte coulde Imparte, suche heates to frendly mynde,
    But for to fynde, thy wordes did her disgrace,
    Whose onely face, the litle heaven ys,
    Whiche whoo dothe myss his eyes are but Dilusyons,
    Barred from his cheefest object of Delightfullnes,
    Throwne on this earthe the Chaos of Confusyons,

COUNTESS OF PEMBROOKES

As for thy wish, to my enraged spytefullnes,
    The Lovely blowe with rare Rewarde my prayer ys,
Thow mayste Love her, that I may see thy spytefullnes,
    The quyet mynde wherof my self ympairer ys,
As thow doest thincke, shoulde moste of all disquyet mee,
    Withoute her Love, then any mynde who fayrer ys,
Her onely Care, from surfett woes can dyet mee,
    Shee holdes the Ballance of my Contentacyon,
Her cleared lookes (nought ellse) in stormes can quyet mee
    Nay, rather then my ease, Discontentatyon
Shoulde breede to her, Lett mee for aye dejected bee,
    From my Joye whiche might her greef occasyon,
With so sweete plaigues my happy harmes infected bee,
    Payne willes mee dye, yet payne of Deathe I mortify,
For thoughe lyfe yrckes, in lyfe my Loves protected bee,
    Thus for eche Chaunge, my Chaungeles harte I fortify.

When they had ended, to the good pleasing of the assistance, especially of *Cleophila*, who never forgatt to give due Comendacyon to her frende *Dorus*, (the more to advaunce hym in his pursute, allthoughe therein hee had brought his matters to a more wisshed Conclusion then yet shee knewe of) Owte startes a Jolly yonker, his name was *Nico*: whose tungue had borne a very ytching silence all this whyle, and having spyed one *Pas* a Mate of his, as madd as hym self, bothe (in deede) Laddes to clyme up any Tree in the worlde, hee bestowed this maner of Salutatyon uppon hym, and was with like reverence requyted.

Nico.   Pas.   Dicus.

Nico. *And are yow there oulde* Pas? *in trouthe I ever thoughte,*
          Amongst us all wee should fynde oute some thing of
          noughte.

Pas.   *And I am here the same, so mote I thryving bee,*
          Dispayrde, in all this flock, to fynde a knave, but thee,

Nico. *A, nowe I see why thow arte in thy self so blynde?*
          Thy gray hoode hydes the thinge that thow dispayrst to
          fynde.

Pas.   *My gray hood ys myne owne, all bee yt bee but graye,*
          Nott as the scripp thow stolest while Dorus *sleeping*
          lay.

Nico. *Myne was the scripp but thow that seeming rayed wth Love,*
    Did snatche from Hyppas *hand her greeny wroughten glove,*

Pas. *Ah foole, so Courtyers doo, but, who did lyvely skipp?*
    When for a Treene dish stollen the father did thee whipp,

Nico. *In deed the witche thy Dame her Crouche from shoulder spredd,*
    For pillfering Lalus *lambe wth Crouche to bless thy hedd.*

Pas. *My voyce the Lambe did wynñ,* Menalchas *was the Judge,*
    Of singing Matche wee made, when hee wth shame did trudge,

Nico. *Couldest thow make* Lalus *flee, so Nightingales avoyde,*
    When with the Cawyng Crowes theyre musick ys anoyde,

Pas. *Na, like to Nightingales, the other byrdes give eare,*
    My pype and songe made hym bothe songe & pype forsweare.

Nico. *I thincke yt well suche voyce woulde make one Musick hate,*
    But yf I had bene there thaddst founde an other Mate.

Pas. *An other sure as ys a Gander from a Goose,*
    But still when thow doest singe mee thinckes a Coulte ys loose.

Nico. *Well aymed by my hatt, for as thow sangest last day,*
    The Neighboures all did crye, Alas what Asse dothe bray,

Pas. *But here ys* Dicus *oulde, Lett hym then speake the worde,*
    To whither with best Cause the Nymphes *fayre flowers afforde,*

Nico. *Content, but I will Lay a wager thereunto,*
    That, proffett may ensue to hym that best can doo.
    I have, and longe shall have a white greate Nymble Catt,
    A Kinge uppon a Mowse a strong foe to a Ratt.
    Fyne eares, Longe tayle hee hathe with lyons curbed Clawe,
    Whiche ofte hee lifteth up and stayes his lifted pawe.

Deepe musing to hym self, w^{ch} (after mewyng) showes,
   Till with likt berde his eye of fyer, espyes his foes.
Yf yow (alas pore yf) doo wynñ, then wynñ yow this,
   And yf I better singe lett mee thy Hyppa kisse.

Pas.   Kisse her, now mayste thow kiss, I have a fitter Matche,
   A prity Curr yt ys, his name, I wus ys Catche.
No eare nor taile hee hathe, least they shoulde hym disgrace,
   A Ruddy hayer his Coate with fyne longe speckled face
Hee never musing standes, but, with hym self will playe,
   Leaping at every flee, and angry with a Flea.
Hee efte woulde kill a Mouse, but hee disdaynes the feighte,
   And makes oure home good sporte wth dauncing bolte uprighte,
This ys my Pawne, the pryce, let Dicus Judgment showe,
   Suche Oddes I willing laye, for hym and yo^w I knowe.

Dicus.   Singe then my Laddes, and singe, wth better vayne, then yett,
   Or else with singing worse, my skill may hardly hitt.

Nico.   Who doubtes but Pas fyne pype, ageane will bringe,
   The auncyent prayse to Arcadia Shepeheardes skill,
Pan ys not deade synce Pas begyns to singe.

Pas.   Who ever more will love Appollos quyll?
   Synce Nico dothe to singe, so wydely gape,
Nico his place farr better furnish will.

Nico.   Was this not hee, who for Siringas scape,
   Raging in woes, first pastors tought to play,
Do yow not heare his voyce, and see his shape.

Pas.   This ys not hee, that fayled her to gayne,
   (Whiche made a Bay) made Bay a holly tree
But this ys one that doth his Musick stayne.

Nico.   O Faunes; O Fayries all, and doo yow see?
   And suffer suche a wronge, a wronge, I trowe,
That Nico must with Pas compared bee.

Pas.   O Nymphes, I tell yow newes, for Pas yow knowe,
   Whyle I was warbling oute youre wonted prayse,
Nico woulde needes with Pas his baggpype blowe.

Nico.   Yf never I did fayle youre holy dayes,
   With Daunces, Carrolls, or with Barley breake,
Let Pas now knowe how Nico maketh layes.

Pas.   *Yf eche day hathe bene holly for youre sake,*
     Unto my Pype, O Nymphes *now help my pype,*
  For Pas *well knowes what Layes can* Nico *make.*

Nico.   *Alas, howe ofte I looke on Cheryes rype,*
     Mee thinckes I see the Lippes my Leuca *hathe,*
  And wanting her, my weeping eyes I wype.

Pas.   *Alas when I in springe mete Roses rathe,*
     And thinck from Hyppas *sweete redd Lippes I live,*
  I leave my eyes unwypte, my Cheekes to bathe,

Nico.   *As I of late, nere Busshes used my sive,*
     I spyde my Thrush, where shee did make her Nest,
  That will I take, and to my Leuca *give.*

Pas.   *But, longe have I a Sparrowe gayly drest*
     As white as Milke, and comming to the Calle,
  To putt yt with my hande in Hyppas *brest.*

Nico.   *I ofte doo sue, and* Leuca *saythe, I shall,*
     But, when I did come nere with heate and hope
  Shee ranne away, and threwe at mee a Balle.

Pas.   Hyppa *once sayde, shee lefte the wickett ope,*
     For mee to come, and so shee did, I came,
  But in the place founde no thinge, but a Rope.

Nico.   *When* Leuca *dothe appeare, the* Sunne *for shame,*
     Dothe hyde hym self, for to hym self hee sayes,
  Yf Leuca *live, shee darcken will my fame,*

Pas.   *When* Hyppa *dothe come forthe, the* Sunne *displayes,*
     His uttmoste Lighte, for well his witt dothe knowe,
  Hyppas *fayre Beames emblemish muche his Rayes.*

Nico.   Leuca *to mee, did yester morninge shewe,*
     In perfect Lighte, whiche coulde mee not deceyve,
  Her naked Legg, more whyte then snowe.

Pas.   *But, yester nighte by Lighte I did receyve,*
     From Hyppas *eyes wch full in Darckenes shyne,*
  I sawe her Arme, where purest Lillyes cleave.

Nico.   *Shee once starcke nakte did bathe a litle tyne,*
     But still mee thoughte with Beutyes from her fell
  Shee did the water washe and make more fyne.

Pas.   *Shee once to coole her self stoode in a well,*
     But ever synce, that well ys well besoughte,
  And for Rose water soulde of rarest smell.

Nico.   *To Rivers bancke, beeyng a wallking broughte,*
      Shee bid mee spye her Baby in the brooke,
    Alas sayde I, this Babe dothe nurse my thoughte.

Pas.   *As in a glasse I helde, shee once did looke,*
      I sayde my handes well payde her for myne eyes,
    Synce in my handes self goodly sighte shee tooke.

Nico.   *O yf I had a Ladder for the skyes,*
      I woulde clyme upp and bringe a p̃ety starr,
    To weare uppon her neck that open lyes.

Pas.   *O yf I had* Appolloes *golden Carre,*
      I woulde come downe, and yeelde to her my place,
    That shyning now shee then might shyne more farr.

Nico.   *No thinge O* Leuca, *shall thy fame deface,*
      Whyles Shepeheardes Tunes bee hearde or Rhymes bee redd,
    Or while that Shepeheardes love a Lovely face,

Pas.   *Thy Name O* Hyppa *shall with prayse bee spredd*
      As farr as any Shepeheardes pyping bee.
    As farr as Love possesseth any hedd.

Nico.   *Thy Monument ys layde in many a Tree,*
      With Name engraved so thoughe thy body dye,
    The after Folckes shall wonder still at thee.

Pas.   *So ofte these woodes have hearde my* Hyppa *crye,*
      That after deathe, to heaven in woodes resounde,
    With Ecchos *help shall* Hyppa, *hippa flye.*

Nico.   *Peace, peace good* Pas, *thow wearest eeven the grounde,*
      With sluttish songe, I pray thee learne to blea?
    For, good thow mayest yet prove in Sheepish sounde.

Pas.   *My father hathe at home a pretty Jay,*
      Goo wynne of hym for chattering prayse or shame,
    For so yet of a Conquest, speake thow may.

Nico.   *Tell mee, (and, bee my* Pan) *the Monsters name?*
      That hathe fowre Legges and with twoo onely goes?
    That hathe fowre eyes, and onely Twoo can frame?

Pas.   *Tell this (and* Phebus *bee,) what Monster growes?*
      With so strange Lyves, that body can not rest?
    In ease, untill that body lyfe forgoes?

Dicus. *Inuff, Inuff, so evell hathe done the best,*
      That since the having of them to neyther ys due,
    Lett Catt and Dogg feight whiche shall have bothe yow.

Some speeche there streight grewe among the hearers, what they shoulde meane by the Riddells of the Twoo Monsters: But this Eglogue of all other was counted the Sportefullest they yet had hearde, and a greater Questyon, whether in deede had wonne ye Wager. *Dicus* still demaunded Justice, that synce hee had bene lawfully appoynted Judge, the Catt and Dogg mighte bee sent for to Trye the *Duello* betuixt them: But, *Cleophila* whose hart better delighted in waylefull Dittyes, as more according to her Fortune, shee desyered *Histor* hee woulde repeate the Lamentation some dayes before hee had toulde them that hee had heard of a Straunger made to the wyse Bowlon. In deede *Cleophila* desyerus to heare of *Plangus* Love, whose valure shee had well seene thoughe ageanst her self in the Combate of the Six Princes: *Basilius* assoone as hee understood *Cleophilas* pleasure, commaunded *Histor* upon payne of his Lyfe, (As thoughe every thinge were a matter of lyfe & deathe to his Masters service) imedyately to sing yt, who with greate Cunning, (varying his voyce according to the diversity of ye persons) thus performed his pleasure.

Histor.

> *As I behynde a Busshe did sitt,*
> *I sylent hearde more Wordes of witt,*
> *Then earst I knew, but first did playne,*
> *The one whiche tother woulde refrayne.*

Plangus.   Boulon.

Plangus. *Alas how longe this Pillgrimage dothe last,*
> *What greater evills have now the Heavens in store?*
> *To cupple comyng harmes with sorrowes past,*
> *Longe synce my voyce ys hoarse, and throate ys sore*
> *With Cryes to skyes, and Curses to the grounde,*
> *But, more I playne, I feele my woes the more.*

> *Ah where was first, that Crewell Cunning founde,*
> *To frame of earthe a vessell of the mynde*
> *Where yt shoulde bee the self destruction bounde,*
> *What needed so hye spirites suche Mansions blynde?*
> *Or wrapt in flessh, what doo they here obtayne?*
> *But gloryous Name of wretched humane kynde,*

Balles to the starres, and Thralles to fortunes raigne,
　Turned from them selves infected with theyre Cage
Where dèathe ys fearde, and lyfe ys helde wth payne,
　Lyke Players placed to fill a filthy stage,
　　Where Chaunge of thoughts one foole to other shewes
　　And all but Jestes, save onely sorowes rage?

The Chylde feeles that the Man that feeling knowes,
　With Cryes first borne, the presage of his lyfe,
Where witt butt serves to have true taste of woes,
　A Shopp of shame, a Booke where Blottes are ryfe,
　　This Body ys, this Body so composde,
　　　As in yt self, to nourish mortall stryfe.

So dyvers bee the Elementes disposde,
　In this weyke worcke, that yt can never bee,
Made uniforme to any estate reposde,
　　Greef onely makes his wretched state to see,
　　　Even lyke a Topp, wch noughte, but whipping mooves,
　　　This Man, this talking beaste, this walking Tree.

Greef ys the Stone whiche fynest Judgment prooves,
　For, who greeves not hathe but a blockish brayne,
Synce Cause of greef, no Cause from lyfe remooves,

Boulon.　Howe longe wilt thow with monefull Musick stayne?
　The Cherefull Notes, these pleasaunt places yeelde,
　Where as good happes a perfect state meynteyne.

Plangus.　Curste bee good happes, and Curst bee they that buylde,
　Theyre hopes on happes, and do not make dispayre,
For all these certeyne Blowes, the surest sheelde,
　Shall I that sawe Eronas shyning hayre?
　　Torne with her handes, and those same handes of
　　snowe,
　　With Losse of purest blood, them selves to teare.

Shall I that sawe those Brestes, where Beutyes flowe
　Swelling with sighes made pale, wth myndes diseaze
And sawe those eyes (those sunnes) suche showers to
　showe
　Shall I whose eares her mornefull wordes do seaze,
　　(Her wordes in Syrop layde of sweetest breathe)
　　Relent those thoughtes wch then did so displease.

No, no, Dispayre, my daily Lesson sayeth,
  And saythe allthoughe I seeke my Lyfe to flye,
Plangus *must live to see* Eronas *deathe*,
  Plangus *must live some help for her to trye*,
    Thoughe Dispayre (for love so forceth mee)
      Plangus *dothe Lyve, and shall* Erona *dye?*

Erona *dye? O heaven, yf heaven there bee,*
  Hathe all the whirling Course so smalle effect?
Serve all thy Starry eyes this shame to see,
  Lett Doltes in haste some Alters fayre erect,
    To those hye powers wch idely sitt above,
      And vertue doo in greatest neede neglect.

Boulon.   *O Man take heede, how thow the goddes do moove,*
  To Causefull Wrathe, whiche thow canst not resist,
Blaspheymous wordes the Speaker vayne dothe prove,
  Alas, whyle wee are wrapt in Foggy Myst,
    Of oure self Love, (so passyons doo deceyve)
      Wee thincke they hurte, where moste they doo
      assist.

To harme us wormes, shoulde they by Justice leave,
  His Nature, nay, hym self for so yt ys,
What glory from oure Losse can wee receyve,
  But still oure daseled eyes theyre way do myss,
    Whyle that wee doo at his sweete scourge repyne,
      The kyndely way to beate us on to bliss.

Yf shee must dye then hathe shee lost the lyne,
  Of loathsome dayes, whose losse how canst thow mone,
That doest so well theyre myseryes defyne,
  But, suche wee are with inward Tempest blowne,
    Of wyndes cleane Contrary, in waves of will,
      Wee moane that Losse, (wch had) wee did bemone.

Plangus.   *And shall shee dye, shall crewell fyer spill?*
  Those Beames that sett so many hartes on fyer.
Hathe shee not force eeven deathe with Love to kyll,
  Nay, eeven coulde Deathe enflamde with whott desyer?
    Her to enjoy, where Joy yt self ys thralle?
      Will spoyle the Earthe of his moste riche attyre.

Thus, Deathe becomes a Rivall to us all,
  And hopes with fowle embracementes her to gett,
In whose decay, vertues fayre shryne must falle,
    O vertue weyke, shall Deathe his Tryumphe sett?
      Uppon thy spoyles whiche never shoulde lye waste
        Lett Deathe first dye, bee thow his worthy Lett.

By what Eclips shall that Sunne bee defaste?
  What Myne hathe earst throwne downe so fayre a
    Tower?
What Sacriledg hathe suche a Sainte disgraste?
  The worlde the garden ys, shee ys the Flower?
    That sweetens all the place, shee ys the guest,
      Of rarest pryce, bothe heaven & earth her Bower.

And shall (O, mee) all this in Asshes rest?
  Alas yf yow a Phenix now will have,
Burnt by the Sunne, shee first must buyld her Nest,
  But well yo^w knowe, the gentle Sunne woulde save,
    Suche Beames so like his owne wch mighte have Myghte,
      In him the thoughtes of Phaetons Dam̃ to grave.

Therefore alas, yo^w use vyle Vulcans spyte,
  Whiche nothing spares to melt that virgin waxe,
Whiche while yt ys, yt ys all Asias lighte,
  O Mars for what dothe serve thy armed Axe,
    To let that witoulde Beast consume in flames,
      Thy Venus Chylde, whose Beuty Venus lackes.

O Venus, yf her prayse, no Envy frames,
  In thy hye mynde gett her thy husbandes grace,
Sweete speaking ofte, a Currish harte reclaymes,
  O Eyes of myne, where once shee sawe her face,
    (Her face whiche was more lyvely in her hart)
      O Brayne, where thoughte of her hathe onely place?

O hande wch tuched her hande when wee did parte,
  O Lyppes that kist that hand with my Teares sprent.
O Toungue then dumbe, not daring tell my smarte,
  O Sowle whose Love, in her ys onely spent?
    What ere yow see thincke, tuche, kisse, speake or Love,
      Let all for her, and unto her bee bent.

Boulon.   *Thy wayling wordes doo muche my Spirites moove,*
    They uttered are in suche a feeling fashion,
    That sorowes worcke ageanst my will I prove,
     Mee thinckes I am partaker of youre passyon,
     And in thy Case do glasse myne owne debility,
      Self guylty folcke, must proove to feele Compassyon.

    Yet Reason saythe, Reason shoulde have hability,
    To holde these worldly thinges in suche proportion,
    As let them come or goo with even facility.
     But, oure Desyers Tyrannicall extortion,
     Dothe force us there, to sett oure cheef Delightfullnes,
      Where, but a Bayting place, ys all oure portion.

    But still allthoughe wee faile of perfect Rightfullnes,
    Seeke wee to tame these Chyldish Superfluityes,
    Let us not wincke, thoughe voyde of purest sightfullnes.
     For, what can breede more peevish Incongruityes,
     Then Man to yeelde to female Lamentacyons.
      Let us some Gram̃er *learne of oure Congruityes?*

Plangus.   *Yf throughe myne eares perse any Consolacyons,*
    By wyse Discourse, sweete Tunes or Poettes *fiction,*
    Yf oughte I cease these Odyous exclamacyons,
     Whyle that my sowle, shee shee Lives in affliction,
     Then lett my Lyfe on earthe longe tyme maynteyned bee,
      To wretched mee, the last worste Malediction.

    Can I that knewe her sacred partes restrayned bee?
    From any Joye, knowe fortunes vyle displacing her?
    In morrall Rules, Lett raging woes conteyned bee,
     Can I forgett, when they in prison placing her,
     With swelling hart in spyte, and due Disdeynfullnes,
      Shee lay for Deade, till I helpt with unlasing her.

    Can I forgett from howe muche mourning playnfullnes?
    With Dyamond in wyndow glasse shee graved
   Erona *dye, and ende this ougly paynefullnes,*
     Can I forgett, in how strange phrase shee craved?
      That quickly they woulde her burne downe or
      smother.
      As yf by deathe shee onely mighte bee saved.

> *Then lett mee eke forgett my hande from other,*
> *Lett mee forgett that* Plangus *I am called,*
> *Lett mee forgett I am sonne to my Mother,*
> *But, yf my memory thus must bee thralled,*
> *To that straunge stroke wch conquerd all my sences,*
> *Can thoughte still thincking so rest unappalled?*

Boulon. *Who still dothe seeke ageanst hym self Offences,*
> *What pardon can avayle, or who employes hym?*
> *To hurt hym self what sheeldes can bee defences.*
> *Woo to pore Man, eche owteward thing anoyes hym,*
> *In dyvers kyndes, yet, as hee were not filled,*
> *Hee heapes in Inward greef, that moste destroyes*
> *hym.*

> *Thus ys oure Thoughte (with payne) for Thistells tilled,*
> *Thus bee oure noblest partes dryed up with sorrowe,*
> *Thus ys oure mynde, with too muche mynding spilled,*
> *One daye layes up store of greef for the morowe.*
> *And whose good happ dothe leave hym unprovyded*
> *Condoling Cause, of Frendship hee will borrowe.*

> *Betuixt the good, and shade of good denyed,*
> *Wee pity deeme that, whiche but weykenes ys,*
> *So are wee from oure hye Creation slyded,*
> *But* Plangus *leste I may youre sicknes mysse,*
> *Or Rubbing hurt the sore I here do ende,*
> *The Asse did hurt when hee did thincke to kisse.*

> *Thus did they say, and then away did wende,*
> *Hye tyme for mee, for scattered were my Sheepe,*
> *While I theyre speeche in my Rude Ryming pend,*
> *Yet for that Nighte my Cabban did them keepe,*
> *Whyle* Plangus *did a Story straunge declare,*
> *But, hoarse and Drye, my Pypes I now must spare.*

So well did *Histors* voyce express the passyon of *Plangus*, that all the Princely beholders were stricken into a silent Consideracyon of yt: In deede every one making that hee hearde of an other, the Ballance of his owne Trubles. *Pamela* was the first that comaunded her thoughtes to give place to some necessary wordes. And so Remembring her self what *Histor* had sayde the other tyme of the Pastoralles, tuching *Musidorus*, whiche as then shee regarded not, desyered hym, yf hee did

beare yt in memory that hee woulde tell what straunge
Adventure yt was, that had ledd away the twoo *Greeke* Princes
from *Erona*, after they had slayne *Otanes* and settled her in her
kingdome. And when shee had asked thus muche having had
no thing, but vehement desyer, to her Counsell her sweete Body
did eeven tremble for feare, leste shee had done a misse: But
glad was her Shepehearde (not to have his doynges spoken of)
but bycause any questyon of hym proceeded oute of that mouthe.
Histor made answer, that *Plangus* had in deede before hee
departed towardes *Thessalia*, and *Macedon*, at his importunate
desyer, made a breef Declaration unto hym therof. But
allwayes with protestation, that suche thinges there were, as
many particularityes of them had beene full worckes to excellent
Historiographers: And that the first adventure was, A man of
monstruous bignes and force and therefore comonly called a
Gyant, who had wasted all the whole Contrey of *Paphlagonia*, by
the help of a stronge Castle in the topp of a hye Rock, where
hee kept a moste terrible Dragon whiche hee had with suche
Arte from his youthe trayned up, that yt was muche more at
his Commaundement, then the best reclaymed Hawke: So that
yt woulde flye abroade, and do incredible Domage, and ever
duely returne ageane to the Castle, where the *Gyant* kept no
living Man but hym self. This (besyde his owne force) forced
the miserable people, to come to what Composicyon hee woulde,
whiche was that monethly they shoulde sende hym twoo Maydes
not above XVI^teene yeares oulde, and twoo Boyes or younge
men under XIX^teene: The Woemen hee used at his beastly
pleasure, and kept them imprisoned in his Castle, the younge
men hee was wonte to sacrifyce to an Idoll. This beeyng come
to the eares of those valyant younge Princes who (the harder a
thinge were the more theyre hartes rase unto yt) went to the
Desolate people, and there after many horrible Compleyntes of
Parentes whose Children by publique force were taken from
them : They offered them selves to pay the next moneths wages
(yf better they coulde not doo). Theyre Beuty made all the
People pity them, but in deede self respect preveyled over the
Pity, and the tyme beeyng come, they armed them selves
secretly under theyre longe garmentes ; and carrying short
swordes under theyre Armes, were in that sorte broughte unto
hym, by a man appoynted to deliver them, for, more the *Gyant*

woulde not suffer to enter. Who, when hee sawe theyre faces, was a prowde Man of so goodly, but they were no sooner in, but drawyng oute theyre swordes they made hym looke to his owne lyfe, whiche hee did, ronning to a Horse Leade of a Mase wch hee allwayes used: And so weaponed, (for, armed hee ever went) hee lett lose his trusty Dragon, and so matched that evell favoured Cuple with the Matchelesse *Princes.* Who having an excellent strengthe and corage, (to make that strengthe a wake) had within smalle space dispatched the worlde of these twoo Monsters. *Pyrocles* having killed the Dragon and *Musidorus* the *Gyant,* what honors were done unto them by that people (wch they continually observe as towardes theyre savers) were superfluous to tell: But thence were they ledd by the fame of a great warre betuixt twoo Brothern, where the younger had rebelled ageanst ye Elder beeyng kinge of *Syria.* Forced there-unto, bycause hee had taken away from hym the Principallity of *Damascus,* wch theyre Father in partage had bestowed uppon hym, there did the shewe as muche theyre wysdome as theyre valure: For the one putting hym self of the one syde, and the other of the other, they so behaved them selves, that eyther parte thoughte they had the bravest Champyon in the worlde, in somuche as bothe were content to let the matter bee tryed by them to save the bloode of so many, wch of bothe sydes were but one people. But they, having ye matter (withoute exception) putt into theyre handes in stede of feighting fell to Arbitrage, and making the Brothers see the shamefullnes of theyre faulte, so to sever them selves: whome nature in theyre very beginning had so nerely knitt, and yet (Remembring that whosoever hathe throwly offended a prince, can never think yt self in perfect savety under hym) they did determyn that ye kinge giving in Riches to his Brother asmuche as the Principallity came unto, shoulde enjoy *Damascus.* And they fynding ye younger a Prince of greate worthynes, did somuche by theyre Credit wth the *Paphlagonians,* that they marryed hym with the Inheritrix of that goodly province; leaving in this sorte a perpetuall Monument of witt, Liberality and Corage. But after this the nexte Notable Chance fell unto them (for many hundred of theyre valyant Actes *Plangus* sayde hee never coulde tell, nor muche tyme coulde serve for the repeating) was by the great Lady of *Palestinas* meanes, called *Andromana*: who, hearing of theyre singuler valor, sente, to beseeche theyre Ayde ageanst a younge Prince of *Arabia*, who had promysed her Mariage, and upon that having gotten a Chylde of her, had now lefte her. They thoughte they knewe shee shoulde have done well, to have bene sure of the Churche, before hee had bene sure of the Bedd: yet pitying womanhood, and desyring to knowe whatt Answer the *Arabian* coulde make for hym self, they went to offer them selves unto her. But they had not beene there a while, and made her see theyre activity in Justice, and theyre valor in theyre particuler Combattes but that shee had quite forgotten her olde fancy, that had cost her so dere; and was growne into the miserablest and straungest passyon of Love, that can bee imagyned, for shee loved them bothe with equall ardency. The oddes was, that when shee sawe *Pyrocles* shee thoughte shee moste desyered hym, and when shee looked on *Musidorus*, then was *Pyrocles* overweyed. At these wordes a Man might have seene the eyes bothe of *Pamela*, and *Philoclea* cast uppon theyre Servauntes, to see whether they had comitted any Trespas or no? But, *Histor* proceeded on in declaring her devyded Desyer, when shee looked on *Musidorus*, then thoughte shee a sweete Browñes the moste delightfull beuty, but when shee marcked *Pyrocles* pure white and Redd, (for suche difference *Plangus* sayde was betwixt them) then Roses and Lillyes were the fayrest flowers. *Musidorus* as the Elder & stronger *Pyrocles* as the younger and more delicate contented her, in fyne shee woulde wisshe some tymes *Musidorus* to bee *Pyrocles* and an other tyme *Pyrocles* to bee *Musidorus*, but still shee woulde have bothe hers: But, those twoo *Princes* (that seemed to love any thing better then Love) did so utterly discomfort her, that shee was forced to flee to force, and putt them bothe by a sleight shee playde, in pryson, where what Allurementes shee used indifferently, were long to tell. But at lengthe they obstinately so muche more refusing her, as theyre Corages disdayned to bee compelled to any thinge, they had lyke to have tarryed there a good nomber of dayes: But that the *Arabian* Prince hearing of theyre Imprisonment grewe prowde of his strengthe and entred into *Palestina*, with hope to Conquer yt. Whiche yᵉ People feeling (whether the Lady woulde or no) delyvered the Prisoners, who having lykewyse by theyre good Conduct delivered them of the *Arabyans*, they them selves went into *Egipt*, aswell to flee suche a hart burning woman (who shortly after as *Plangus* sayde had likewyse forgotten them and after dyvers Chaunges at last marryed her self to an Apple monger) as bycause they hearde greate fame of the Kinge of *Egiptes* Courte ; to bee by reason of his magnificence full of valyant Knightes: As allso his Contry well pollicyed with good Lawes and Customes worthy to bee learned. But many notable accidentes mett with them, as they passed the Dezart way betuixt *Palestina* and *Egipt* worthy to have whole Bookes written of them: But *Plangus* a passionate mynde coulde not brooke longe discourses, and therefore hasted hym self to lett mee knowe the generallity of theyre Dooynges, whiche certeynly were suche as made mee greately delighted to heare them. But did hee tell yo^w no further sayde the sweetest *Philoclea*, of those Princes? yes answered *Histor*, of a straunge chaunce fell to them in *Egipt*, and that was this. Ryding together aboute sixe myles from the greate City of *Memphis* they hearde a pityfull Crye, as of one whome eyther extreeme greef or present feare, had made his voyce his best instrument of defence. They went the next way they thoughte shoulde guyde them to the party, and there founde they a younge man well apparelled, and handsomely proportioned, in the handes of Foure Murderinge villaynes, who were redy to slay hym. Having stayde for no thinge, but that hee toulde them hee knewe a place where great Tresure was hidd: The Covetusnes of that made them delay the Killing of hym, till one of the fowre (weary to follow hym any longer) was redy to have given his mortall wounde, at the wch hee Cryed. But the other three stopped theyre fellow, when (in good tyme for hym) came in these Twoo Princes, who seeynge (howe Justly soever hee had deserved deathe) that the maner was unjust, by whiche they sought to lay yt uppon hym, came in, among them with threatninges yf they did not let hym loose: But the Fowre, better knowyng theyre owne nomber, then the others valor, scorned theyre Commaundement, till by the Deathe of three of them, the fourthe was taughte by ronning away to leave the Prisoner to theyre Discretion: Who falling on his knees unto them as to the Bestowers of a Lyfe uppon hym, toulde them the grounde of his myschaunce to this purpose. That hee was a Servant, and of nearest Creditt to *Amasis*, sonne and heyre to *Sesostris* kinge of *Egipt*, and beeyng of one Aige, and was allso

148

like hym, as hardly (but by the greate difference of theyre owtewarde estates) the one coulde bee knowne from the other: That yᵉ Kinge *Sesostris* after the deathe of *Amasis* mother, had marryed a younge woman, who had turned the ordenary Course of Stepmothers hate to so unbrydeled Love towardes her husbandes Sonne *Amasis*, that neyther the name of a Father in hym, of a Husband in her, nor of a Mother and sonne betweene them selves coulde keepe her back from disorderly seeking that of *Amasis*, whiche ys a wickednes to accept. But, hee besydes his Duety to vertue (having his hart allredy pledged to *Artaxia* Queene of *Persia*) the more shee loved hym, the more detested her: whiche fynding her whott spirites to worcke uppon shame, Disdayne and Lust converted all her affection to a moste revengefull hatred, in somuche, that all her studye was for some Naughty pollicy to overthrowe hym, wherof in the ende this young man offered her occasyon. For, Considering the Resemblance hee bare to his Master, shee began to make the pore youthe beleeve, shee did extremely affect hym in respect of that likenes whiche hee (privy to all his Masters Counsell) well knewe shee imoderately loved. *Thermuthis*, (for so the young man was called) thought hym self advaunced to the Starres: when hee sawe so fayre a Queene bend her good will towardes hym, whiche shee (so farre was shee become a Slave unto synne) sealled unto hym with the fruition of her unchaste body; When shee had thus angled *Thermuthis*, then began shee to accuse *Amasis* to his father, as having soughte to defyle his bedd: wᶜʰ opinyon beeyng some thing gotten in, thoughe not fully imprinted in *Sesostris* heade, shee caused *Thermuthis* (who was fully at her devotion) to come one nighte in his Masters apparell, hee had that day worne, to her Chamber, with his sworde redy to have killed yᵉ kinge, as hee slept, for so shee had perswaded hym to doo. But as soone, as hee entred into the Chamber, shee awaked the Kinge, and making hym see hym, hee tooke to bee his Sonne (beeyng deceyved by Candle lighte and his rayment) in that order coming to kill hym: The pore *Thermuthis* astonisshed, and ronning away shee sent those foure Trusty servauntes after hym, to whome shee had before given charge to have eye of hym. And assoone as hee shoulde flee oute of the Chamber to followe hym (under Coloure to help hym by her Comaundement) till they trayned hym into some secrett place, and there murder hym:

And thus muche one of them appoynted to kill hym (who was the Man the Queene of *Egipt* moste trusted) had reveyled unto hym, thinckyng his speedy deathe shoulde keepe yt from beeyng opened. And sayde *Thermuthis* by this tyme, I feare the kinge hathe done some hurt to my Deare Master, whome thus myserably I have Ruyned: And in deede, so the Kinge ment to have done, and presently meant to have killed hym, whome shee Caused to bee broughte by force oute of his Lodging, as thoughe thither hee had fledd to shyfte hym self and so escape, (The pore Prince beeyng newly come oute of his sleepe, and with his amasednes rather Condempning hym self then otherwyse). But the Kinge neyther taking paynes to examen the matter to the utter moste, nor so muche as to heare what *Amasis* coulde say in a matter by many Circumstances easy enoughe to have bene refelled hee presently Caused hym to bee carryed to the Redd sea, there to bee putt in a Shippe, with oute any Man but hym self in yt; and so to bee lefte to the wyndes discretion: But the twoo *Princes* having understood the beginning of the matter by *Thermuthis*, taking hym with them, they entred into *Memphis*, as the pore Prince was some fewe myles all redy carryed towardes his Shipp of deathe. Whiche they understanding, and (fearing they shoulde not have leasuer to tell the Kinge, and save hym) they first pursewed after hym, and by force of Armes joyned with the help of some of the Contry who were willing to help theyre Prince, they rescued hym of theyre handes: And bringing hym back to the Kinge, made hym understand the whole Circumstance by *Thermuthis* Confession whose pardon they gott, considering what a faulte the Kinge hym self had done to ronne so hastely in yᵉ Condempning his onely soñe in a Cause, mighte, bothe by *Thermuthis* absence and many other wayes have beene prooved contrary: As for his wyfe shee was past eyther pardoning or punisshing, for, when shee heard the matter was reveyled, shee killed her self. Thence, *Plangus* sayde, (having lefte the Father and sonne in unity, and *Amasis* acknouledging his lyfe of them with greate Love, whiche not-withstanding hee coulde not have done, yf hee had knowne how *Artaxia* hated them) they returned, as yt was thoughte, to *Grece* warde: whom hee had still followed, and by many mysfortunes coulde never fynde, and now his last hope ys in one of theyre Contryes, beeyng nevertheless in great doubte, that they are all redy perisshed by Sea. Thus, did *Histor* epitomyse the worthy actes of those Twoo Worthyes, making (thoughe unknowne) theyre owne eares witnesses of theyre glory, whiche in no respect rejoyced them somuche, as that theyre Beloved Ladyes hearde yt, of whose esteeming them, they had then dearest Regarde, and cheefly desyered they might knowe yt, was no Dishonor they soughte unto them ; whose Honors they helde in more precyous reconing then theyre owne Lyves. But in deede unmeasurable was the Contentment of the twoo Ladyes (who besydes Love, had taughte them to trust) mighte fynde by the Circumstances of these thinges, that these coulde bee no others then theyre Lovers: Allthough eythers hart was so deepely plunged in her owne, that shee never payned her self to Calle in questyon her Sisters Case, so, y^t neyther *Pamela* tooke conceipte of the *Amazon*, nor, *Philoclea* of the Shepeheard. As for *Ginecia*, suche an inward Lordship *Cleophila* helde in her, that shee onely sawe her, shee hearde no body but her, and thoughte of no thinge but of her: So that *Histors* Discourse passed throwe her eares withoute any marcking, judging, (as Comonly they doo that are full of thoughtes) by the beginning, that yt shoulde no thinge aperteyne to the party, uppon whome shee knitt all her ymagening power. The *Duke* woulde dyvers tymes very fayne have broken of *Histors* speeche but, that fynding *Cleophila* yeelde hym acceptable audyence, hee was in doubte to displease her: But well afrayde hee was that the prayse hee gave to the famous *Pyrocles* mighte kyndle *Cleophilas* harte unto hym. For, Comparing theyre worthynes, hee was forced to Confess in hym self, there woulde proove a Noble Matche betweene them, whiche made hym feare leaste *Cleophilas* younge mynde mighte bee styrred that way : Therefore assoone, or rather before *Histor* had ended, leste hee mighte renewe ageane some mention of those twoo Princes, hee called to *Philisides*. Who (according to his Custome) satt so Malencholye as thoughe his mynde were banisshed from the place hee loved, to bee imprisoned in his body : And desyered hym hee woulde begyñ some *Ecclogue* with some other of the Shepeheardes, according to the accustomed guyse. *Philisides* thoughe very unwilling at the *Dukes* comaundement offered to singe with *Lalus*, but *Lalus* directly refused hym, sayinge hee shoulde within fewe dayes bee marryed to the fayre *Kalla*, and synce hee had gotten his desyer, hee woulde singe no more. Then the *Duke* willed *Philisides* to declare the Discourse of his owne fortunes unknowen to them, as beeyng a Straunger in that Contry: But hee prayed y^e *Duke* to pardon hym, the tyme beeyng farr to joyfull, to suffer ye rehearsall of his myseryes. But, to satisfy *Basilius* some way hee began an *Eglogue*, betuixt hym self and the *Eccho*, framinge his voyce so in those Dezert places, as what wordes hee woulde have the *Eccho* reply unto, those hee would singe higher then ye rest: And so kyndely framed a Disputatyon betuixt hym self and yt, with these *Hexameters* in the followyng order.

Philisides.	Eccho.
Fayre Rockes, goodly Rivers, sweete Woodes, when shall I see peace?	*peace.*
Peace? what barres mee my toungue, who ys yt y^t comes mee so nye?	*I.*
Oh I, do knowe what Guest I have mett, yt ys Eccho.	*yt ys* Eccho.
Well mett Eccho, *approche then tell mee thy will too?—*	*I will too.*

$$- - - \cup \cup - - - \cup \cup - \cup \cup - -$$

Eccho, *what doo I gett yeelding my spirit to my greeves?—*	*greeves.*
What Medcyn may I fynde for a payne y^t drawes mee to deathe?	*Deathe.*
O poysonus Medecyn what worse to mee, can bee then yt?—	*yt.*
In what state was I then when I tooke this Deadly disease?	*ease.*
What maner of a mynde, wch had to that Honor a vayne?	*vayne.*
Hathe not Reason enoughe vehemency the Desyer to reproove?	*proove.*
Ofte proove I but what salve, when reason seekes to bee goñ?	*One.*
Oh what ys yt, what ys yt that may bee a salve to my Love?	*Love.*
What doo Lovers seeke for, Long seeking for to enjoy?	*Joye.*

What bee the Joyes for wch to enjoy they want to the paynes?   paynes.

Then to an earnest Loove, what dothe best victory lende?   Ende.

Ende, but I can never ende, love will not give mee the Leave.   leave.

Howe bee the myndes disposde that can not taste thy Phisick?   Sick.

Yet, say ageane thy advyse, for the evills that I tolde thee?   I tolde thee.

Dothe the Infected wretche of his evell the extremity knowe?   No.

But yf hee knowe not his harmes what guydes hathe hee while hee ys blynde?   blynde.

What blynde Guydes can hee have that leanes to a fancye?   a fancy.

Can fancyes want eyes? or hee falle that steppeth a lofte?   ofte.

What Causes first made these Tormentes on mee to lighte?   Light.

Can then a Cause bee so lighte, that forceth a Man to go dye?   I.

Yet tell mee what lighte thing I had in mee to draw mee to dye?   ey.

Eye sight made mee to yeelde but what first prest to myne eyes?   eyes.

Eyes hurters eyes hurte but what from them to mee falles?   falles.

But when I first did falle what broughte moste falle to my hart?   Arte.

Arte? What can bee that Arte wch thow doest meane by thy speeche?   speeche.

What bee the fruites of speaking Arte, what growes by the wordes?   wordes.

O muche more then wordes, those wordes seemd more to mee blesse.   lesse.

O when shall I bee knowne where moste to bee knowne I doo longe?   Longe.

Long bee thy woes for suche Newes: But how Reckes shee my thoughtes?   oughtes.

Then, then what do I gayne, since unto her will
    I do wynde?   *wynde.*
Wynde Tempestes and stormes yet in ende what gives
    shee desyer?   *Ire.*
Silly Rewarde, yet among women hathe shee of
    vertue ye moste.   *moste.*
What greate name may I give to so heavenly a woman?   *a woman.*
Woe, but seemes to mee Joy y^t agrees to my thoughtes so?   *I thought so.*
Thincke so, for of my desyered blisse yt ys onely the
    Course.   *Curse.*
Curst by thy self for cursing y^t wch leades mee to Joyes?   *toyes.*
What bee ye sweete Creatures where lovely demaundes
    bee not hearde?   *harde.*
Hard to bee gott, butt gott constant to bee helde like
    steeles.   *eeles.*
How can they bee unkynde speake for thow haste
    nerely pryed?   *pryde.*
Whence can pryde come there, since springes of beuty
    bee thence?   *thence.*
Horrible ys thy Blasphemy, unto the moste holy.   *O ly*
Thow lyest false Eccho, *theyre myndes as vertue bee*
    Just.   *Just.*
Mockest thow those Dyamondes wch onely bee matcht
    by ye goddes.   *oddes.*
Oddes? what an oddes ys there synce them to y^e
    heavens I preferr.   *err.*
Tell yet ageane mee the names of these fayre formd
    to do evells?   *Devills.*
Devills? yf in hell suche Devills do abyde to the helles
    I do go?   *go.*

Philisides was Commended for the placinge of his Eccho but litle did hee regarde theyre prayses, who had sett the foundacyon of his Honor there, where hee was moste despysed: And therefore, returning ageane to the Trayne of his desolate pensivenes, *Cleophila* seeyng no body offer to fill the Stage, as yf her longe restrayned Conceipt did now burst oute of prison, shee (thus desyering her voyce shoulde bee according to no thing, but to *Philocleas* eares) threwe downe the burden of her mynd in *Anacrions* kynde of verses.

⌣ – ⌣ – ⌣ – –

My *Muse*, what ailes this *Ardoure*?
To blase my onely *Secrettes*:
Alas yt ys no glory,
To singe my owne decayed state:
Alas yt ys no Comfort,
To speake withoute an aunswer,
 Alas yt ys no wisdome,
  To shewe the woundes without Cure.

My *Muse* what ailes this *Ardoure*?
My eyes bee Dym̃, my Lym̃es shake,
My voyce ys hoarse, my throate scortche,
My toungue to this my Roof cleaves,
My fancy amasde, my thoughtes Dulde.
My hart dothe ake, my lyfe fayntes,
My sowle begins to take leave,
So greate a passyon all feele.
 To thincke a sore so Deadly,
  I shoulde so rashly ripp up.

My *Muse* what ailes this *Ardoure*?
Yf unto Songe thow arte bent,
Goo singe the falle of oulde Thebes,
The warres of ougly Centaures,
The Lyfe, the Deathe of Hector,
So may thy Songe bee famous.
Or yf to love thow arte bent,
Recounte the Rape of Europe
Adonis *ende*, Venus *Nett*.
 The Sleepy Kisse, the Mone stale
  So may thy Songe bee pleasant.
My *Muse* what ailes this *Ardoure*?
To blase my onely Secrettes.
Wherein doo onely florish,
The sory fruites of Anguish,
The Songe therof, alas will,
The Tunes bee cryes, the Wordes playntes,
The Singer ys the songes Theme,
Wherein no eare can have Joy,
 Nor eye receyves an object,
  Myne plesure here in fame gott.

My Muse what ailes this Ardoure?
Alas shee saythe I am thyne,
So are thy paynes, my paynes too?
Thy heated hart my seate ys,
Wherein I burne, thy Breathe ys,
My voyce to hott to keepe in,
Besydes, to heare the Aucthor
Of all my harmes, lo here shee,
   That onely can redress thee,
   Of her I will demaund help.

My Muse I yeelde, My Muse singe?
But all thy Song herein knitt,
The Lyfe wee Leade ys all Love,
The Love wee holde ys all deathe.
Nor oughte I crave to feede deathe,
Nor oughte I seeke to shone deathe.
   But onely that my Goddess
   My lyfe my Deathe dothe Counte hers.

Basilius, when shee had fully ended her songe, fell prostrate uppon the grounde, and thancked the *Goddes* they had preserved his lyfe so longe, as to heare the very Musick they them selves used in an earthly body; And then with like grace to *Cleophila* never lefte entreating her till shee had (taking a *Lyra Basilius* helde for her) songe this *Phaleuciackes.*

$$- - - \cup \cup - \cup - \cup - \cup$$

Reason, tell mee thy Mynde, yf here bee Reason?
In this straunge vyolence to make resistance,
Where sweete Graces erect the stately Banner?
Of Vertues Regiment shyning in harness
   Of Fortunes Dyadems by Beauty mustered,
   Say then Reason (I say) what ys thy Counsell?

Her Loose hayer bee the shott, The Brestes the Pykes bee,
Skoutes eche Motion ys, The handes the Horsemen,
Her Lyppes are the Riches, the Warryers to meyntayne,
Where well Couched abydes a Coffer of Perle,
   Her Legges, Cariage ys of all the sweete Campe,
   Say then Reason (I say) what ys thy Counsell?

Her Cannons bee her eyes, Myne eyes, the Walles bee?
Whiche at first volley gave to open entrie,

Nor Ramper did abyde, my Brayne was up blowne,
Undermynde wth a speeche, the perser of thoughtes,
    Thus weykened by my self, no help remayneth.
    Say then Reason *(I say) what ys thy Counsell?*

And now Fame, *the Herralde of her true Honor,*
Dothe proclayme with a sounde made all by mens mouthes,
That Nature, *Soveraigne of Earthly Dwellers*
Comaundes all Creatures *to yeelde obaysance?*
    Under this her owne her onely Darling.
    Say then Reason *(I say) what ys thy Counsell.*

Reason *sighes, but in ende hee thus dothe answer?*
Noughte can Reason *avayle in heavenly Matters*
Thus Natures *Dyamond receyve thy Conquest,*
Thus Pure Perle I do yeelde my sences and sowle,
    Thus sweete payne I do yeelde what ere I can yeelde.
    Reason *looke to thy self I serve a* Goddess.

Dorus had longe, (hee thoughte,) kept silence from singing somewhat whiche mighte tend to the glory of her, in whome all glory (to his seeming) was enclyned: But nowe hee brake yt, singing these verses, called,

         − − − ◡ ◡ − − ◡ ◡ − ◡ ◡   Asclepiadickes.

O sweete woodes, the Delighte of Solitarynes?
O howe muche I doo like youre solitarynes,
Where Mans mynde hathe a freed Consideracyon,
Of goodnes, to receyve Lovely direction,
Where Sences do beholde the order of heavenly Hoaste,
And wyse thoughtes do beholde what the Creator ys,
Contemplacyon here holdeth his onely seate,
Bounded with no Limittes borne wth a winge of hope,
Clymes even unto the Starres Nature *ys under yt.*
Naughte disturbes thy quyett all to thy service yeelde,
Eche sighte Drawes on a thought, thoughte Mother of scyence,
Sweete Byrdes kyndely do graunte harmony unto thee.
    Fayre Trees, shade ys ynoughe fortification,
    Nor Daunger to thy self, yf not in thy self.

O sweete woodes the Delighte of Solitarynes?
O howe muche do I like youre solitarynes,
Here, no treason ys hidd vailed in Innocency,

Nor Envyes snaky eye fyndes any harboure here,
Nor Flaterers venymous Insinuations,
Nor Cunning Humoristes pudled opinyons.
Nor Courteous Ruyning of proffered usury,
Nor Tyme prattled away, Cradle of Ignorance,
Nor tryffling Tytle of vanity daseleth us.
Nor golden Manackles stande for a Paradyse,
Here wronges name ys unhearde, Sclaunder a Monster ys.
> *Keepe thy Spirite from abuse, here no abuse dothe haunte,*
> *What Man graftes in a Tree dissimulation.*

O sweete woodes the Delighte of Solitarynes?
O howe well do I like youre solitarynes?
Yet Dere sowle, yf a Sowle closde in a Mansion,
As sweete as vyolettes, fayre as a Lilly ys,
Streighte as a Cedar, *a voyce staynes the* Canarie *Birdes*
Whose shade safety dothe holde, Daunger avoydeth her.
Suche wysdome, that in her lives speculation.
Suche goodnes, that in her Simplicity *tryumphes,*
Where Envyes snakye eye wincketh or else dyeth,
Slaunder wanteth, a Pretext Flatery gone beyonde.
O yf suche a one hathe bent to a Lovely lyfe,
Her stepps glad wee receyve, glad wee receyve her eyes,
> *And thincke not shee dothe hurt oure solitarynes?*
> *For, suche Company deckes suche solitarynes.*

The other Shepeheardes were offering them selves to have Continewed the Sportes: But the Nighte had so quyetly spent moste parte of her self amonge them, that the *Duke* for that tyme lycensed them. And so bringing *Cleophila* to her lodging, who woulde muche rather have done the same for *Philoclea*, of all sydes they went to Counterfeit a sleepe in theyre Bedd: For, a true one theyre Agonyes coulde not afforde them, yet there they Lay, (for so mighte they bee moste Solitary for the foode of theyre Thoughtes) till yt was nere Noone the nexte day after: While *Basilius* was to continewe his *Appollo* Devotions, and the other to meditate uppon theyre private desyers.

Here ende the Second Eglogues.
and Second Booke.

The Thirde Booke or Acte.

THE next day wch followed a Night full of passyons, and yet brought in yt self newe matter to encrease them (Tyme uppon Tyme still adding groweth to a well rooted inclination) while the *Duke* in the after noone tyme was buysy aboute *Appollos* Rytes, *Cleophila*, to whome the not enjoying her Frend *Dorus*, had beene one of her burdenous greeffes, took holde of this oportunity ; And, called her beloved Cossyn wth her went to the same place, where first shee had Reveyled unto hym her inclosed passyon, and was by hym as yo^w may remember with a Frendly sharpenes reprehended. There sitting downe amongst the sweete flowers wherof that Contry was very plentyfull, under the pleasant shade of a Brodeleaved *Sicamor*, they recoumpted one to an other theyre straunge Pilgrimage of passyons, omitting no thinge wch the open harted Frendship ys wonte to lay forthe, where there ys Cause to comunicate bothe Joyes & sorowes: For, in Deede there ys no sweeter Taste of Frendship then the Cuppling of theyre Sowles in this Mutuality eyther of Condoling or Comforting. Where the oppressed mynde, fyndes yt self not alltogether miserable, since yt ys sure of one, wch ys feelingly sory for his misery: And the joyfull spendes not his Joy eyther alone or there where yt may bee envyed, but may freely send yt to suche a well grounded object, from whence hee shall bee sure to receyve a sweete reflection of the same Joyes, and as in a Clere Mirror of syncere good will see a Lyvely picture of his owne gladnes. Then woulde there aryse betuixt them Loving Debates of theyre Ladyes Beautyes, of theyre owne Constancyes, and some tymes gloryously stryve whether had bene the moste wretched: O my *Dorus*, my *Dorus* (saide *Cleophila*) who woulde ever have thought so good a Schoole Master as yo^w were to mee coulde for lack of Living bene driven to Shepeherdry. Even the same (saide *Dorus*) that woulde have thoughte so true a Chaste boy as yo^w were coulde have become a Counterfeit Curtizan: But saide hee see whether yo^w can shewe mee so fayer spoyles of youre victory: And therewith hee drewe oute a glove of *Pamelas*, done with Murrey silk and golde Lace, and not withoute tender teares kissing yt hee putt yt ageane in his bosome, & sange these twoo staves.

O sweete glove the witness of my secrett Blisse,
(Whiche hyding did preserve that beutyes lighte)
That (opened forthe) my sealle of Comfort ys,
Bee thow my Starr in this my Darckest nighte,
Thow that myne eyes theyre Cherefull Sunne dothe misse,
Which Daseling still doste still meyntayne my sighte,
Bee thow Sweete glove, the Anchor of my Mynde,
Till my frayle Barcke his Haven ageane do fynde.

Sweete glove, the sweetest spoyles of the sweetest hand,
Fayre hande, the fayrest pledg of fayrer harte,
True harte, whose truthe dothe yeelde to trusty bande,
Cheef Bande I say wch tyes my cheefest parte,
My Cheefest parte, wherein doo cheefly stande
Those secrett Joyes wch heaven to mee imparte,
Unite in one, my state thus still to save
Yow have my thanckes, Let mee youre Comfort have.

Alas, sayde *Cleophila*, (when shee had a while pawsed after her frendes Musick) Can yow not joye sufficyently in youre joyes, but yow must use youre joyes, as yf yo^w woulde vauntingly marche over youre frendes myseryes? Bee happy still my *Dorus*, but wishe the same happe to hym, whome good will dothe make to place muche of his hope in yow. Not the same happ (sayde *Dorus* smyling) *Philocleas* happ I freely graunte yow, but I pray yo^w lett not youre *Amazon* eyes bee busyed upon the Lady *Pamela*, For youre Lookes have an attractive power in them, and youre harte ys not made of the hardest Metell: And are yow affrayed of that (sayde *Cleophila*) from henceforthe bee not, for hardly are Starres seene in daylight, but I woulde fayne knowe, what assurance yo^w have of ye Chaunging favor of Fortune. I have hearde of them that dreamed muche of holding greate Treasures, and when they awaked founde no thinge in theyre handes but a Bedstaff: Glad woulde I bee to bee assured of youre well beeyng, for mee thinckes, the goddes bee too un-equall to Mankynde, yf they suffer not good to come from one Kynseman to an other, by a secrett confusion as wee fynde daily evell dothe by manifest infection. Therefore, synce youre Joy was suche as yo^w woulde fynde in youre harte to singe yt, doo

now for my sake vouchesafe to say yt : My Joyes are suche,
saide *Dorus* as neyther suffer in them selves uncerteynty, nor
are in daunger by inconstancy, Lett mee therefore, Doo no
wronge to my Motherly Destenyes (whiche have woven mee so
blessed a webb) by ungratefull forgetting theyre favoures. And
since I have often tyered yᵉ *Muses* with the hidyous Tune of
my Dolefull affectes, I will nowe sawce those Sorowes wᵗʰ some
more pleasaunt exercyses : And so tooke hee his Shepeheardes
pype, and with sounding that first seeming to invite the Byrdes
to marcke his musick, hee after layde downe his pype, and sange
these followyng.

> *The Merchaunt Man, whome gayne dothe teache yᵉ Sea,*
>   *Where Rockes do weyte for them, the wyndes do chase,*
> *Beaten wᵗʰ waves, no sooner kenns the Bay,*
>   *Where hee was bounde to make his Martyng place,*
>   *But (feare forgott and paynes all overpast)*
>   *Make present ease receyve the better Taste.*
>
> *The Labourer wᶜʰ cursed earthe up teares,*
>   *With sweaty Browes, some tymes wᵗʰ watery eyes,*
> *Ofte scorching Sunne ofte cloudy darcknes feares,*
>   *While uppon Chaunge his fruite of Labor lyes.*
>   *But, Harvest come, and Corne in fertile store.*
>   *More in his owne hee toylde hee gladdes the more.*
>
> *Thus in my Pilgrimage of mated mynde,*
>   *Seeking the Sainte, in whome all graces dwell,*
> *What stormes founde mee, what Tormentes I doo fynde,*
>   *Who seekes to knowe acquayntes hym self wᵗʰ Hell,*
>   *But, now, Success hathe gott above anoyes,*
>   *That, Sorowes weighte, dothe ballance up these Joyes.*

Truly (saide *Cleophila*) amonge so many quallityes, as all ages
have attributed to *Cupid*, I did never thincke hym so good a
Mynstrell that in suche short space, coulde make his scoller so
musicall, as yow bee : But allthoughe for my parte the Starres
have not helde wholy an angry respect towardes mee, yet leste
envyous fortune shoulde spyte at the boasting of youre too
muche blessednes I will mingle youre Comycall tunes with my
longe used Tragicall notes, and will stayne a litle the fullnes of
youre hopes with the hanging on of my tedyous feares : Therewith, lyinge downe with her face upwardes toward heaven with

her Eye so setled, as one might well perceyve yt was no thing her eye coulde there see wch buysyed her Comon sence with a faynting kynde of voyce, shee thus sange.

> *The Merchaunt man, whome many seas have taughte,*
>   *What horrors breedes where wynde Dominyon beares,*
> *Yet never Rock, nor Rage suche terror broughte,*
>   *As nere his home, when storme or shelf hee feares,*
>   *For Nature hathe that never faylling scope,*
>   *Moste loathe to Loose the moste approching hope.*
>
> *The Labourer whome tryed body makes,*
>   *Holde dere his worcke, wth sighe eche chaunge attendes,*
> *But at no Chaunge, so pinching Care hee takes,*
>   *As happy shewes of Corne when Harvest sendes,*
>   *For, Reason, will greate sight of hoped blisse*
>   *Make greate the Losse, so greate the feare to misse.*
>
> *Thus tossed in my Shippe of Huge desyer,*
>   *Thus toyled in my worcke of Raging Love,*
> *Nowe that I spye the Haven my thoughtes aspyer,*
>   *Nowe that some Flower of Fruites my paynes do proove,*
>   *My Dreades augment the more in passyons mighte,*
>   *Synce Love with Care, and Hope wth feare do feighte.*

As shee had ended the last worde, shee tooke *Dorus* in her armes, A, my *Dorus* (sayde shee) These bee as yet my Harvestes these bee as yet the gaynes of my Traffique? But I conjure thee by the Inviolate Name of oure Frendship, or (yf youre newe Flames have made that smoake) by the fayre hayer of *Pamela*, that yo^w tell mee the Story of youre Loving Adventures, that thus shorte of mee (as I thincke in affection) yow have gotten somuche the forefoote in affections Rewarde. Alas (saide *Dorus* with a chaunged Countenaunce) the Cruell Schoole master makes the silly Chylde thincke a litle play great sporte, and howe muche the more wee neede greate help, smalle help, seemes the greater unto us: For longe beaten in mysery yt makes us measure oure myndes by oure powers and not by oure wisshes, and the harte stuffed with wofullnes, ys glad greedily to sucke the thinnest ayer of Comfort: Farr am I (God knowes) from the place, where I hope to stoppe, But yet well advaunced I am from thence where I tooke my start. Then did hee declare unto her the Discourse of all that, wth whiche heretofore, fayre Ladyes,

I have trubled yo^w, howe *Pamela*, oute of a vertuous Resolucyon in respect of his oute ward inequality had wholy disdayned to speake with hym and mysliked the shewes hee had reade of his Love. The strayte hee was in to make hym self knowne (hee beeyng enviously looked uppon and shee beeyng narrowly guarded) that in the ende hee was forced to Counterfeit a Love to *Mopsa* & tell her what soever hee woulde have *Pamela* understand. Howe in his tale hee answered *Pamelas* witt and abused *Mopsas* ignorance; the maner wherof yow have before, (Fayre Ladyes) understoode: And furder since that tyme having founde there wanted no lykinge in *Pamela*, yf shee might have assurance in his worthynes, hee had still (under the Coloure of asking her whether yt were not fitt for *Mopsa* so to doo) Concluded with her the stealling her away to the next sea porte: Under vehement Oathe to offer no force unto her, till hee had invested her in the Duchy of *Thessalia*. That one of the greatest Causes had wonne her to this was the straunge humor shee sawe her Father lately fallen unto and unreasonable restreynt of her Liberty: wherof shee knewe no Cause, but light grounded Jelosy added to the hate of that maner of Lyfe and Confidence shee had in his vertue, that nowe they wanted for nothing, but some fitt tyme by the absence of her Three Loathsome Companyons in whome folly engendered suspicyon. And therefore now saide *Dorus* my Dere Coszen to whome Nature began my Frendship, Education confirmed yt and vertue hathe made yt eternall, here have I discovered the very foundacyon whereuppon my Lyfe ys buylt: Bee yo^w ye Judge betwixt mee and my fortune. The vyolence of Love ys not unknowne unto yow, and I knowe my Case shall never want pitty in youre Consideracyon. Howe all the Joyes of my harte do leave mee in thincking, I must for a tyme bee absent from yo^w. The eternall Truthe ys witness unto mee, I knowe I shoulde not so sensibly feele the Panges of my last Departure: But this enchauntmēt of my Restles Desyer hathe suche aucthority in my self above my self, that I am become a Slave unto yt. I have no more freedome in myne owne Determinacyons, my thoughtes are all bent to carry away my burdenous blisse. Yet moste beloved Coszen, rather then yo^w shoulde thincke I doo herein vyolate that holy bande of true Frendship wherein I unworthy am knitt unto yo^w, Comaunde my staye: Perchaunce, the force of youre Comaundement may worck suche impressyon, wch no Reason of my owne can imprint unto yt, for the Goddes forbid, the fowle worde of abandoning *Pyrocles* mighte ever bee objected to the faythfull *Musidorus*. But yf yo^w can spare my absence, whose presence no way serves yow, and by the Devision of these twoo Lodges ys not ofte with yow, Nay yf yow can thincke my absence may (as yt shall) stand yo^w in stede by bringing suche an Army hether, as shall make *Basilius* willing or unwilling to knowe his owne happ in graunting yo^w *Philoclea*: Then I will chere-fully goo aboute this my moste desyered enterpryse, I shall thincke the better half of yt allredy atcheeved beeyng begun in the fortunate hower of my Frendes Contentment. These wordes as they were not knitt together with suche a Constant Course of flowynge eloquence as *Dorus* was wonte to use, so was his voyce interrupted, with sighes, and his Countenaunce with enterchaunging Coloure dismayde: So muche his owne harte did fynde hym faulty, to unbynde any way the continuall use of theyre dere frendshipp. But, Oh feminine Love, what power thow haste in mens hartes? Many tymes hee had bene desyerous to signify his happy success and finall determinacyon wth *Pamela*: But his harte woulde never serve to come to this poynte, till one worde emboldened an other kyndely to discover to his Frende his owne unkyndenes. *Cleophila*, who had beefore purposed to make the like declaracyon uppon what slippery grounde her hope stoode, and yet how farr her hopes in *Philoclea* were advaunced, how farre by *Ginecia* they were hindered; when this last Determinatyon of *Dorus* strake her attentive eares, shee stayed a great while oppressed with a Deade amasement. There came streighte before her mynde, made tender with wooes, the Images of her owne Fortune, her tedyous longinges, her Causes to dispayer, the Combersome folly of *Basilius*, the enraged Jelosy of *Ginecia* her self a Prince withoute Retinewe a Man anoyed with the trubles of woman-kynde, Loathsomely Loved, and daungerusly Loving, and now for the perfecting of all her Frende to bee taken away by hym self to make the losse ye greater by the unkyndenes. But, within a while shee resolutely passed over all inward objections, and therefore preferring her Frendes proffitt to her owne desyer, with a quyet but harty Looke shee thus answered hym. Yf I bare thee this Love (vertuous *Musidorus*) for myne owne Sake, and that oure Freendship grewe bycause I for my parte mighte rejoyse, to enjoy suche a Freend, I shoulde nowe so throughly feele myne owne Losse, that I shoulde Calle the heavens and earthe to witnes, howe cruelly yo^w robbe mee of my greatest Comfort, measuring the breache of Frendshipp, by myne owne passyon : But bycause, in deede I Love thee for thy self, and in my judgment, Judge of thy worthynes to bee beloved, I am content to leave all that wch mighte please my self. I am content to buylde my pleasure upon thy Comforte, and then will I deeme my happ in Frendship greate when I shall see thee whome I Love, happy ; Lett mee bee sure, tho^w Lovest mee still, the onely pryce of true affection : Goo therefore on worthy *Musidorus* with the guyde of vertue, and service of fortune, Lett thy Loves bee Loved, thy Desyers prosperus, thy escape safe, and thy Journey easy, Let every thinge yeelde his help to thy Desert. For my Parte, absence shall not take the frome myne eyes, nor afflictions shall barre mee from gladding in thy good, nor a possessed harte shall keepe thee from the place yt hathe for ever allotted unto yo^w : *Dorus* woulde fayne have replyed ageane to have made a Liberall Confession, that, *Cleophila* had of her syde the advauntage of well performing Frendshipp, but partly his owne greef of parting frome one hee Loved so derely, partly the kynde Care in what state hee shoulde Leave *Cleophila* bred suche a Conflict in his mynde, that many tymes he wisshed hee had eyther never attempted or never reveyled this secrett enterpryse. But *Cleophila* (who had now looked to the utter-moste of yt and establisshed her mynde uppon assured Deter-mynacyon) my onely Frende sayde shee, since to so good towardnes youre Curtuous Destenyes have conducted yo^w, Lett not a Ceremonyall Consideracyon of oure mutuall Love bee a Barr unto yt ? I joy in youre presence, but I joye more in youre good, that Frendship bringes forthe the fruites of enmity wch preferrs his owne tendernes before his Frendes Domage, For my parte, my greatest greef herein shall bee, I can bee no further servisable unto yow. O *Cleophila* (sayde *Dorus* with his eyes eeven covered with water) I did not thincke so soone to have displayed my Determynacyon unto yo^w, but to have made my way first into youre Loving judgment, But, alas as youre sweete Disposicyon drewe mee so farr, so dothe yt more strengthen mee in yt : To yow therefore bee the due

Comendacyon given who can conquer mee in Love and Love in Wysdome. As for mee, then shall goodnes turne to evell, and ingratefullnes bee the token of a true harte when *Pyrocles* shall not possess a Principall seate in my sowle, when the name of *Pyrocles* shall not bee helde of mee in devoute Reverence. I thincke, they woulde never have come to the Cruell instant of parting, nor the yll Faring worde of Farewell, had not *Cleophila* seene a farr of the oulde *Basilius* who had beene every where to seeke her synce hee had ended his Sacrifyce: And nowe. beeyng come within Compass of discerning her, hee began to frame the Lovelyest countenaunce hee coulde, stroking upp his Legges, setting his Bearde in due order & standing bolt upprighte. Alas (sayde *Cleophila*) beholde an evill for tooken of oure sorowfull Departure, yonder, see I one of my furyes wch dothe dayly vexe mee, Fare well, Farewell my *Musidorus*, the goddes make fortune to wayte on thy vertues, and make mee wade throughe this Lake of wretchednes: *Dorus* burste owte into a fludde of teares wringing her fast by the hande. No no, saide hee I goo blyndfolde whether the Course of my yll happ carryes mee, for nowe too late my harte gives mee, this oure seperating can never bee prosperus: But, yf I Live, attend mee here shortly with an Army. Thus bothe appalled with the greevous Rending of theyre longe Combynacyon, having first resolved with them selves, that what soever evill fell unto them, they shoulde never uppon any occasyon utter theyre names, for the Conserving of theyre Honor of theyre Royall Parentage, but tooke other Names they agreed uppon: They tooke dyvers wayes, *Dorus* to the Lodge warde where his hevy eyes mighte bee refresshed, *Cleophila* towardes *Basilius*, saying to her self with a scornefull smylinge, yet hathe not my frend Fortune deprived mee of a pleasant Companyon. *Basilius* had inquyred of his Daughter *Philoclea*, what Receipte his Desyers founde in *Cleophila* and had some Comfort of her: That by her owne good Interteynement shee did imagyn his Cause was not ungratefull unto her, and now having with muche searche come to her presence Doubt and Desyer bred a greate quarrell in his mynde. For late experyence had taughte hym to doubte, and true Feeling of Love made Doubtes daungerus, but the worcking of his Desyer, had ere longe wonne the fielde: And therefore with moste submissive maner his behavyor coulde yeelde,

O Goddess (sayde hee) toward whome I have the greatest feeling of Religion, bee not displeased at some shewe of Devotion I have made to *Apollo*. Synce hee, (yf hee knewe any thinge) knowes that my harte beares farr more and full reverence to youre self, then to any unseene *Diety*: yow will ever bee deceyved in mee (answered *Cleophila*) I will make my self no Competitor with *Appollo*, neyther can Blasphemyes to hym bee Duetyes unto mee, with that *Basilius* tooke oute of his bosome certeyn verses hee had written: And kneeling downe presented them unto her. They conteyned this.

> Phaebus *Farewell, a sweeter Sainte, I serve,*
> *The hye Conceyptes, thy heavenly wisdome breede,*
> *My thoughtes forgett My thoughtes wch never swerve,*
> *From her in whome ys sowne theyre Freedoms feede,*
> *And in whose eyes my daily Doome I reede.*

> Phebus *Farewell a Sweeter Sainte, I serve,*
> *Thow arte farr of, thy Kingdome ys above,*
> *Shee heaven on Earthe wch beutyes doo preserve,*
> *Thy Beames I like, but her Clere Rayes I Love,*
> *Thy force I feare, her force I still doo proove.*

> Phebus *yeelde up thy Title in my mynde?*
> *Shee dothe possess, thy Image ys defaste?*
> *But yf thy Rage, some brave Revenge will fynde,*
> *On her, in mee who hathe thy Temple raste;*
> *Employ thy mighte, that shee thy fyers may taste.*
> *And howe muche more her wrothe surmounteth thee,*
> *Make her asmuche more base by Loving mee.*

This ys my Hymne to yow (saide Hee) not lefte mee by my Auncestors, but begun in my self, the Temple wherein yt ys daily sunge, ys my Sowle: And the Sacrifice I offer to yow wth all ys all what soever I am. *Cleophila,* who ever thoughte shee founde in his speeches the yll taste of a Medicyn, and the operation of a poyson woulde have suffered a Disdaynefull Looke to have bene the onely witness of his good acceptation: But that *Basilius* began a fresshe to lay before her many pityfull prayers, and in the ende to Conclude, that hee was fully of opinyon the hatefull influence wch had made hym embrace this Sollitary lyfe, was nowe past over hym, and with all, Living so weykely garded, the late Tumulte had Taughte hym what

Daungers hee mighte falle into. Therefore hee was now enclyned to returne to his Pallace in *Mantinea*, & there hee hoped, hee shoulde bee better able to shewe how muche hee desyered to make all hee had herrs, with many other suche hony wordes, wch my penn growes allmoste weary to sett downe: This in deede nerely pearsed *Cleophila*, for the good beginning shee had obtayned of *Philoclea* made her desyer to continew the same Trade till unto the more perfecting of her Desyers, and to come to any publique place, shee did deadly feare, least her Maske by many eyes mighte the sooner bee discovered, and so her hopes stopped and the state of her Joyes endangered. Therefore, a while, shee rested musing at the daily chaunging Labyrinth of her owne fortune but in her self Determeyned yt was, her onely best, to keepe hym there, and with favoures to make hym love the place where ye favoures were receyved, as Disgraces had made hym apte to chaunge the soylle: Therefore, casting a kynde of Comfortable Looke upon hym yt ys truely saide (saithe shee) that aige cooleth the blood. Howe soone (good man) yow are terrifyed, before yow receyve any hurte, Doo yow not knowe, that Dayntynes ys kyndely unto us, and y^t harde obtayning ys the excuse of woemens graunting? yet speake I not as thoughe yow were like to obtayne, or I to graunte, But bycause I woulde not have yo^w imagyn I am to bee wonne by Courtely vanityes or esteeme a Man the more bycause hee hathe handsome men to weyte upon hym, when hee ys afrayde to live withoute them. Yow mighte have seene *Basilius* humbly swell, and with a Lowly looke stand uppon his tipptoes; suche diversity her wordes delivered unto hym. O *Hercules* (answered hee) *Basilius* afrayde? or his blood Colde that boylles in suche a Furnace? Care I who ys with mee, while I enjoy youre presence? Or ys any place good or badd to mee, but as yt pleaseth yow to bless or Curse yt? O lett mee bee but armed in youre good grace, and I Defye what ever there ys or can bee ageanst mee: No, no, youre Love ys forcible, and my Age ys not withoute vigor. *Cleophila* thought yt not good for his stomack to receyve a surffeit of too muche favor, and therefore thinckking hee had ynoughe for the tyme, to keepe hym from any sodeyn remooving, with a certeyn gracyous bowing downe of her head towardes hym shee turned away: Sayinge shee woulde leave hym at this tyme, to see how

168

temperatly hee coulde use so bountyfull a measure of her kyndenes. *Basilius*, that thoughte every Dropp a floode, that bredd any Refreshment, durst not furder press her, but with an ancyent modesty lefte her to the sweete repast of her owne fancyes: *Cleophila*, assoone as hee was departed went towardes *Pamelas* Lodge in hope ageane to have seene her frend *Dorus*, to have pleased her self with a newe paynefull farewell. But beeyng come even nere the Lodge, shee sawe ye mowthe of a Cave, made, as yt shoulde seeme by nature in despyte of Arte, so fittly did the riche growyng Marble serve to beutify the vaulte of the first entrie: Under foote the ground seemed mynerall yeelding suche a glistering shewe of golde in yt as they say the River *Tagus* carryes in his sandy bedd, the Cave framed oute to many good spacyous Rowmes, even suche as the self liking men have with long and learned Delicacy founde oute the moste easefull. There rann throwe yt a litle sweete River, wch had lefte the face of the earthe, to drowne her self for a smalle way in this Darck but pleasant mancyon: The very firste shewe of the place entysed the Melancholy mynde of *Cleophila* to yeelde her self over there, to the Floode of her owne thoughtes. And therefore sitting downe in the first entrie of the Caves mowthe, with a Songe shee had lately made, shee gave dolefull way to her bitter affectes shee sange to this effect.

> *Synce that the Stormy Rage of passyons darcke,*
> *(Of passyons darcke made darck by Beutyes Lighte,)*
> *With Rebell force hathe closde in Dongeon darcke,*
> *My mynde ere nowe led forthe by* Reasons *lighte,*
> *Synce all the thinges wch gives my eyes theyre lighte,*
> *Do Foster still the fruite of Fancyes Darcke.*
> *So that the wyndowes of my Inward Lighte,*
> *Do serve to make my Inwarde powers Darcke.*
>
> *Synce, (as I say) bothe mynde and Sences darcke,*
> *Are hearde, not helped, with pearsing of the Lighte,*
> *While that the Lighte may shewe the horrors darcke*
> *But can not make resolved Darcknes Lighte.*
> *I like this place where at the Least the Darcke,*
> *May keepe my thoughtes from thoughte of wonted lighte.*

COUNTESS OF PEMBROOKES

In steade of an Instrument, her Songe was accompanyed wth the wringing of her handes, the Closing of her weary eyes, and even some tyme cutt of with the swelling of her Sighes, whiche did not suffer the voyce, to have the free and native passage: But, as shee was a while musinge uppon her songe, Raysing up her Spirittes wch were somewhat fallen in to the weykenes of Lamentacyon Considering solitary Complayntes do no good to hym whose help standes with oute hym self, shee mighte a farr of first heare a whispering sounde whiche seemed to come from the inmoste part of the Cave, and beeyng kept together with the Close hollownes of the place, had, (as in a Truncke) the more Liberall access unto her eares: And by and by shee mighte perceyve the same voyce deliver yt self into Musicall tunes, and with a base *Lyra* gave forthe this songe.

Hearke playntfull Ghostes, Infernall furyes harcke?
  Unto my wooes, the Hatefull heavens doo sende,
The Heavens conspirde, to make my vitall sparcke,
  A wretched wrack, a Glass of Ruyns ende.

Seeyng, (alas) so mighty powers bende,
  Theyre irefull shott ageanst so weyke a Marcke
Come Cave, become my grave, Come deathe and lend,
  Receipte to mee within thy Bosome darcke.

For, what ys lyfe to daily dyinge mynde?
  Where Drawyng breathe I suck the Ayer of Wooe,
Where, too muche sighte makes all the body blynde,
  And highest thoughtes Downeward moste hedlong throwe
    Thus then my forme, and thus my state I fynde,
    Deathe wrapt in Flesh to Living grave assygnde.

And pawsing but a litle with Monefull Melody yt continewed this Octave.

Lyke those sicke folckes in whome straunge Humors flowe,
  Can taste no sweetes, the sower onely please,
So, to my Mynde, while passyons daily growe,
  Whose fyery Chaynes uppon his freedome seaze,
  Joyes Straungers seeme, I can not byde theyre shewe,
  Nor brooke oughte ellse, but well acquaynted wooe,

  Bitter greef tastes mee best, paynes ys my ease,
  Sicke to the deathe, still Loving my Diszease.

O *Venus*, sayde *Cleophila*, who ys this, so well acquaynted wth mee, that can make so lyvely a Purtraiture of my myseryes? yt ys surely, the Spirite appoynted to have Care of mee, wch dothe now in this darcke place beare parte with the Complayntes of his unhappy Charge; For yf yt bee so, that the Heavens have at all tymes mesure of theyre wrathfull harmes, surely so many have come to my blissles Lott, that the rest of the worlde have too smalle a proportion, to make so waylefull a Lamentatyon. But, (saide shee) what soever thow bee, I will seeke the oute, for thy Musick well assures mee wee are at least hande fellowe Prentyzes to one ungracyous Master: So, rase shee, and went guyding her self by the still playing voyce, till shee sawe upon a stone a litle waxe lighte sett, and under yt a peece of paper wth these verses, very lately (as yt should seeme) written.

> *Howe ys my Sunne (whose Beames are shyning brighte,*
> *Become the Cause of my Darcke ougly Nighte?*
> *Or howe do I captyved in this darck plighte,*
> *Bewayle the Case, and in the Cause delighte?*
>
> *My mangled mynde huge Horrors still do frighte,*
> *With Sence possest, and claymde by reasons Righte,*
> *Betwixt whiche twoo in mee I have this fighte,*
> *Where, who so wynnes, I putt my self to flighte.*
>
> *Come cloudy feares, close up my daselled sighte,*
> *Sorow suck up the Marowe of my Mighte.*
> *Dewe Sighes blowe oute all sparckles of joyfull Lighte?*
> *Tyre on Dispayer uppon my Tyered spirite*
> *An ende, an ende, my Dullde penn can not wryte,*
> *Nor masde heade thincke, nor faultering tongue resyte.*

And hard under neathe the Sonett were these wordes written.

> *This Cave ys Darcke, but yt had never Lighte,*
> *This waxe dothe waste yt self, yet payneles dyes,*
> *These wordes are full of woes, yet, feele they none,*
> *I darckened am, who once had clearest sighte,*
> *I waste my harte, whiche still new Torment tryes,*
> *I Playne with Cause, my woes are still myne owne,*
> *No Cave, no wasting waxe, No wordes of greef,*
> *Can holde, shewe, tell my paynes withoute Releef.*

Shee did not longe stay to reede the wordes, for, not farr of from ye Stone shee mighte discerne in a darcke Corner, a Lady lyinge wth her face so prostrate uppon the grounde, as shee coulde neyther knowe nor bee knowne: But, as the generall nature of Man ys desyerus of knowledge and sorowe especially glad to fynde Fellowes, shee went as softely as shee coulde convey her feete nere unto her, where shee hearde these wordes come with vehement sobbing from her. O Darcknes (saide shee) whiche dothe lightsomely mee thinckes make mee see the picture of myne inward Darcknes, synce I have chosen thee to bee the secret witnes of my Sorowes, Lett them receyve a safe receypte in thee, and esteeme them not tedyous: But, yf yt bee possible, lett the uttering them bee some discharge to my overladen brest. Alas, Sorowe, now thow haste the full Sacke of my Conquered Spirites, rest thy self a while, and sett not still newe fyers to thyne owne Spoylles: O accursed Reason how manye eyes haste thow to see thy evills and howe dumbe, nay blynde arte thowe in preventing them? Forlorne Creature that I am, I woulde I mighte bee freely wicked, since wickednes dothe prevayle. But the Foote steppes of my over troden vertue ly still as bitter accusacyons unto mee; I am devyded in my self, how can I stande? I am over throwne in my self who shall rayse mee, vyce ys but A Nurse of Newe Agonyes, and the vertue I am devorced from, makes the hatefull Comparyson the more manifest. No, no vertue either I never had but a shadowe of thee, or thow thy self are but a shadowe. For how ys my sowle abandoned? How are all my powers layde waste? My desyere ys payned bycause yt can not hope, and yf hope came, his best shoulde bee but myscheef, O straunge mixture of humane myndes, onely somuche good lefte, as to make us Languish in oure owne evills: Yee infernall Furyes (for yt ys to late for mee to awake my Deade vertue or to please my Comfort in the Angry godes) yee infernall Furyes (I say) ayde one that dedicates her self unto yo^w. Lett my Rage bee satisfyed since the affect of yt ys fitt for youre service: Neyther bee afrayed to make mee too happy, synce no thing can come to appease the smarte of my guylty Conscyence, I desyer but to asswage the sweltering of my hellish Longing dejected *Gynecia*?

Cleophila no sooner hearde the Name of *Gynecia* but, that wth a Colde sweate all on her, as yf shee had bene redy to treade uppon a deadly stinging adder, shee woulde have withdrawne her self, but her owne passyon made her yeelde more unquyett motyons then shee had done in Commyng. So, that shee was perceyved, and *Gynecia* sodenly risen up, for in deede yt was *Gynecia* gotten into this Cave, (the same Cave wherein *Dametas* had safely kept *Pamela* in ye late uprore) to passe her panges with chaunge of places: And as her mynd rañ still upon *Cleophila*, her pearcing Lovers eye had soone founde, yt was shee, and seeyng in her a Countenaunce to flee away, shee fell downe, at her feete. And catching fast holde of her, alas sayde shee whether or from whome doest thow flee away? The savagest Beastes are wonne wth service, and there ys no Flinte but may bee mollifyed: Howe ys *Gynecia* so unworthy in thy eyes, or whome can not abundance of Love make worthy? O weighe alas, weighe with thy self ye newe effectes of this mighty passyon, that I unfitt for my estate, uncomely for my sexe must become a Supplyant at thy feete? By the happy woeman that bare thee, by all the Joyes of thy harte, and success of thy desyer, I beseche thee, turne thy self into some Consideracyon of mee: And rather shewe pitty in nowe helping mee, then in, too late repenting my deathe whiche howerly threatens mee? *Cleophila* imputing yt to one of her continuall myshappes, thus to have mett wth this Lady, with a full weary Countenaunce Withoute Doubte Madame (sayde shee) where the desyer ys suche as may bee obteyned, and the party well deserving as youre self yt must bee a greate excuse that may well coloure a denyall: But when the firste Motion carryes wth yt a direct unpossibility then must the onely answer bee Comfort wth oute help, and sorowe to bothe partyes, to yow not obteyning, to mee not able to graunte. O saide *Gynecia*, howe good Leysure yo^w have to frame these scornefull answers? ys *Gynecia* thus to bee dispysed? Am I so vyle a worme in youre sighte? No, No, trust to yt harde harted Tygre, I will not bee the onely Actor of this Tragedy, synce I must falle, I will press downe some others wth my Ruyns? synce I must burne, my spytefull Neighboures shall feele of my fyer? Doest thow not perceyve that my diligent eyes have persed thorowe ye Cloudy Maske of thy Disguysement? Have I not tolde thee O foole (yf I were not muche more foole) that I knowe thow wouldest abuse us with thy owtewarde shewe? Wilt thow still attend the Rage of Love in a womans hart? The Girle thy well chosen Mistris perchaunce shall defend thee, when *Basilius* shall knowe howe thow haste sotted his mynde with falsehood, and falsely soughte the Dishonor of his howse: Beleeve yt beleeve yt unkynde Creature I will ende my myseryes with a Notable example of Revenge, and that accursed Cradell of myne shall feele the smarte of my wounde, thow of thy Tyranny, and lastly (I Confess) my self of myne owne worke. *Cleophila*, that had longe before doubted her self to bee discovered by her, and now playnely fynding yt was (as the proverb saythe) like them that holde the wolf by the eares, bitten while they holde, & slayne yf they loose, yf shee holde her of in these wonted Termes shee sawe Rage woulde make her Love worcke the effectes of hate: To graunte unto her, (her harte was so bounde uppon *Philoclea*) yt had bene worse then a Thowsand Deathes, yet founde shee yt was necessary for her to come to a Resolutyon. For, *Gynecias* sore could ebyde no Leysure, and (once discovered) besydes the daunger of *Philoclea* her desyer shoulde bee for ever stopped utterly: Shee Remembred with all the wordes of *Basilius* how apte hee was to leave this lyfe and returne to his Courte (a greate barr to her hopes). Lastly she Considered *Dorus* enterpryze mighte bringe some straunge alteration of this theyre welllyked fellowshipp, so that (compassed with these instant difficultyes) shee bent her Spirites to thinck of a Remedy wch mighte at once bothe save her from them and serve her to ye accomplishment of her onely pursuite: Lastly shee determeyned thus, that there was no way but to yeelde to the vyolence of theyre Desyers, since stryving did the more chafe them, and that followyng theyre owne Current at lengthe of yt self, yt woulde bring her to the other syde of her burning desyers. But mee thinckes I heare the Shepeheard *Dorus* calling mee to tell yow something of his hopefull adventures, who soever hathe founde by experyence, how unspeakeable a Comfort a true Frende ys: where there ys so synceare a participating of eche others fortunes, as a Man ys sure, eyther to have help or Comforte, may holde easily in his Conjecture the present Case of Devyded *Dorus* devyded betuixt Love and Frendshipp. But Love carrying with yt, besydes all force of suche Argumentes (of wch affectionated braynes are never unprovyded) the continuall stynge of insatiate desyer had (as yow have hearde) gotten the forte, thoughe withoute prejudice of his Loyall frendship, wch dothe never barr the mynde from his Free satisfaction: yet still, *Dorus* (a cruell Judge over hym self) thoughte hee was some wayes faulty, and applyed his mynde, howe to amend yt with a speedy and behovefull returne. But then was his first studye how to gett a way, whereto allredy hee had *Pamelas* Consent Confirmed and Concluded under the Name of *Mopsa* in her owne presence. *Dorus* taking this way, that, whatsoever hee woulde have of *Pamela* hee woulde aske her whether in suche a Case yt were not best for *Mopsa*, so to behave her self: Thus was *Mopsas* envy made an instrument of that shee did envy, as allredy yo^w have understood by the relacyon *Dorus* made therof to *Cleophila*. Now, that *Dorus* had passed over his firste moste feared difficulty hee buysyed his spirits howe to come to the Harvest of his Desyers, wherof hee had so fayre a shewe: And thereunto having gotten leave for some dayes of his Master *Dametas*, who began to accoumpt hym as his Sonne in Lawe, hee romed rounde aboute the Dezert to fynde some unknowne way that mighte bringe hym to the next Sea porte, asmuche as mighte bee oute of all Course of other passingers. Whiche all very well succeeding hym, and hee having hyered a Barcke for his lyves traffique, and provyded horses to carry her thether, returned homewarde, now come to the last ende of his Care, howe, to goo beyond the Loathsome watchfullnes of his three Comely Companyons: And therein did wysely Consider, how they were to bee taken wth whome hee had to dealle, Remembring that in the particularityes of every bodyes mynde and Fortune there are particuler advauntages by whiche they are to bee helde. The Muddy mynde of *Dametas* hee founde moste easily stirred wth Covetusnes: The Curst myscheevous harte of *Miso* moste apte to bee tickled wth Jelosy, as whose rotten brayne coulde thinck well of no body but younge Mistris *Mopsa*, who coulde open her eyes uppon no thinge that did not all to beewonder her, hee thoughte Curyosity the fittest Bayte for her. And first for *Dametas*, *Dorus* having employed a whole dayes worcke aboute x myles of from the Lodge quite contrary way to that hee meant to take with *Pamela* in digging and opening the grounde under an auncyent oake, that stoode there, in suche sorte as mighte longest holde *Dametas* greedy hopes in some shewe of Comfort: Hee came to his Master wth a Countenaunce mixte betweene cherefullnes and haste, and taking hym by the Right hande, as yf hee had a great matter of Secretsy, to Reveile unto hym; Master, saide hee I did never thinck that the Godds had appoynted my mynde freely brought up to have so longing a Desyer to serve yow, but that they mynded thereby to bringe some extraordenary fruite to one so beloved of them as youre Honesty makes mee thincke yow are. This byndes mee in my Conscyence to disclose that, wch I perswade my self ys allotted unto yo^w that youre Fortune may bee of equall Ballance with youre Desertes: Hee sayde no furder bycause hee would lett *Dametas* play uppon the Bitt a whyle, who, not understanding what his wordes intended, yet well fynding they carryed no evill Newes, was somuche the more desyerus to knowe ye matter as hee had free scope to ymagyn what measure of good happ hym self woulde. Therefore putting of his Capp to hym, whiche hee had never done before, and assuring hym hee shoulde have *Mopsa* (thoughe shee had beene all made of Clothe of golde) hee besoughte *Dorus* not to holde hym longe in hope, for that hee founde yt a thing his hart was not able to beare: Master answered *Dorus*, yo^w have so satisfyed mee with promysing mee the uttermoste of my desyered blisse, that yf my Duety bounde mee not, I were in yt sufficyently rewarded. To yow therefore shall my good happ bee vowed, and the fruite of all my Laboure dedicated: Therewth hee toulde hym, howe under an auncyent Oake (the place hee made hym easely understand by sufficyent Marckes hee gave unto hym) hee had founde digging but a litle Depthe, scatteringly lying a great nomber of *Medaillas*. And that pearsing further into ye grounde hee had mett wth a greate Stone, wch by the hollow sounde yt yeelded seemed to bee the Cover of some greate vaulte, and upon yt a Boxe of *Cypres* with the name of the valyant *Aristhomenes* graven uppon yt: And within the Boxe hee founde certeyn verses wch signifyed that some depthe ageane under that, all his tresures laye hidden, what tyme for the Discorde fell oute in *Arcadia*, hee lived banished. Therewith hee gave *Dametas* a certeyn *Medailla* of golde hee had longe kept aboute hym, and asked hym (bycause yt was a thinge muche to bee kept secrett, and a Matter one Man in xx^{ti} howres mighte easily performe) whether hee woulde have hym goo and seeke the Bottom of yt? Whiche hee had refrayned to doo till hee knewe his mynde, promysing hee wolde faythfully bringe hym what hee founde, or ellse that hee hym self woulde doo yt and bee the first beholder of y^t comfortable spectacle. No man neede doubte whiche parte *Dametas* woulde chose, whose fancy had all redy devoured all this greate Riches, and even nowe began to grudge at a Partener before hee sawe his owne share. Therefore, taking streighte a strong Jade Laden with spades & mattockes (wch hee ment to bringe back otherwyse Laden) hee went in all speede thetherward, taking Leave of no body: Onely desyering *Dorus* hee woulde looke well to the Princes *Pamela*, promising hym Mounteyns of his owne Laboure, wch nevertheles hee litle meante to performe, like a Foole, not considering, that no man ys to bee mooved wth parte that neglectes the whole. Thus away went *Dametas* having allredy made an Image in his fancy, what Pallaces hee woulde buylde how sumptuously hee woulde fare, and amonge all other thinges imagined what money to employ in making Coffers to keepe his money: His Tenn myles seemed twyse so many Leagues, and yet contrary to the nature of yt, thoughe yt seemed longe yt was not wearysome. Many tymes hee cursed his horses want of Consideratyon that in so ymportunate a Matter woulde make no greater speede, many tymes hee wisshed hym self the back of an Asse to help to carry away his newe soughte Riches: An unfortunate wissher, for yf hee had aswell wisshed the hedd, yt had beene graunted hym, at lengthe, beeyng come to the Tree whiche hee hoped shoulde beare so golden Ackornes, downe went all his instrumentes, and forthewith to the Renting up of the hurtles earthe. Where, by and by hee was caughte wth the Lyme of a fewe promysed *Medialles*, whiche was so perfect a pawne unto hym of his furder expectation that hee deemed a great Nomber of howers well employed in groping furder unto yt, wch with Logges and greate Stones was made as combersome as mighte bee: At lengthe wth sweaty browes hee came to the greate stone, a Stone (God knowes) full unlike to the Cover of a Monument, but yet, there was the Cypres Boxe with *Aristhomenes* graven uppon yt and these verses written in yt.

> *A Banisshed man longe barrd from his Desyer,*
> *By inward lettes of them his State possest :*
> *Hidd here his Hopes by whiche hee mighte aspyer,*
> *To have his harmes with wisdomes help redrest.*

COUNTESS OF PEMBROOKES

Seeke then and see what Man esteemeth best.
All ys but this, this ys but Laboures hyre,
Of this wee Love, in this wee fynde oure Rest,
Who holdes this fast, no greater Wealth requyer,
Looke furder then, so shalte thow fynde at leaste,
A Bayte moste fitt for hungry mynded guest.

Hee opened the Boxe, and to his greate Comfort redd them, and with fresh Corage went aboute to lifte up that Stone; But in the meane tyme, I must tell yow that *Dametas* was not half a Myle gone to the Treasure warde when *Dorus* came to *Miso*, whome hee found sitting in the Chimneyes ende, babling to her self, and showyng in all her gestures that shee was loathsomely weary of the Worlde: Not for any hope of a better lyfe, but fynding no one good, neyther in mynde nor body, whereat shee mighte nourish a quyet thoughte, having longe synce hated eche thing else, began nowe to hate her self. Before this sweete Hony woord Dame, *Dorus* sett hym self, and framed towardes her suche a smyling Countenaunce, as mighte seeme to bee myxte betwixt a Tickled Myrthe, and a forced pitty: *Miso* (to whome Cherefullnes in others was ever a Sawse of envy in her self) tooke quickly marcke of his behavyor, and with a Looke full of forworne spyte, Now, the Devill (sayde shee) take these villeynes that can never leave gryning, bycause I am not so fayre as Mistris *Mopsa* to see howe the Skipp Jack lookes at mee? *Dorus* that had the occasyon hee desyered, truely Mistris, answered hee, my smyling ys not at yow, but at them that are from yow, and in deede I must needes a litle accorde my Countenaunce with others sporte: And there with all tooke her in his Armes, and Rocking her to and froo, In faythe Mistris, (sayde hee) yt ys hye tyme for yow to bydd us good nighte for ever, synce others can possess youre place in youre owne tyme? *Miso*, that was never voyde of mallice, to suspect the uttermoste evill, to satisfy a furder shrewdnes, tooke on a present myldenes and gently desyered hym to tell her what hee meante? for sayde shee, I am lyke ynoughe to bee knavishly dealte wth all by that Churle my Husband. *Dorus* fell of from the matter ageane, as yf hee had meante no suche thinge, till by muche refusing her Intreaty and vehemently stirring up her Desyer, to knowe, hee

178

had strengthened a Creditt in her, to that hee should say, and then with a formall Countenaunce, as yf the Conscience of the Case had tuched hym self: Mistrys (saide hee) I am muche perplexed in myne owne Determinacyon, for my thoughtes doo ever will mee to doo honestly, but my Judgment fayles mee, what ys honest betuixt the generall Rule that in trusted secrecyes are wholy to bee observed, and the particuler exception, that the Dishonest secretsies are to bee reveiled, especially there where by Reveiling they may eyther bee prevented, or amended. Yet in this Ballaunce youre judgment weyghes mee downe, bycause I have Confidence in yt, that yow will use what yow knowe, moderately, and rather take suche faultes, as an advauntage to youre desertes then by youre bitter using yt, bee Content to bee revenged on others wth youre owne harmes. So ys yt, Mistris (sayde hee) that, yesterday dryving my Sheepe up to the stately Hill, whiche liftes his heade over the fayre Citty of *Mantinea*, I hapned uppon the syde of yt in a litle fawling of ye grounde wch was a rampier ageanst the Sunnes rage, to perceyve a younge Mayde, truely of the fynest stamp of Beuty, and that wch made her beuty the more admirable, there was at all no Arte added to ye helping of yt. For her apparell was but suche as Shepeheardes Daughters are wonte to weare, and as for her hayer yt hanged downe, at the free liberty of his goodly lengthe. But, that some tymes falling before the clearest starrs of her sighte, shee was forced to putt yt behynd her eares, and so open ageane the Treasure of her perfections, wch that for a while had in parte hidden in her Lapp: There lay a Shepeheard so wrapped up in y^t well liked place, that I coulde discerne no peece of his face, but, as myne eyes were attent in that her Angelike voyce, strake myne eares with this Songe.

> *My true Love hathe my harte, and I have his,*
>   *By just exchaunge one for the other given,*
> *I holde his deare, and myne hee can not misse,*
>   *There never was a better Bargayne driven.*
> *His harte in mee keepes mee and hym in one,*
>   *My hart in hym his Thoughtes and sences guydes,*
> *Hee Loves my Harte, for once yt was his owne,*
>   *I Cherish his, bycause in mee yt bydes.*

179

His Harte his wounde receyved from my sighte,
  My harte was wounded wth his wounded hart,
For, as from mee on hym his hurt did lighte,
  So still mee thoughte in mee his hurt did smarte:
  Bothe equall hurte in this Chaunge soughte oure Bliss:
  My true Love hathe my harte and I have his.

But as yf the Shepeheard that lay before her had bene Organes whiche were onely to bee blowne by her Breathe shee had no sooner ended with the joyning her sweete Lippes together, but that hee Recorded to her Musick this Rurall Poesy.

O wordes whiche falle like Somer Deawe on mee,
  O breathe more sweete then ys the growyng Beane,
O Toungue in whiche all Hony Liquors bee,
  O voyce, that dothe the Thrussh in shrillnes stayne,
  Do yow say still this ys her promyse Due,
  That shee ys myne, as I to her am true.

Gay hayer, more gay, then Strawe, when harvest lyes,
  Lippes Redd and plume as Cheryes ruddy syde,
Eyes fayre and greate, like fayre great Oxes eyes,
  O Brest in whiche twoo white Sheepe swell in pryde,
  Joyne yow with mee, to sealle this promyse due,
  That shee bee myne, as I to her, am True.

But thow white skynn as white as Curdes well prest,
  So smoothe as Slikestone, like yt smoothes eche parte,
And thow Dere flessh as Softe as Woolle new drest,
  And yet, as hard as Brawne made hard by Arte,
  First Fower, but say, next Fower theyre saying sealle.
  But, yow must pay the gaige of promist weale.

And with the Conclusyon of this Songe hee embraced her, aboute the knees, O sweete *Charita* saide hee, when shall I enjoy the Rest of my Toylling thoughtes? and when shall youre Blisfull promyse now Due bee verifyed with Just performance: with that I drewe nere to them, and sawe, (for nowe hee had lifted up his face to glasse hym self in her fayre eyes) that yt was my Master *Dametas*. But, here *Miso* interrupted his Tale with rayling at *Dametas* wth all those exquisite Termes, whiche I was never good Schould ynough to ymagyn: But, *Dorus*, as yf hee had bene muche offended with her Impacyence, woulde proceede no further till shee had vowed more stillnes, for (sayde hee) yf the first Drũ thus Chafe yow, what will yow bee when yow come to the Blowes. Then hee tould her how after many familier interteynementes betwixt them, *Dametas* layinge before her his greate Creditt with the *Duke*, and with all giving her very fayre presentes with promyse of muche more, had in the ende concluded together, to meete as that Nighte at *Mantinea* in the *Oudemian* streete at *Charitas* unckles howse aboute Tenñ of the Clock: After wᶜʰ Bargayne *Dametas* had spyed *Dorus*, and calling hym to hym, had with a greate Bravery tolde hym all his good happ. Willinge hym in any Case to returne to the olde witche *Miso*, (for so in deede Mistris, of Lyvelynes and not of evill will hee termed yow) and to make some honest excuse of his absence: For (saide hee) kissing *Charita* yf thow didest knowe what a Lyfe I leade with that Dryvill, yt woulde make thee eeven of pitty receyve mee into thy onely Comfort? Now Mistris (sayde hee) exercyse youre Discretion, whiche yf I were well assured of I woulde wissh yoʷ to goo youre self to *Mantinea*, and lye in secrett in some of youre Gossipps howses till the tyme appoynted come, so may yow fynde them together, and using mercy Reforme my Master from his evell wayes: There had nothing more enraged *Miso*, then the prayses *Dorus* gave to *Charitas* beuty, whiche made her Jelosy swell the more with the poyson of Envy, and that beeynge increased with the presentes shee hearde *Dametas* had given her (wᶜʰ all seemed torne oute of her Bowells) her hollow eyes yeelded suche wretched Lookes, as one might well thincke *Pluto* at that tyme might have had her sowle very good Cheape. But when the fyer of spighte had fully caughte houlde of all her Inward partes, then (whosoever woulde have seene the picture of *Alecto*, or with that maner of Countenaunce *Medea* kyllde her owne Children) needed but take *Miso* for the full satisfaction of that poynte of his knowledge: Shee that coulde before scarce goo but by Crouches, now Flue aboute the howse borne up wᵗʰ the Winges of Anger, there was no one sorte of mortall Revenge that had ever come to her eares, but presented yt self now to her gentle mynde. At lengthe with fewe wordes (for her wordes were chookte up wᵗʰ the Rysing of her revengefull harte) shee ranñ downe and wᵗʰ her owne handes sadled a Mare of hers, (a Mare that seaven yeares before had not beene acquaynted with a Saddle) and so to *Mantinea* shee went: Casting with her self, how shee mighte cuple shame, with the punishment of her Cursed husband, but the person ys not worthy in whose passyon I shoulde too longe stand. Therefore, now must I tell yow, that Mistris *Mopsa* (who was the last party *Dorus* was to practize his Cunning with all) was at the parting of her Parentes attending upon the Princess *Pamela* : whome bycause shee founde to bee placed in her Fathers howse, shee knewe yt was for suspicyon the *Duke* had of her, this made *Mopsa* with a Righte base nature, (which Joyes to see any hard happ happen to them they deeme happy) growe prowde over her, and use greate ostentation of her owne diligence in prying curiously into eche thinge yt *Pamela* did. Neyther ys there any thing sooner overthrowes a weyke harte, then Opinyon of authority, (Like too stronge a Liquor for so feeble a glasse) whiche joyned yt self to the humor of envying *Pamelas* beuty: So farr, that, ofte shee woulde say to her self yf shee had beene borne a *Duchess* aswell as *Pamela*, her perfection then shoulde have bene aswell seene, as *Pamelas*. With this maner of woemen and placed in these Termes, had *Dorus* to play his last parte, wch hee woulde quickly have dispatched, in tying her up in suche a maner that shee shoulde litle have hindered his enterprise : But that the vertuous *Pamela*, when shee sawe hym so mynded, by Countenañce absolutely forbad yt, Resolutely determeyning shee woulde not leave behynde her any Token of wronge, since the wronge done to her self was the best excuse of her escape. So that *Dorus* was Compelled to take her in the manner hee first thoughte of, and accordingly *Pamela* sitting musing at the straunge attempt shee had Condiscended unto, and *Mopsa* hard by her (Looking in a Glasse with very partiall eyes) *Dorus* putt hym self betueene them, and Casting up his face, to the Topp of the howse, shrugging all over his Body, and stamping some-tymes uppon the grounde, gave *Mopsa* occasyon (who was as Buysy as a Bee to know any thinge) to aske her Lover *Dorus*, what ayled hym, that made hym use so straunge a behavyor : Hee, (as yf his Spirites had bene ravished with some supernaturall Contemplatyon) stood still Mute, some tyme Rubbing his foreheade, some tymes starting in hym self, that hee sett *Mopsa* in suche an ytche of Inquiry, that shee woulde have offered her

182

Maydenhead, rather then to bee kept longe from yt. *Dorus* not yet answering to the purpose, still keeping his Amasement O *Hercules* (sayde hee) Resolve mee in this Doubte, a Tree to graunte ones wishes? ys this the Cause of the *Dukes* solitary lyfe? O whiche parte shall I take, happy in eyther, unhappy bycause I can not knowe wch were my best happe. These Doubtfull self speeches made *Mopsa*, yet in a furder longing of knowing the matter, so that the pritty Pigg laying her sweete Burden aboute his neck: My *Dorus* sayde shee, tell mee these wonders or else I knowe not what will befalle mee? Hony *Dorus* tell them mee? *Dorus* havinge stretched her Mynde uppon a Right Last, extremely loved *Mopsa* sayde hee, the matters bee so greate, as my harte fayles mee in the Telling them, But, since yow holde the greatest seate in yt, yt ys reason youre Desyer shoulde add lyfe unto yt. Therewith hee tolde her a farr fett tale, how that, many Millyons of yeares before *Jupiter* fallne oute with *Appollo* had throwne hym oute of heaven, taking from hym the priviledge of a God: So that pore *Appollo* was fayne to leade a very myserable Lyfe, unaquaynted to worcke and never used to begg, that in this order having in tyme learned to bee *Admetas* heardeman, hee had uppon occasyon, (of fetching a certeyne Breede of goodly Beastes oute of *Arcadia*) come to that very Dezert, where wearyed with Travell and resting hym self in the Boughes of a pleasant Asshe tree, stoode a litle of from the Lodge, hee had with pityfull Complayntes gotten Father *Jupiters* pardon, and so from that Tree was receyved ageane to his golden share: But having that Right Nature of a god, never to bee ungratefull to *Admetas*, hee had graunted a duble lyfe, and bycause that Tree was the Chappell of his prosperus prayers, hee had given yt this quallity, that whosoever of suche estate and in suche maner as hee then was satt downe in that Tree, they shoulde obtayne what soever they wished. This, *Basilius* having understood by the Oracle, was the onely Cause whiche made hym trye, whether framing hym self to the state of a Heardeman, hee might have the Priviledge of wisshing, onely graunted to that Degree: But that having often attempted yt in vayne, bycause, in deede hee was not suche, hee had nowe opened the secrett to *Dametas*, making hym sweare hee shoulde wisshe according to his direction. But, bycause (saide *Dorus*) *Appollo* was at that tyme with extreme greef muffled rounde aboute his face with a Skarlett Cloake *Admetas* had given hym: And bycause they that must wisshe must bee muffled in lyke sorte, and with like stuff, my Master *Dametas* ys goñ I knowe not whether to provyde hym a Scarlett Cloake, and to morow dothe poynte to returne wth yt. My Mistris I can not tell howe having gotten some ynckling of yt ys trudged to *Mantinea*, to gett herself a Cloke before hym, bycause shee woulde have the first wishe: My Master at his parting of greate Trust toulde mee this secrett, Commaunding mee to see no body clyme that Tree, but now my *Mopsa* (sayde hee) I have here the like Cloke of myne owne, and I am not so very a foole, as thoughe I kept his Comaundement in others, to barre my self. I Rest onely extremely perplexed bycause having no thing in the worlde I wish for, but the enjoying yo^w and youre favoure, I thincke yt a muche pleasaunter Conquest to come to yt; by youre owne Consent, then to have yt by suche a Charming force as this ys: Nowe, therefore choose, synce have yo^w I will in what sorte I shall have yow. But never Chylde was so desyerus of a gay puppett, as *Mopsa* was to bee in the Tree, And therefore withoute sqweymishnes promysing all hee woulde shee Conjured hym by all her precyous Loves, that shee mighte have the first possession of the wisshing Tree, assuring hym, that for the enjoyng of her hee shoulde never neede to Clyme farr: *Dorus* to whome tyme was precyous made no greate Ceremonyes wth her but helping her up, to the Toppe of the Tree, (from whence likewyse shee coulde yll come downe withoute help) hee muffled her Rounde aboute the face so truely that shee her self coulde not undoo yt. And so hee tolde her the maner was shee shoulde holde her mynde in Continuall Devotion to *Appollo*, with oute making at all any Noyse till at the furdest within xii howres space shee shoulde heare a voyce call her by name three tymes, and that till the thirde tyme shee shoulde in no wyse answer, and then yo^w shall not neede to doubte youre Cominge downe: For at that tyme (saide hee) bee sure, but to wishe wysely, and in what shape soever hee come unto yow, speake bouldly unto hym and youre wish shall have as certeyne effect as I have a desyer to enjoy youre sweete Loves: In this plighte did hee leave *Mopsa* resolved in her harte to bee the greatest Lady in the worlde and never after to feede on worse then Furmenty.

Thus *Dorus* having delivered his handes of his Three

Tormentors, tooke speedily the benefit of his Devise, and mounting the gratious *Pamela* uppon a fayre horse hee had provyded for her, hee thrust hym self forthewith into the wyldest parte of the Dezart: where hee had lefte Marckes, to guyde hym from place to place to the next sea porte, disguysing her very fitly with skarffes, allthoughe hee rested assured hee shoulde meete that wth nobody till hee came to his Barke into whiche hee ment to enter by nighte. But *Pamela*, who all this while trãsported with desyer and trubled with feare had never free scope of Judgment to looke with perfect Consideracyon into her owne enterpryse, but even by the Lawes of Love had layde ye Care of her self upon hym, to whome shee had given her self: Nowe that the pange of Desyer with evident hope was quyeted, & moste parte of the feare passed, Reason began to Renewe his shyning in her harte, and make her see her self in her self, and weighe with what wynges shee flewe oute of her Native Contry and upon what grounde shee buylt her Determinacyon. But Love fortifyed with her Lovers presence kept still his owne in her harte, so that as they Ridd together with her hand uppon her faythfull Servauntes shoulder, sodenly, Casting her Basshfull eyes to the grounde, and yet bending her self towardes hym (lyke the Clyent that committes the Cause of all his worthe, to a well Trusted Advocate,) from a mylde spirite, sayde unto hym these sweetly delyvered wordes. Prince *Musidorus* (for so my assured hope ys, I may justly calle yow) synce with no other my harte coulde ever have yeelded to goo, and yf so I do not rightly terme yow, all other woordes are as booteles, as my Deede myserable, and I as unfortunate as yo^w wicked: My Prince *Musidorus* I say nowe, that ye vehemẽt shewes of youre faithfull Love towardes mee have brought my mynde to answer yt, in so a due a proportyon, that contrary to all generall Rules of Reason I have layde in yow my State, my lyfe, my honor. Yt ys nowe youre parte, to duble youre former Care and make mee see youre vertue, no less in preserving, then in obtayning and youre faythe to bee a faythe asmuche in free-dome as bondage: Tender now youre owne worckmanship, and so govern youre Love towardes mee, as I may still remayne worthy to bee Loved, youre promyse yow Remember, wch here by the Eternall givers of vertue I Conjure yo^w to observe. Lett mee bee youre owne, as I am, but by no unjust Conquest, Lett not oure Joyes, wch oughte ever to last, bee stayned in oure owne Conscyences, Lett no shadow of Repentance steale into the sweete Consideracyon of oure mutuall happynes? I have yeelded to bee youre Wyffe, stay then till the tyme that I may Rightly bee so, Let no other Defyled name burden my harte? What shoulde I more say, yf I have chossen well, all Doubt ys past synce youre action onely must determeyn whether I have done vertuously or shamefully in followyng yow? *Musidorus* (that had more abundance of Joy in his harte then *Ulisses* had, what tyme wth his owne Industry hee stale the fatall *Paladium*, imagined to bee the onely Relique of *Troyes* safty) taking *Pamelas* hande, and many tymes kissing yt: What I am (sayde hee) the goddes, I hope will shortly make youre owne eyes Judges, and of my mynde towardes yow, the meane tyme shall bee my pledge unto yow, youre Contentmēt ys derer to mee then myne owne. And therefore Doubt not of his mynde, whose thoughtes are so thralled unto yo^w, as yo^w are to bende or slack them as yt shall seeme best unto yow: yow doo wronge to youre self, to make any Doubte that a base estate coulde ever undertake so hye an enterpryse, or a spotted mynde bee ever able to beholde youre vertues: Thus muche onely I must Confess I can never doo to make the worlde see yo^w have chosen worthely, since all the worlde ys not worthy of yo^w. In suche delighttfull Discourses kept they on theyre Journey meyntayning theyre hartes in that right Harmony of affection, whiche dothe enterchaungeably deliver eche unto other, ye secrett worcking of theyre Sowles: Till with the unused traveyll, the *Princess* beeyng weary, they alighted downe in a fayre thick wood wch did entyse them with the pleasauntnes of yt to take theyre Rest there. It was all of Pyne Trees, whose brode heades meetinge together, yeelded a perfect shade to the grounde where theyre Bodyes gave a spacyous and pleasaunt Rowme to walke in: They were sett in so perfect an order, that every way the eye beeyng full, yet no waye was stopped, and even in the mydst of them there were many sweete Springes wch did Lose them selves uppon the face of the earthe. Here *Musidorus* drewe oute suche provision of Fruites and other Cates, as hee had broughte for that dayes Repast, and layde yt down uppon the fayre Carpet of the greene grasse: But *Pamela* had muche more pleasure to walke under those Trees, making

186

in theyre Barckes prity knottes wch tyed together the names of *Musidorus* and *Pamela*, sometymes intermixedly chaungyng them to *Pamedorus* and *Musimela*, with xx^{ti} other Flowers of her traveling fancyes wch had bounde them selves to a greater Restraynt, then they coulde withoute muche payne well endure : And to one Tree more beholding to her then the Rest, shee entrusted the Treasure of her thoughtes in these verses.

> *Doo not Disdayne O streighte upraysed Pyne?*
> *That, wounding thee, my Thoughtes in thee I grave,*
> *Synce that my thoughtes as Streighte as streightnes thyne,*
> *No smaller wounde, (Alas) furr deeper have?*
>
> *Deeper engraved whiche salve nor Tyme can save,*
> *Given to my harte by my fore wounded eyen*
> *Thus Cruell to my self, how Canst thow Crave;*
> *My Inwarde Hurt shoulde spare thy owteward Rhyne?*
>
> *Yet still fayre Tree lyfte up thy stately Lyne?*
> *Live longe, and longe witness my Chosen smarte?*
> *With barrd Desyers, barrd by my self imparte*
> *And in this growyng Barcke, growe verses myne.*
>
> *My Harte my worde my worde hathe given my harte?*
> *The Giver given from Gifte shall never parte.*

Uppon a Roote of the Tree that the Earthe had lefte some thinge Barer then the Rest, shee writt this Couplett.

> *Sweete* Roote *say thow, the* Roote *of my Desyer?*
> *Was vertue cladd in Constant Loves Attyer.*

Musidorus seeyng her Fancyes drawne up to suche pleasaunt Contemplations, accompanyed her in them, and make the Trees aswell beare the Badges of his passyons : As this Songe engraved in them did Testify.

> *Yow goodly Pynes whiche still with brave assent,*
> *In Natures pryde youre heades to heaven warde heave,*
> *Thoughe yo^w besydes suche graces Earthe hathe lent,*
> *Of some late grace, a greater grace Receyve?*
>
> *By her, who was (O blessed yow) content,*
> *With her fayre hande youre tender Barckes to cleave,*
> *And so by yow (O blessed yow) hathe sent,*
> *Suche persing woordes, as no thing else Conceyve,*

Yet, yeelde youre graunte, a Baser hande may Leave,
  His Thoughtes in yo^w where so sweete thoughtes were spent,
For how woulde yo^w the Mistris thoughtes bereave,
  Of wayting thoughtes all to her service ment.

Nay, higher thoughtes thoughe Thralled thoughtes I calle
  My Thoughtes then hers, who first youre Rhyne did Rent,
Then hers to whome my thoughtes a Lovely thralle
  Rysing from Love are to the highest bent,
  Where hers whome worthe makes highest over all,
  Comĩng from her can not but Downeward falle.

While *Pamela* sitting her downe under one of them, and
making a Poesy of the fayre under growing Flowers, filled
Musidorus eares with the heavenly sounde of her Musick whiche
before hee had never hearde: So that yt seemed unto hym a
newe Assaulte given to the Castle of his hart allredy conquered,
whiche to signify and with all Reply, to her sweete Notes, hee
sange in a kynde of still (but Ravishing) Tune, a few verses, her
songe was this, and hys Reply followes.

Pamela.   *Lyke Dyvers Flowers whose dyvers Beutyes serve,*
             To decke the Earthe with this well coloured weede,
           Thoughe eche of them his private forme preserve,
             Yet joyning Formes, one sighte of Bewty breede
             Right so my thoughtes whereon my harte I feede.

           Right so my Inwarde partes and owteward glasse,
             Thoughe eche possess a dyvers worcking kynde,
           Yet all well knitt, to one fayre ende do passe,
             That hee to whome these sondry giftes I bynde,
             All what I am still one his owne to fynde.

Musidorus. *All that yow are still one his owne to fynde,*
             Yow that are Borne to bee the worldes eye,
           What were yt ellse but to make eche thing blynde,
             And to the Sunne with Waxen winges to flye,
           No, No, suche force with my smalle force to trye
             Ys not my skill, nor reache of mortall mynde.
           Calle mee but youres, my Tytle ys moste hye?
             Holde mee moste youres, then my Longe sute ys signde?

Yow none can clayme, But, yo^w youre self by Righte
For yow doo pass youre self in vertues mighte,
So bothe are youres, I bounde with gaged harte,
Yow onely youres too farr beyond Desert.

In these vertuous wantonyes, suffering theyre myndes to descend to eche tender enjoying theyre united thoughtes, *Pamela* having tasted of the fruites, and growyng extreme sleepy, havinge bene longe kept from yt with the perplexity of her daungerus attempt laying her heade in his lapp, was invited by hym to sleepe with these softly uttered verses.

Locke up fayre Liddes, the Treasures of my harte,
Preserve those Beames, this Ages onely Lighte,
To her sweete Sence, sweete Sleepe some ease imparte
Her Sence too weyke to beare her Spirites mighte,
And whyle, O Sleepe, thow closest up her sighte,
(Her sighte where Love did forge his fayrest Darte)
O Harboure all her partes in easefull plighte,
Lett no straunge Dreame make her fayre body starte:

But, yet O Dreame yf thow wilt not Departe?
In this rare Subject from thy Comon Righte,
But wilt thy self in suche a Seate delighte,
Then take my Shape and play a Lovers parte.
Kisse her from mee, and say unto her Sprite,
Till her eyes shyne, I live in darckest lighte.

The sweete *Pamela* was broughte into a sweete Sleepe with this Songe whiche gave *Musidorus* oportunity at leysure to beholde her excellent Beutyes: Hee thoughte her fayre Foreheade was a feelde, where her fancyes foughte, and every hayer of her heade seemed a stronge Chayne that tyed hym. Her fayre Liddes then hyding her fayrer eyes, seemed unto hym sweete Boxes of Mother of perle Riche in them selves but conteyning in them farr Richer Jewells: Her Cheekes with theyre Colour moste delicately myxed woulde have interteyned his eyes some while but that the Roses of her Lippes (whose seperating was wonte to bee accompanyed with moste sweete speeches) now by force drewe his sighte, to marcke howe prittily they lay one over an other uniting theyre devided beutyes: And throwe them the Eye of his fancy delyvered to his memory, the lyinge as in Ambush under her Lippes those armed Ranckes, all armed in moste pure white, and keeping the moste precyse order of Military Disciplyn. And leste this Beuty mighte seeme the Picture of some excellent Artificer forthe there stale a softe Breathe carrying good Testimony of her Inwarde sweetenes, and so steallingly yt came oute, as yt seemed lothe to leave his contenfull Mansyon: But that yt hoped to bee drawne in ageane to that well closed Paradyse, that did so tyrannize over *Musidorus* affectes, that hee was compeld to putt his face as Lowe to hers as hee coulde, sucking the Breathe with somuche Joy, that hee did determẽyn in hym self there had bene no Lyfe, to a Camelyons yf hee mighte bee suffred to enjoy that foode. But eche of these having in his harte a severall worcking all joynde together did so drawe his will into ye nature of theyre Confederacy, that now his promyse begãn to have but a faynting force, and eche thoughte that rose ageanst those desyers was receyved but as a Straunger to his Counseyll, well experyencing in hym self, that no vowe ys so stronge as ye avoyding of occasions: So that rysing softely from her overmastered with the fury of delighte (having all his Sences parciall ageanst hym self, and enclyned to his wellbeloved Adversary) hee was bent to take the vauntage of the weykenes of the watche, and see whether at that season hee coulde wynñ the Bullwarck before tymely help mighte come. And now hee began to make his aproches when to the just punishment of his broken promyse, and moste unfortuned barr of his longe pursued & atcheeved desyers, there came by a Doszen Clownish villeynes armed with dyvers sortes of weapons: And for the Rest bothe in face and apparrell so farr wasted, that they seemed to beare a great Conformity with the Savages, who (myserable in themselves thoughte to encrease theyre myscheef in other bodyes harmes) came with suche Cryes, as they awaked *Pamela*, whose sleepe had beene sett uppon with twoo daungers, the one of whiche had saved her from the other, and made *Musidorus* turne unto them full of a vyolent Rage with the Looke of a Shee Tyger, when her whelpes are stolne away: But *Cleophila*, whome I lefte in the Cave hardly bestedd, (having bothe greate wittes and sturring passyons to dealle with) makes mee lend her my penñ a whyle, to see with what dexterity shee coulde putt by her Daungers: *Cleophila* who had in one instant, bothe to resist rage, and goo beyonde wysdome, having to dealle with a Lady that had her wittes awake in every thinge but in helping of her owne hurt, sawe nowe none other Remedy in her Case but, to qualify her Rage with hope, and to satisfye her wittes with playñes. Yet, least too abrupt a falling into yt shoulde yeelde to greate an Advauntage unto her shee thought good to come to yt by Degrees wth this kynde of Insinuatyon: Youre wyse but very darcke speeches (moste excellent Lady) are wounde up in so intricate a mañer, as I knowe not howe to proportion myne answer unto them? So are youre Prayers myxt with Threates, and so ys the shewe of youre Love hidden wth the name of Revenge the naturall effect of mortall hatred. Yow seeme displeased with the opinyon yow have of my disguysings and yet yf I bee not disguysed, yow must needes bee muche more displeased: Hope, then the onely succoure of perplexed myndes beeyng quite cutt of, yow desyer my affection, and yet yo^w youre self thinke my affection allredy bestowed, yo^w pretend Cruelty before yow have the Subjection, and are jelous of ye keeping that, whiche as yet yow have not gotten. And that wch ys strongest in youre Jelosy ys bothe the unnaturall unjustice of yt, in beeyng Loathe, that shoulde come to youre Daughter wch yow deeme good, and the vayñes synce yo^w twoo are in so dyvers respectes that there ys no necessity one of yowe shoulde falle to bee a barr to the other: For, neyther, yf I bee suche as yow fancy can I marry yo^w whiche muste needes bee the onely ende I can aspire to in her, neither neede the marrying of her keepe mee from a gratefull Consideracõn howe muche yow honor mee in the Love yo^w vouchesafe to beare mee. *Gynecia* to whome the fearefull agonyes shee still Lived in made any smalle Reprivall sweete, did fynde her wordes falling to a better way of Comfort, and therefore with a mynde redy to shewe no thinge coulde make yt rebellyous ageanst *Cleophila*, but too extreme Tyranny, shee thus sayde. Alas toomuche beloved *Cleophila*, the thoughtes are but outeflowynges of the mynde, and the Tòungue ys but a Servaunt to the Thoughtes, therefore marvell not that my wordes suffer contraryetyes, sithe my mynde dothe howerly suffer in yt self whole Armyes of mortall Adversaryes: But alas yf I had but the use of myne owne Reason, then shoulde I not neede for wante of yt to fynde my self in this desperate mischeef. But bycause my Reason ys

COUNTESS OF PEMBROOKES

vanisshed, so have I likewyse no power to correct myne un-reasonablenes, Doo yow therefore accept ye protection of my mynde wch hathe no other resting place, and dryve yt not by beeyng unregarded to putt yt self into unknowne extremityes: I Desyer but to have myne affection answered, and to have a Right Reflection of my Love in yo^w. That graunted, assure youre self myne owne Love will easely teache mee to seeke youre Contentment, and make mee thincke my Daughters a very meane pryce to keepe still in myne eyes the foode of my Spirittes: But take heede that Contempt drawe mee not into dispayer, the moste vyolent Cause of y^t miserable effect. *Cleophila*, that all redy sawe some fruite of her last determyned fancy, so farr as came to a mollifying of *Gynecias* Rage seeyng no other way to satisfy suspicyon, wch was helde open wth the Continuall prickes of Love, (resolved now with playnnes, to wynñ trust, wch Trust shee mighte after deceyve wth a greater subtillty). Therefore looking uppon her with a more relenting grace then ever shee had done before pretending a great bash-fullnes before shee coulde come to Confess suche a faulte, shee thus sayde unto her. Moste worthy Lady, I did never thincke till nowe, that pitty of an other coulde make one betray hym self nor that the sounde of wordes coulde overthrowe any wyse bodyes determynacyon: But youre worthe I thinck hathe charmed mee, and youre grace bewitched mee, youre Compassyon makes mee open my harte to yo^w, and leave unharboured myne owne thoughtes. For proof of yt I will disclose my greatest secrett, whiche well yo^w might suspect but never knowe and so have youre wandering hope in a more paynefull wildernes beeyng neither way able to bee Lodged in any perfect Resolutyon: I will (I say) unwrapp my moste hidden estate, and after make yo^w judge of yt perchaunce directer. The troathe ys, I am a Man. Nay; I will say furder to yo^w, I am borne a Prince, and to make up youre mynde in a throwe understanding of mee since I came to this place, (I may not Deny) I have had some sprinckling of I knowe not what good liking to my Lady *Philoclea*: For howe coulde I ever ymagyn the heavens woulde have rayned downe somuche of youre favoure uppon mee? and of that syde there was a shewe of possible hope, the moste Comfortable Counseylor of Love. The Cause of this my chaunged Attyer, was a Journey twoo yeares agoo I made amonge the *Amazons*

192

where having soughte to trye my unfortunate valor I mett not one in all the Contry but was too hardd for mee: Till in the ende in the presence of theyre Queene *Senicia* I (hoping to prevayle ageanst her) challenged an oulde woman of Lxxx^ti yeares to feight on horseback to the uttermoste with mee, who having overthrowne mee (for saving of my lyffe) made mee sweare I shoulde goo like an unarmed *Amazon*, till, the Cõming up of my Beard, did with the discharge of my oathe deliver mee of that Bondage. Here *Cleophila* ended not coming to a full Conclusyon, bycause shee woulde see what this wrought in *Gynecias* mynde, having in her speeche soughte to wynñ beleef of her: And (yf yt mighte bee) by the Disgrace of her self to diminish *Gynecias* affection, for the first yt had muche prevayled. But *Gynecia* whose ende of Loving her was not her feightinge neyther coulde her Loove too deepely grounded receyve diminishmẽt, and besydes shee had seene her self sufficyent prooffes of *Cleophilas* admirable prowess: Therefore straytly passing over y^t poynte of her fayned Dishonour, but taking good holde of ye Confessing her Manly sexe with the shamefast Looke of the Suiter (who having all redy obteyned muche, ys yet forced by wante to Demaunde more) putt forthe her sorow-full suite in these wordes. The Goddes (sayde shee) rewarde thee for thy vertuous pitty of my overladen sowle, who yet hathe receyved some breath of Comforte by fynding thy Confession to meyntayne some possibility of my anguisshing hope: But alas as they who seeke to enriche them selves by Mynerall Industry theyre first Laboure ys to fynde the myne, whiche to theyre cherefull Comfort beeying founde, yf after any unlooked for stopp or Casuall Impediment keepe them from getting the desyered Owir, they are somuche the more greeved as the late conceyved hope addes Tormentes to theyre former want. So falleth yt oute with mee, happy or happles woman as yt pleaseth yo^w to ordayne, who am now eyther to receyve some guerdon of my longe wofull Laboures, or to returne into a more wretched Darcknes, having had some glimmering of my blisfull Sunne: O *Cleophila*, treade not uppon a Sowle, that lyes under youre feete? Lett not the abasing of my self make mee more base in youre eyes, but judge of mee according to that I am and have bene, and lett my errors bee made excusable by the Immortall Name of Love. With that (under a fayned

Rage tearing her Cloathes) shee discovered some partes of her fayre body, whiche yf *Cleophilas* hart had not beene so fully possest (as there was no place lefte for any newe Guest) no doubt yt woulde have yeelded to that gallaunt assaulte: But, *Cleophila* somuche the more arming her Determinatyon, as shee sawe suche force threatned, (yet still Remembring shee must wade betwixt Constancy and Curtesy, embrasing *Gynecia*, and · once or twyce kissing her) Deare Lady (sayde shee) hee were a great Enimy that woulde refuse suche offered blisse, in the purchase of whiche a Mans lyfe were blessedly bestowed. Nay howe can I over yeelde due Reverence for suche excessive a favour, but having no more to give yo^w but my self, take that, (I must Confess a smalle, but a very free present), and what soever other affectyon I have had shall give place to as greate perfections working besydes uppon the bonde of gratefullnes : The Godds forbidd I shoulde bee so foolish as not to see, or so wicked, as not to Remember howe muche my smalle Desertes are overballaunsed by youre unspeakeable goodnes. Nay happy may I well accoumpt my myshapp amonge the *Amazons*, synce that Dishonor hathe beene so true a pathe to my greatest honor, and the Chaunging of my owteward Rayment hathe cloathed my Mynde in suche Inwarde Contentatyon : Take therefore Noble Lady asmuche Comfort to youre hart, as the full Comaundement of mee can yeelde yo^w, wype youre fayre eyes, and keepe them for Nobler services. And now I will presume thus muche to say unto yo^w, that yo^w make of youre selffe for my sake, that the Joyes of my newe obtayned Riches may bee accomplisshed in yow: But let us leave this place least yo^w bee too long missed, and henceforward quyett youre mynde from any further Care, for I will nowe to my too muche Joy take the Charge uppon mee within fewe dayes to worcke youre satisfaction and my felicity. Thus shee sayde, and withall ledd *Gynecia* oute of the Cave, for, well shee sawe the boylinge mynde of *Gynecia* did easely apprehend the fittnes of that Lonely place: But in deede this direct promyse of a short space joyned wth the Combersome familier of Womankynde (I meane Modesty) stayed so *Gynecias* mynde, that shee tooke thus muche at that present for good payment. Remayning with a paynefull Joy and wearysome kynde of Comfort not unlike the Condempned Prisoner, (whose mynde still ronning uppon the vyolent aryvall of his Crewell deathe) heares that his pardon ys promysed but not yet signed: In this sorte the bothe issewed oute of that obscure Mansion, *Gynecia* allredy half perswaded in her self (O weykenes of humane Conceipt) that *Cleophilas* affection was turned towardes her. For suche, alas, are wee all in suche a Moulde are wee cast, that with too muche Love wee beare oure selves, beeyng first oure owne flatterers wee are easily hooked with others flattery, wee are easily perswaded with others Love: But *Cleophila* who had now to play her pryze, seeying no way thinges coulde longe remayne in that estate, and now fynding her promyse had tyed her Tryall to a smalle Compass of tyme, began to throwe her thoughtes into eche Corner of her Inventyon howe shee mighte atcheeve her Lyves enterpryse. For well shee knewe, Deceipt can not otherwyse bee maynteyned but by deceipt, and howe to deceyve suche heedefull eyes, and howe to satisfy and yet not satisfy suche hopefull desyers yt was no smalle skille: But, bothe theyre thoughtes were called from them selves with the sighte of *Basilius*, who then lying downe by his Daughter *Philoclea*, uppon the fayre (thoughe naturall) Bedd of greene grasse seeyng the Sunne what speede hee made to leave oure West, to doo his office in the other Hemisphere, his Inwarde Muses made hym in his best Musick singe this Madrigall.

Whye doest thow haste away,
O Tytan *fayre, the Giver of the day,*
Ys yt to Carry Newes?
To westerne Wightes, what Starres in Easte appeare?
Or doest thow thincke that heare
Ys lefte a Sunne, whose Beames thy place may use,
Yet stay, and well peruse,
What bee her giftes, that make her æquall thee,
Bend all thy Lighte to see,
In Earthly Clothes enclosed a Heavenly sparcke,
Thy Ronning Course can not suche Beutyes marck.
No, No, thy motyons bee
Hastened from us with Barr of shadowe darck,
Bycause that thow the Author of thy sighte,
Disdaynes wee see, thee stayned with others Lighte.

And having ended, Deare *Philoclea* (sayde hee) singe some

thinge that may divert my thoughtes from the Continuall Taste of theyre Ruynous Harboure: Shee obaydyent to hym, and not unwilling to disburden her secrett passyon, made her sweete voyce bee hearde in these wordes.

> *O, Stealing tyme, the Subject of Delay,*
> *Delay the rack of unrefraynde Desyer,*
> *What straunge desyer, haste thow my hopes to stay?*
> *My hopes whiche doo but to myne owne aspyer.*
>
> *Myne owne (O worde) on whose sweete sounde dothe pray,*
> *My greedy sowle, with grype of Inwarde fyer,*
> *Thy title great I justly challenge may*
> *Synce in suche phrase his faythe hee did attyer.*
>
> *O Tyme become the Charyott of my Joyes?*
> *As thow drawest on, so lett my Bliss drawe nere,*
> *Eche Moment lost parte of my happ Destroyes,*
> *Thow arte the Father of occasyon Deere,*
> *Joyne with thy Sonne, to ease my Longe Annoyes.*
> *In speedy help, thancke worthy freendes appeare.*

Philoclea brake of her Songe, assoone as her Mother w[th] *Cleophila* came nere unto them, rysing up with a kyndly bashfullnes, beeyng not ignorant of the Spyte her Mother bare her, & striken with the sighte of that person, whose Love made all those Trubles seeme fayre Flowers of her dearest garland, Nay rather all those Troubles made her Love encrease: For as the Aryvall of Enimyes makes a Towne to fortify yt self, as ever after yt remayneth stronger, (so that a Man may say Enimyes were no smalle Cause of the Townes strength) So to a mynde once fixed in a well pleasing Determination, who hopes by annoyance to overthrowe yt, dothe but teache yt to knitt together all his best groundes, and so perchance of a Chaungeable purpose, make an unchaungeable Resolucyon. But no more did *Philoclea* see the wonted signes of *Cleophilas* affection towardes her, shee thoughte shee sawe an other Lighte in her eyes, with a bolde and Careles Looke uppon her, w[ch] was wonte to bee daszelled with her Beuty: And the framing of her Curtesyes rather Ceremonyes, then affectionate, and (that whiche worse liked her) was that yt proceeded from suche a quyett setlednes, as yt rather threatned a full purpose, then any sodeyn passyon. Shee founde her Behavyor bent alltogether to her Moother, &

presumed in her self shee discerned the well acquaynted face of his fancyes nowe turned to an other Subject, shee sawe her Mothers worthynes and too well knew her affection, these joyning theyre dyverse working powers together in her mynde: But yet a Prentys in the paynfull mystery of passyons broughte *Philoclea* into a new Traverse of her thoughtes, and made her keepe her Carefull Looke, the more attentive uppon *Cleophilas* behavyour. Who in deede, thoughe wth muche payne and condempning her self to Committ a Sacriledge ageanst ye sweete Sainte that lived in her Inmoste Temple, yet strengthning her self in yt beeyng the surest way, to make *Gynecia* byte of her other Baytes did so quyte overrule all wonted shewes of Love to *Philoclea*, and Convert them to *Gynecia*, that the parte shee playde did worcke in bothe a full and lyvely perswasion to *Gynecia* suche excessive Comfortes as the beyng preferred to a Rivale dothe deliver to swelling desyer: But, to the delicate *Philoclea*, whose Calme thoughtes were unable to nourish any straunge debate, yt gave so stinging a Hurte, that faynting under the force of her Inwarde Tormentes shee withdrew her self to the Lodge, and there, (weary of supporting her owne Burden) cast her self uppon her Bedd, suffering her sorowe to melt yt self into abundance of teares. At lengthe cloasing her eyes, as yf eche thinge shee sawe were a picture of her Myshapp, and turning her uppon her hart syde, (whiche wth vehement panting did so moove her to Consider her Fortune) shee thus beemoned her self: Alas *Philoclea*, ys this the pryce of all thy paynes? ys this the Rewarde of this thy given away Liberty? hathe too muche yeelding bredd Cruelty? Or can too greate acquayntance make mee bee helde for a Straunger? hathe the Chosinge a Companyon made mee bee left alone? or dothe graunting desyer, cause the Desyer to bee neglected? Alas despysed *Philoclea*, why didest thow not holde thy thoughtes in theyre simple Course, and Content thy self with the Love of thyne owne vertue, wch woulde never have betrayed thee: Ah, silly foole, diddest thow looke for truthe in hym, that with his owne mouthe Confesseth his fallshood? for playne proceeding in hym, that still goes disguysed, they say the fallsest men will yet beare outeward shewes of a pure mynde. But hee that even outewardly beares the badge of treachery, what helles of wickednes must needes in the depthe bee conteyned? But, oh

wicked mowthe of myne, how darest thow thus blaspheyme the
Ornament of the earthe the vessell of all vertue? O wretche
that I am y^t will anger the goddes, Dispraysing theyre moste
excellent worcke, O no, no there was no faulte but in mee,
that coulde ever thincke so hye eyes woulde looke so Lowe? or
so great perfection woulde stayne them selves with my
unworthynes. Alas why, coulde I not see, I was too weyke a
Bande, to tye so heavenly a hart, I was not fitt to Limitt the
Course of his wonderfull Destinyes, was yt ever like that upon
onely *Philoclea* his thoughtes shoulde rest? Ah silly sowle, that
coulde please thy self with so impossible an Imaginacyon, an
universall happynes ys to flowe from hym, howe was I so
inveigled to hope I mighte bee the Anchor of suche a mynde?
Hee did thee no wronge *Philoclea*, hee did thee no wronge, yt
was thy weykenes to fancy the Beames of the Sunne shoulde
give lighte to no eyes but thyne. And yet, O Prince *Pyrocles*
for whome I may well begyn to hate my self but can never
leave to Loove thee, what Tryumphe canst thow make of this
Conquest? what spoylles wilt thow carry away of this my
undeserved overthrowe? Coulde thy force fynde oute no fitter
fielde, then the feeoble mynde of a pore Mayde, who at the
first sighte did wish thee all happynes, shall yt bee sayde the
Mirrour of Mankynde hathe beene employed to destroy a
hurtles gentlewoman? O *Pyrocles*, *Pyrocles*, let mee yet calle thee
before the Judgment of thyne owne vertue? Let mee bee
accepted for a pleyntiff in a Cause wch Concernes my lyffe?
What neede hadst thow to arme thy face wth the inchaunting
Maske of thy paynted passyons? what neede hadst thow to
fortefy thy excellencyes wth so exquisite a Cunning in making
oure owne artes betray us? What needest thow discend so farr
from thy incomperable worthynes, as to take on the habite of
weyke womankynde? was all this to wynñ the undefended
Castle of a frende, wch beeyng wonne thow wouldest after Rase?
Coulde so smalle a Cause allure thee, or did not so unjust a
Cause stopp thee? O mee, what say I more, This ys my Case,
my Love hates mee, vertue dealles wickedly with mee, and hee
dooeth mee wronge, whose doyng I can never accoumpte
wronge. With that, the sweete Lady turninge her self uppon
her weary Bedd, shee happely sawe a Lute, upon the Belly of
w^{ch} *Gynecia* had written this Songe, what tyme *Basilius* had

imputed her Jelous motyons to proceede of the Doubte shee had of his untymely Loves: under wch vaile shee (contented to Cover her never Ceassing anguish) had made the Lute a Monument of her mynde. Whiche *Philoclea* had never muche marked till nowe the feare of a Competitor more stirred her then before the Care of an other: The verses were these.

> *My Lute within thy self, thy Tunes enclose?*
> *Thy Mistris Songe ys now a Sorowes Crye,*
> *Her hande benomde with Fortunes dayly blowes.*
> *Her mynde amasde can neythers help apply,*
> *Weare these my wordes, as Mourning weedes of woes?*
> *Black Incke become the State wherein I Dye.*
> > *And thoughe not my moanes bee not in Musick bounde*
> > *Of written greefes yet bee the sylent grounde.*

> *The worlde dothe yeelde suche yll Consorted showes,*
> *With sircled Course, wch no wyse stay can trye,*
> *That Chyldish stuff, wch knowes not frendes from foes,*
> *(Better despysde), bee wonder gasing eye.*
> *Thus Noble golde downe to the bottome goes,*
> *When worthles Corck alofte dothe floating lye.*
> > *Thus in thy self, Leste stringes are Lowdest founde,*
> > *And Lowest Stoppes doo yeelde the highest sounde.*

Philoclea redd them, and throwyng downe the Lute, ys this the Legacy yow have bequeathed mee? O kynde mother of myne (sayde shee) did yow bestowe the Light uppon mee for this, or did yow beare mee to bee the Author of my Buryall? A trym̃ purchase, yo^w have made of youre owne shame? Robbed youre Daughter, to Ruyn youre self: The Byrdes unreasonable yet use somuche Reason as to make Nestes for theyre tender younge ones: My Crewell Mother turnes mee oute of myne owne Harboure: Alas playntes bootes not, for my Case can Receyve no help, for who shoulde geve mee help, shall I flee to my Parentes? they are my Murderers, shall I goo to hym, who allredy beeyng wonne and lost, must needes have killed all pitty? Alas, I can bringe no newe Intercessions, hee knowes all redy what I am ys his. Shall I come home ageane to my self? O mee Contempned wretche I have given away my self. With that, the pore sowle bett her Brest, as yf that had beene guilty of her faultes, neyther thinking of Revenge nor studying of Remedy, but the sweete Creature gave greef a free Dominyon, keeping her Chamber a few dayes after: Not, needing to fayne her self sick, feeling even in her sowle the panges of extreme payne. But litle did *Gynecia* Reck that neyther when shee sawe her goo away from them neyther when shee after founde, that sicknes made her hyde her fayre face, so muche had fancy prevayled ageanst Nature: But, yow, that have ever knowne howe tender to every Motion Love makes the Lovers hart, howe hee measures all his Joyes uppon her Contentment, and dothe with respectfull eye hange all his behavyour uppon her eyes? Judge I pray yow nowe of *Cleophilas* trubled thoughtes? when shee sawe *Philoclea* with an amased kynde of sorowe carry away her sweete presence & easily founde (so happy a Conjecture unhappy affection hathe) that her Demeynor was guylty of that Trespas. There was never foolish softe harted Mother that, (forced to beate her Chylde) did weepe first for his paynes, and (dooyng that shee was loathe to doo, did repent before shee began) did fynde half that motion in her weyke mynde as *Cleophila* did, now that shee was forced by Reason to give an outeward blowe to her passyons: And for the lending of a smalle tyme, to seeke the usury of all her Desyers. The unkyndenes (shee Conceyved *Philoclea* might conceyve) did wounde her sowle, eche Teare (shee doubted) shee spent, drowned all her Comforte, her sicknes was a Deathe unto her: Often woulde shee speake to the Image of *Philoclea*, whiche Lived and Ruled in the highest of her Inward parte, and use vehement Oathes and protestacyons unto her, that no thinge shoulde fallsify the free chosen vowe shee had made. Often woulde shee desyer her, that shee woulde looke well to *Pyrocles* harte, for as for her, shee had no more Interest in yt to bestowe yt any way: Alas woulde shee say, onely *Philoclea* haste thow not somuche feeling of thyne owne force, as to knowe no new Conqueror can prevayle ageanst thy Conquestes? was ever any daszelled with the Moone, that had used his eyes to the Beames of the Sunne? Ys hee carryed away with the greedy desyer of Ackornes, that hathe had his sences ravisshed with a garden of moste Delightfull Fruites? O *Philoclea*, *Philoclea* bee thow but as mercyfull a Princess to my mynde, as thow arte a sure possessor, and I shall have asmuche Cause of gladnes as thow haste no Cause of mysdoubting. O, No, No, when a Mans owne hart ys the gage of his Debt, when a Mans owne thoughtes are willing witnesses to his promyse, Lastly, when a Man ys the Jaylour over hym self, there ys litle Doubt of breaking Creditt and less doubte of suche an escape: In this Combat of *Cleophilas* doubtfull Imaginacyons, in the end Reason well backed wth the vehement Desyer, to bring her Matters soone to ye desyered haven did ever Rule the boylling of her Inward kyndenes, though as I say, with suche a Manifest stryfe, that bothe *Basilius* and *Gynecias* well wayting eyes had marcked her Muses had laboured in deeper subject then ordenary. Whiche shee like wyse perceyving they had perceyved, awaking her self oute of those thoughtes, and principally Caryng howe to satisfy *Gynecia* (whose Judgmẽt and passyon, shee stoode moste in Regarde of) bowyng her heade, to her attentive eare, Madame (sayde shee) with practize of my thoughtes I have founde oute a way by wch youre Contentment shall drawe on my happynes: *Gynecia* delivering in her face as thanckfull a Joyfullnes as her hart coulde holde, sayde, yt was then tyme to retyre them selves to theyre Restes, For what with the Tumult the day before, and late sitting up for the *Eglogues* theyre bodyes had dearely purchased that nightes qwyett, so went they home to theyre Lodge. *Cleophila* framing of bothe sydes, bountyfull measures of Loving Countenaunces to eythers Joy, and neythers jelosy, but to the specyall Comfort of *Basilius*, whose weyker bowells were streight full with the leste liquor of hope: So that still holding her by the hand and some tymes tickling yt, hee went by her with the moste gay Conceytes that ever had entred his braynes, growyng now so, hawty in his Resolutyon, that hee litle respected *Gynecias* presence. But with a Lustyer note then wonted, Clearing his voyce, and chearing his Spirites, Looking still uppon *Cleophila*, (whome nowe the Moone did beutify with her shyning all moste at the full) as yf her eyes had beene his Songebooke, hee did the Message of his mynde in singing these verses

> *When Twoo* Sunnes *doo appeare,*
> *Some say yt dothe betoken wonders nere,*
> *   As Princes Losse or Chaunge:*
> *Twoo gleaming* Sunnes *of splendor like I see*
> *And seeyng, feele in mee*
> *   Of Princes hart quite lost, the Ruyñ straunge.*
> *   Butt nowe eche where dothe Raunge,*

With ougly Cloake the Darck envyous Nighte,
Who full of guilty Spyte,
  Suche Living Beames shoulde her black seate assayle
  Too weyke for them, oure weyker sighte dothe vayle,
No sayes fayre Moone, my Lighte,
  Shall barr that wronge, and thoughe yt not prevayle,
Lyke to my Brothers Rayes, yet those I sende,
Hurt not the face wch no thing can amend.

And by that tyme, beeyng come to the Lodge, and having
vizitted the sweete *Philoclea*, with muche less then naturall Care
of ye Parentes and muche lesse then wonted kyndenes of
Cleophila, eche party full fraughte with dyversly worcking
fancyes, made theyre pillowes weyke proppes of theyre over-
loden heades: yet of all other were *Cleophilas* braynes moste
turmoyled, trubled with Love bothe active and passive, and
lastly and specially wth Care howe to use her short limitted
tyme, to the full performance of her vyolent affection, by some
wyse and happy diverting her Twoo Lovers unwellcome desyers.
Cleophila having had ye Nighte her onely Counseylor in the
buysy enterpryse shee was to undertake, and having all that
tyme mused, and yet not fully resolved, howe shee mighte joyne
obtayning with preventing: was offended with the dayes bolde
entrie into her Chamber, as yf hee had now by Custome growne
an assured bringer of evill Newes, whiche shee (taking a *Cittron*
to her) did lay to *Auroras* charge wth these well songe verses.

  Aurora *nowe thow shewest thy blusshing Lighte,*
    (Whiche ofte to hope layes oute a guylefull Bayte)
  That trustes in tyme, to fynde the way a Righte,
    To ease those paynes, wch on desyer doo wayte;

  Blusshe on for shame, that, still with thee do lighte,
    On pensive sowles (in stead of Restfull bayte)
  Or uppon Care (in steade of Dooyng Righte)
    To overpressed Brestes more greevous weighte,

  As oh my self, whose wooes are never lighte,
    (Tyde to the stake of Doubte) strong passyons Bayte,
  Whyle thy knowne Course observing Natures Righte
    Sturres mee to thinck what Daungers lye in wayte
      For Mischeefes great, day after day do shewe
      Make mee feare still, thy fayre appearing hewe.

ARCADIA

Alas saide shee, am I not Ronne into a straunge Gulffe that am fayne for Love, to hurt her I Love, and bycause I detest the others, to please them I detest: O onely *Philoclea* whose Beuty ys matched with nothinge but with the unspeakeable buty of the fayrest mynde. Yf thow didest see upon what a Rock my Tormented sowle ys sett, Litle woulde yow thinck I had Free scoape nowe to leape to any newe Chaunge: with that with hasty handes shee gott her self up turning her sighte, to every thinge, as yf Chaunge of object mighte help her Invention. So went shee ageane to the Cave, where forthewith yt came into her heade, that shoulde bee the fittest place to performe her exployte, of whiche shee had now a kynde of Confused Conceypte, allthoughe shee had not sett downe in her fancy the meeting with eche particularity that mighte falle oute: Butt, as a Paynter dothe at the first shewe a Rude proportion of the thinge hee imitates, whiche after wth more Curyous hande hee drawes to the representing eche Lineament; So had her thoughtes (beaten aboute yt Continually) receyved into them, ground plott of her devyse, allthoughe shee had not in eche parte shapte yt according to a full determeynacyon. But in this sorte having earely vizitted the Morninges beuty in those plesant Dezertes, shee came to the *Duke* and *Duchess* and toulde them that for ye performance of certeyne her Contry Devotyons (wch onely were to bee exercysed in solitarynes) shee did desyer theyre Leave shee might for a fewe dayes lodge her self in the Cave, the fresh sweetenes of whiche did greately delyte her in that whott Contry: And that, for that smalle space, they woulde not otherwyse truble them selves in vizitting her, but at suche tymes as shee woulde come to wayte uppon them, whiche shoulde bee every day at certeyne howres neyther shoulde yt bee Longe shee woulde desyer this priviledged absence of them. They, whose myndes had allredy taken oute that Lesson perfectly, to yeelde a willing obaydyence to all her desyers with Consenting Countenaunce made her soone see her pleasure was a Lawe unto them; Bothe in deede inwardly glad of yt: *Basilius* hoping that her Devyding her self from them mighte yet give hym some freer occasyon of Coming in secrett unto her, whose favourable face had lately strengthened his faynting Countenaunce. Butt *Gynecia* of all others moste Joyous, houlding her self assured that this was but a Prologue to the play shee had promysde her: Thus bothe flattering them selves with dyversly grounded hopes, they Range a Bell wch served to Calle certeyne pore woemen (wch ever lay in Cabyns not farr of) to doo the howsholde services of bothe Lodges, and never came to eyther but beeyng Called for. And comaunded them to Carry forthewith *Cleophilas* Bedd & furniture of her Chamber into the pleasaunt Cave, and to deck yt up as fynely as yt was possible for them, that theyre Sowles Rest mighte rest her body to her best pleasing maner: That was wth all diligence performed of them, and *Cleophila* all redy in possession of her newe chosen Lodging, where shee like one of *Vestas* Nuñes enterteyned her self for a fewe dayes in all shewe of streytnes, yet once a day Cōming to doo her Duty to the *Duke* and *Duchess*. In whome the sildomnes of the sighte encreased the more unquyett Longing, thoughe somewhat quallifyed, as her Countenaunce was decked to eyther of them with more Comfort then wonted: Especially to *Gynecia*, who seeyng her wholly neglect her Daughter *Philoclea* had nowe promysd her self a full possession of *Cleophilas* hart, still expecting the fruite of the happy & hoped for Invention. But bothe shee and *Basilius* kept suche a Continuall Watche aboute the precinctes of the Cave, that eyther of them was a Barr to the other for having any secrett Comoning with *Cleophila*: While in the meane tyme the sweete *Philoclea* (forgotten of her Father, despysed of her Moother, and in appearance lefte of *Cleophila*) had yeelded upp her sowle to bee a pray to sorowe and unkyndenes, not with Raging conceipte of Revenge, as had passed throwe ye stowte and wyse hart of her Mother, but with a kynde of meekenes taking uppon her self the weighte of her owne woes. And suffering them to have so full a Course in her, as yt did not alitle weyken the estate of her body, aswell for whiche Cause as for that shee coulde not see *Cleophila*, withoute expressing (more then shee woulde) howe farr nowe her Love was imprisoned in extremity of sorowe, shee bounde her self to the Limittes of her owne Chamber: But *Cleophila* having now a full Liberty to Cast aboute every way howe to bringe her conceyved attempt, to a desyered success, was ofte so perplexed with the Difficulty of yt, that some tymes shee woulde Resolve by force, to take her away, though yt were with the deathe of her Parentes. Sometyme, to goo away her self with *Musidorus*

and bringe bothe theyre Forces to wynñ her, but Lastly, even
the same day that *Musidorus* by feeding the humors of his three
lothsome Gardyans had stolne away the Princess *Pamela*:
whether yt were that Love ment to matche them every way or
y^t in Deede *Cleophila* forbare the practizing her devyse, till shee
founde her Frende had past thorowe his. The same day I say
thus shee governed her purpose, having Curyously trymed her
self to the beutifying her Beutyes, that beeyng now at her last
tryall, shee mighte come to yt in her best Armoure: Havinge
putt on that kynde of mylde Countenaunce, wch dothe encorage
the Looker on to hope for a gentle answer, according to her
late receyved maner shee lefte the pleasant Darcknes of her
Melancholy Cave, to goo take her Dynner of the *Duke* and
Duchess & give unto bothe them a pleasaunt foode of seeyng the
Owner of theyre Desyers. But even as the *Persians* were
auncyently wonte to Leave no Rysing Sunne unsaluted, (But
as his fayre Beames appeared Cleared unto them woulde the
more hartely Rejoyse) laying uppon them a greate foretoken of
theyre followinge fortunes: So was there no tyme that *Cleophila*
encountered theyre eyes with her beloved presence, but that yt
bredd a kynde of burning Devotyon in them, yet so muche the
more gladding theyre greedy sowles, as her Countenaunce were
cleared with more favour unto them. Whiche now beeyng
determinately framed to the greatest descent of kyndenes, yt
tooke suche holde of her Infortunate Lovers that like Children
aboute a tender Father, from a longe voyage returned, with
loving Chyldishnes hange about hym, and yet, with simple
feare measures by his Countenaunce, howe farr hee acceptes
theyre Bouldenes: So were these twoo throwne into so servisable
an affection, that the turning of *Cleophilas* eye was a stronge
sterne, ynoughe to all theyre motions wynding no way, but as
the enchaunting force of yt guyded them. But having made a
light Repast of the pleasaunt fruites of that Contry enterlarding
theyre foode wth suche maner of generall discourses as Lovers
are wonte to Cover theyre passyons in, (when respect of a
thirde person keepes them from playner particulers) at the
earnest intreaty of *Basilius, Cleophila* (first saluting the *Muses*
with a Base vyoll honge hard by her) sent this Ambassade in
versifyed Musick to bothe her yll Requited Lovers.

Beuty hathe force to catche the Humane sighte,
  Sight dothe bewitch the Fancy evell awaked,
Fancy (wee feele) eludes all passyons mighte,
  Passyon Rebeld, often Reasons strength hathe shaked,

No wonder then, thoughe Sighte, my Sighte did taynte,
  And thoughe thereby my Fancy was infected,
Thoughe (yoked so) my mynde with sicknes faynte,
  Had Reasons weyght for passyons ease rejected,

But nowe the Fitt ys past, and Tyme hathe given,
  Leysure to weyghe what due Desert requyreth,
All Thoughtes so sprunge are from theyre dwelling driven,
  And wysdome to his wonted seate aspyreth.
    Crying in mee, I hopes deceyptfull proove,
    Thinges rightly prysde Love ys the bande of Love.

And after her Songe with an affected modesty, shee threwe downe her eye, as yf the Conscyence of a secrett graunt her inwarde mynde made, had sodenly cast a basshfull vayle over her: whiche *Basilius* fynding, and thincking now was the tyme to use his paynefull petition, beseeching his wyfe wth more Carefull eye, to accompany his sickly Daughter, *Philoclea* beeyng ridd for that tyme of her, who was Content to graunt hym any scope, that shee mighte after have ye like freedome (with a gesture governed by the force of his passions making his knees his best supporters) hee thus sayde unto her. Yf eyther (sayde hee O Lady of my Lyfe) my Deadly panges coulde beare delay or that this were the first tyme the same were manifested unto yo^w, I woulde now but meyntayne still the Remembrance of my mysfortune w^thoute urging any furder Rewarde then tyme and pity mighte procure for mee: But alas, synce my Martyrdome ys no less paynefull then manifest, & that I no more feele the myserable Daunger then yo^w know the assured truthe therof, why shoulde my Toungue deny his service to my hart, why shoulde I feare the breathe of my wordes who dayly feele the flame of youre worckes? Embrace in youre sweete Consideracyon I beseeche yo^w the mysery of my Case, acknowlledge youre self to bee the Cause, and thinck yt ys Reason for yow to redress the effectes? Alas let not certeyne Imaginatyve Rules (whose truthe standes but upon opinyon) keepe so wyse a
206

ARCADIA

mynde from gratefullnes and mercy whose never fayling Lawes *Nature* hathe planted in us. I playnely lay my deathe unto yow, the deathe of hym y^t Loves yow, the Deathe of hym whose lyfe yow may save: Say youre absolute Determenacyon, for hope yt self ys a payne while yt ys over mastered with feare, and yf yo^w do Resolve to bee Crewell, yet is the speedyest Condempnatyon as in evills moste wellcome. *Cleophila* who had fully sett to her self the Trayne shee woulde keepe, yet knowyng that who soonest meane to yeelde dothe Well to make the bravest parley keeping her Countenaunce alofte. Noble Prince sayde shee youre wordes are too well Couched to come oute of a Restles mynde and thancked bee the goddes youre face threatens no Daunger of Deathe; These bee but those swelling speeches wch give the uttermoste Name to every Tryfle wch all were worthe no thing yf they were not enamyld with the goodly outesyde of Love. Truly Love were very unlovely yf yt were half so deadly as yo^w Lovers still Living terme yt, I thincke well, yt may have a certeyne Chyldish vehemency wch for the tyme to one Desyer will engage all the Sowle so longe as yt lasteth, but with what Impacyence yow youre self shewe, who Confess the hope of yt a payne: And thincke yo^w youre owne desyer so unworthy as yo^w woulde fayne bee ridd of yt? and so with over muche Love sue hard for a hasty Refusall. A Refusall cryed oute *Basilius*? amased withall, but persed with ye last, Now assure youre self whensoever yo^w use that worde definitively yt will bee the undoubted Doome of my approching deathe; And then shall youre owne experyence knowe in mee, howe soone the Spirittes dryed up with anguish leave the performañcy of theyre Ministery, whereuppon oure Lyfe dependeth. But alas what a Cruelty ys this, not onely to torment, but to thincke the Tormentes lighte? The Terriblest Tyrauntes woulde say by noo man they killde, hee dyed not, nor by no man hee punisshed, that hee escaped free, for of all other there ys lefte hope of mercy where there ys no acknoulledging of the payne. And wth like Cruelty are my wordes breathed oute from a flamy hart accounpted as Messingers of a quyett mynde, yf I speake no thing, I choke my self, and am in no way of Releef; yf simply, neglected, yf Confusedly, not understood, yf by the bending together all my inward powers, they bringe forthe any Lyvely expressing of that they truely feele,

207

that ys a Token forsoothe, the thoughtes are apte to too muche Leysure, thus ys sylence desperate folly punisshed and witt suspected. But in Deede yt ys vayne to say any more, for wordes can bynde no beleef: Lady I say determyn of mee, I must Confess I can not beare this Battell in my mynde, and therefore lett mee soone knowe what I may accoumpt of my self, for, yt ys a hell of Dolors when the mynde still in doubt for want of Resolucyon can make no Resistance. In deede answered *Cleophila*, yf I shoulde graunte to youre Request I shoulde shewe an example in my self that I esteeme the holy band of Chastety to bee but an Imaginative Rule as yow termed yt and not the truest observance of Nature: The moste noble Comaundement that mankynd can ever have of them selves, as in deede bothe Learning teacheth and inward feeling assureth. But first shall *Cleophilas* grave become her mariage bedd before my sowle shall Consent to his owne shame, before I will leave a Marcke in my self of an unredeemable Trespas: And yet must I Confess that yf ever my harte were sturred, yt hathe beene with ye manifest and manifolde shewes of the Misery yow Live in for mee. For in truthe so yt ys, *Nature* gives not us her degenerate Children any more generall precept, then one to help the other, One to feele a true Compassyon of the others Myshapp: But, yet yf I were never so Contented to speake with yow (for further, O, *Basilius* never looke for at my handes) I knowe not howe yow can avoyde youre wyves Jelous attendance, but that her suspicyon shall bringe myne honor into questyon. *Basilius* whose smalle Sailes the leste wynde did fill was forthewith as farr goñ into a Large promising hym self his desyer, as before hee was stricken downe with a threatning denyall: And therefore bending his Browes (as thoughe hee were not a Man to take the matter as hee had done) What saide hee shall my wyffe become my Mistriss? Thincke yow not that thus muche tyme hathe taughte mee to Rule her? I will mewe the gentlewoman tyll shee have Cast all her Fethers, yf shee Rowse her self ageanst mee. And with that hee walked up and downe nodding his heade as though they mystooke hym muche, that thoughte hee was not hys wyves Master. But *Cleophila*, now seeyng yt was tyme to Conclude, Of youre wisdome & Manhood (sayde shee) I Doubt not, but that suffyseth not mee, for bothe they can hardly tame a Malicyous toungue, and Impossibly barr the freedome of thoughte: whiche bee the thinges that must bee my onely witnesses of Honor or Judges of Dishonor. But that yow may see I do not sett light youre affection, yf to Night, after youre wyffe bee assuredly a sleepe (wherof by youre Love I Conjure yow to have a moste precyse Care) yow will steale handsomely to the Cave to mee: There do I graunt yo^w as greate proportyon as yow will take of free Conference with mee. *Basilius*, that was oulde ynoughe to knowe that woemen are not wonte to appoynt secrett Nighte meetinges for the purchasing of Lande (holding hym self allredy an undoubted possessor of his desyers) kissing her hande, and lifting up his eyes to heaven as yf the greatnes of the benefitt did goo beyonde all measure of thanckes, sayde no more: Lest sturring of more wordes might bring forthe some perhapps contrary matter. In whiche Traunce of Joy *Cleophila* went from hym saying shee wolde leave hym to the Remembrance of theyre appoyntment: And for her shee woulde goo vizitt the Lady *Philoclea*, into whose Chamber beeyng comĕ, keeping still her late taken on gravity, and asking her howe shee did (rather in the way of Dutyfull Honor, then any speciall affection) with extreme Inward anguish to them bothe, shee turned from her. And taking the Duchess *Gynecia*, ledd her into a Bay wyndowe of the same Chamber, Determening in her self not to utter to so excellent a witt as *Gynecia* had the uttermoste poynte of her pretended Devyse: But to keepe the Clause of yt, for the last instant, when the shortenes of ye tyme shoulde not give her spirittes leysure to looke into all those Doubtes that easily enter into an open Invention. But with smylinge eyes and with a Delivered over grace (fayning asmuche Love to her as shee did Counterfeit litle Love to *Philoclea*) shee began with more Credible then eloquent speeche to tell her: That with muche Consideracyon of a Matter so nerely importing her owne fancy and *Gynecias* honor shee had now concluded, that the Nighte followyng shoulde bee the fittest tyme for the joyning together of theyre severall desyers. What tyme sleepe shoulde perfectly doo his office uppon the *Duke* her husband, and that the one shoulde come to the other to the Cave: whiche place as yt was the first receypte of theyre promysed Love, so yt mighte have the first Honor of the due performance. That the Cause whye those fewe dayes past shee had not sought the like, was leste the new Chaunge of her Lodging might make the *Duke* more apte to marcke any sodeyn event, wch now the use of yt woulde take oute of his mynde : And therefore nowe moste excellent Lady (sayde shee) there resteth no thinge, but, that, quickly after Supper yow trayne up the *Duke* to vizitt his Daughter *Philoclea*, and then framing youre self not well at ease, by youre gooyng to bedd drawne hym not longe to bee after yow. In the meane tyme I will bee gonñ home to my Lodging, where I will attend yo^w with no Less Devotion (but as I hope) wth better fortune then *Thisby* did the twoo muche Loving and too muche Loved *Pyramus* : The blood that quickly came into *Gynecias* fayre face was the onely answer shee made, but that one mighte easily see Contentment and Consent were bothe to the full in her. Whiche shee did testify with the wringing *Cleophila* fast by the hand, Closing her eyes and letting her heade falle, as yf shee woulde give her to knowe, shee was not ignorant of her faulte, allthoughe shee were transported with the vyolence of her evill : But in this triple agreement did the day seeme tedyous of all sydes, till his never erring Course had given place to the Nightes succession, and the Supper by eche hand hasted was with no less speede ended. When *Gynecia* presenting a heavy sleepynes in her Countenaunce brought up bothe *Basilius* and *Cleophila* to see *Philoclea*, sicke in her bedd and farr more sick in mynde then in body and more greeved then Comforted with any suche vizitacyon : Thence, *Cleophila* (wisshing easefull Rest to *Philoclea*) did seeme to take that Nightes Leave of that Princely Crewe. When *Gynecia* lyke wyse seeming somewhat Diszeazed, desyered *Basilius* to stay a while with her Daughter while she Recomended her sicknes to her Beddes Comfort : In deede desyerus to determyn ageane of the maner of her stealling away, to no less Comfort of *Basilius* who the sooner shee was a sleepe, the sooner hoped to Come by his long pursewed pray. Thus bothe were bent to deceyve eche others, and to take the advauntage of eyther others disadvantage, But, *Gynecia* having taken *Cleophila* into her Bedchamber, to speake a litle with her of theyre sweete Determinatyon : *Cleophila* uppon a sodeyn (as thoughe shee had never thought of yt before) Nowe the goddes forbid (sayde shee) so greate a Lady as yo^w are shoulde come to mee, or that I shoulde leave yt to the handes of fortune, yf by eyther the evill governing of youre passyon, or youre husbandes sodeyne waking any daunger might happen unto yo^w. No, yf there bee any Superiority in the poyntes of true Love yt shall bee youres, yf there bee any Daunger, (synce my self am the author of this Devyse) yt ys Reason yt shoulde bee myne: Therefore, doo yo^w but leave with mee the keyes of the gate, and upon youre self take my upper garment (that yf any of *Dametas* howse see yow they may thincke yo^w to bee my self) and I will presently lye downe in youre place so muffled for youre supposed sicknes, as the *Duke* shall no thing knowe mee. And then assoone as the *Duke* ys asleepe will I (as muche better becomes mee) wayte uppon yo^w: And yf the uttermoste of myscheefes shoulde happen, I can assure yo^w the *Dukes* lyfe shall sooner pay for yt, then youre Honor. And with the ending of her wordes shee threwe of her gowne, not giving *Gynecia* any space to take the full Image of this Newe Chaunge into her fancy: But seeying no objection ageanst yt in her harte, and knowing there was no tyme then to stand longe disputing. Besydes, remembring the Giver was to order the maner of his gifte, yeelded quickly to this Conceypte, in deede, (not amongst the smallest Causes tickled thereunto by a certeyne Wanton desyer) that her husbandes deceypte mighte bee the more notable: In this sorte did *Cleophila* nymbly disarming her self possess *Gynecias* place, hyding her heade in suche a Close maner, (as greevous and over watched sicknes ys wonte to invite to yt self the solace of sleepe). And of the other syde the *Duchess* putting on *Cleophilas* uppermoste garment went first into the Closett there, quickly to beutify her self with the best and sweetest Night deckinges: But there Casting a hasty eye over her precyous thinges, whiche ever synce *Cleophilas* Comming (her heade otherwyse occupyed had lefte unseene) shee happened to see a Bottell of golde, uppon wch downe alonge were graved these verses.

> *Let him drincke this, Whome longe in Armes to folde,*
> *Thow doest desyer, and with free power to holde.*

Shee Remembred her Bottell, for yt had beene kept of longe tyme by the Kinges of *Cyprus*, as a thinge of Rare vertue, and given to her by her Mother, when shee beeyng very younge maryed to her Husband of muche greater age: Her Mother (perswaded yt was of property to force Love with Loves effectes)

had made a precyous present of yt to this her wellbeloved
Chylde, though yt had beene rather receyved by tradicyon to
have suche quality then by any approoved experyment. This,
Gynecia, (according to the Comon disposicion) not onely (thoughe
especially) of wyves, but of all other kynde of people, not to
esteeme muche ones owne, but to thincke that Laboure lost
employed aboute yt) had never Cared to give yt to her Husband,
but suffered his affection, to ronne according to his owne scope:
But now that, Love of her particuler Choyse had awaked her
spirites and perchaunce the very unlawfullnes of yt had a litle
blowne the Cole (among her other ornamētes) with glad mynde
shee tooke moste parte of the liquor, and putting yt into a fayre
Cupp all sett with Dyamondes (for what dare not Love undertake armed with the nighte and provoked with Lust). And this
done, shee went to the Cave warde, guyded onely by the
Moones fayre shyning, suffering no other thoughte to have any
familiarity wᵗʰ her braynes, But that wᶜʰ did present unto her a
picture of her approching Contentment: Shee that had longe
disdayned this solitary Lyfe her Husband had entred into, now
wisshed yt muche more solitary, so shee mighte onely obtayne
the private presence of *Cleophila*, shee that before woulde not
have goñ alone so farr, (especyally by Nighte, and to so darcke
a place) now tooke a pryde in the same Corage and framed in
her mynde a plesure oute of yᵉ payne yt self. Thus with thick
dubled pases shee went to the Cave receyving to her self for
her first Contentment the onely lyinge where *Cleophila* had done
whose pillowe shee kist a thowsand tymes : For having borne
the prynte of that beloved hedd, and so keeping with panting
harte, her traveyling fancyes so attentyve, that the wynde
woulde sturr no thinge, but that shee styrred her self, as yf yt
had bene the pase of the longed for *Cleophila*. Shee kept her
syde of the Bedd, defending onely and cherisshing the other syde
with her Arme, (till after a while wayting) Coumpting with her
self howe many stepps were betuixt the Lodge and the Cave:
And ofte accusing *Cleophila* of more Curyous stay then needed,
shee was vizited as yoʷ shall presently heare. For, *Basilius*
assoone as his Wyfe was gone to her fayned Repose as Longe
as hee remayned with his Daughter, (to give his wyffe tyme of
unreddying her self) yt was easily seene what a very thorny
aboade hee made there: And the Discourses with wᶜʰ hee

212

enterteyned his Daughter, not unlike to those of earnest Players, when in ye midst of theyre game, Triffling questyons bee putt unto them. His eyes still looking aboute, and hym self still chaunging places, began to speake of a thinge, and brake yt of before yt were half done, to any speeche *Philoclea* ministred unto hym, with a sodeyne starting and Casting up his hedd hee woulde make an answer farr oute of all *Grañer*, with a certeyne deepe musing, and by and by oute of yt uncerteyne motions, unstayed graces: Havinge borne oute ye limitt of a reasonable tyme wth asmuche payne as mighte bee, hee came darckling into his Chamber, forcing hym self to treade as softely as hee coulde, but the more Curyous hee was, the more every thing creaked under hym: And his mynde beeyng oute of the way with an other thoughte, and his eyes not serving his turne in that darcke place, eche Coffer or Cupborde hee mett, one saluted his shinnes, an other his ellbowes, sometymes redy in Revenge to stryke them ageane with his face. Till at lengthe lifting upp the Cloathes, as gently as I thincke pore *Pan* did, when in steade of *Ioles* bedd, hee came into the roughe embracinges of *Hercules*, and laying hym self downe, as tenderly as a Newe byrd, rested a while wth a very open eare, to marcke eche breathe of his supposed wyffe: And some tymes hee hym self woulde yeelde a longe fetched sighe as thoughe that had beene a Musick to drawe on an other to sleepe, till within a very litle whyle, with the other partyes Counterfeited sleepe (who was as willing to bee ridd of hym, as hee was to bee gotten thence) assuring hym self hee lefte all safe there, in the same order stale oute ageañe. And putting on his Night gowne, with muche groping and scambling, hee gott hym self oute of the litle howse, and then did the Moone lighte serve, to guyde his feete. Thus with a greate deale of payne did *Basilius* goo to her, whome hee fledd, and with muche Cunning lefte the person for whome hee had employed all his Cunning. But, when *Basilius* was once gotten (as hee thoughte) into a clere Coste, what Joye hee then made? how eche thinge seemed vyle in his sighte in Comparyson of his fortune? Howe farr allredy hee deemed hym self in the cheef Tower of his Desyers yt were tedyous to tell: But once his harte coulde not chuse but yeelde this Songe, as a Fayring of his Contentment.

Gett hence fowle greeffe, the Cancker of the mynde,
Farewell Complaynte, the Misers onely pleasure,
Away vayne Cares, by whiche fewe men do fynde,
theyre sought for Treasure.

Yee helples sighes blowe oute youre Breathe to noughte,
Teares, drowne youre selves, for woe youre Cause ys wasted,
Thought, thincke to ende, too Longe the fruite of thoughte
my mynde hathe tasted.

But thow, sure Hope, tickle my leaping harte?
Comfort, sleepe thow in place of wonted sadnes,
Forefelt Desyer, begynñ to savoure parte,
of my Cunning gladnes.

Lett voyce of sighes into clere Musick ronne,
Eyes lett youre teares with gasing, now bee mended,
Insteade of thoughte, true pleasure bee begun,
and never ended.

Thus imagening as then with hym self his Joyes so held hym
upp, that hee never touched grounde, like a righte oulde beaten
Soldyour that knowe well ynoughe the greatest Capteynes do
never use longe Orations, when yt comes to the poynte of
execution: Assoone as hee had gotten into the Cave, and to the
Joyfull though silent expectation of *Gynecia* came close to the
bedd, (never Recking his promyse of looking for nothing but
Conference) hee lepte into that syde preserved for a more wellcome Guest. And laying his loving holde uppon *Gynecia*,
O *Cleophila* (sayde hee) embracing youre favoure, this humble
Servaunt of youres, holde wth mee my harte whiche pantes to
leave his Master, to come unto yow: In what Case pore
Gynecia was, when shee knewe the voyce and felt the body of
her husband? Fayre Ladyes, yt ys better to knowe by
imaginacyon, then experyence? For streight was her mynde
assaulted partly with the beeyng deprived of her unquenched
desyer, butt principally with the Doubt that *Cleophila* had
betrayed her to her husband, besydes the Renewed stinge of
Jelosy, what in the meane tyme mighte befall her Daughter:
But of the other syde, her Love with a fixed perswasion shee
had had toughte her to seeke all reason of hopes, and therein

214

thoughte best before discovering of her self to marcke the behavyour of her Husband. Who bothe in deedes and wordes, still using her, (as taking her to bee *Cleophila*) made *Gynecia* hope, that this mighte bee *Basilius* owne enterpryse whiche *Cleophila* had not stayed, leste shee shoulde discover the matter, wch mighte bee performed at another tyme: whiche hope accompanyed with *Basilius* maner of dealling (hee beeyng at that tyme fuller of lyvelyer fancyes, then many yeares before hee had beene, besydes the remembrance of her Daughters sicknes and late straunge Countenance betwene her and *Cleophila* all Cōming together into her mynde, wch was loathe to condempne yt self of an utter overthrowe) made her frame her self (not truely with a sugred joye, but with a determyned patyence) to lett her Husband thincke hee had founde a very gentle and supple mynded *Cleophila*: whiche hee (good man) making full Reckening of, did melt in asmuche gladnes, as shee was oppressed with dyvers ungratefull burdens. But, *Pyrocles* who had at this present, no more to play the parte of *Cleophila*, having (as I toulde yow) so naturally measured the maner of his breathing that *Basilius* made no doubt of his sounde sleeping, having lyen a prety while with a quyett unquyetnes to satisfy his greedy desyer: Assoone as by the debate betweene *Basilius* shynnes and the unregarding Formes, he perceyved that hee had fully lefte the Lodge after hym went hee with stealling steppes. Having his sworde under his Arme (still doubting leste some myschaunce mighte turne *Basilius* back ageane) downe to the gate of the Lodge, whiche (not content to lock fast) hee barred and fortefyed with asmany devyses as witt and haste coulde suffer hym: Resolving to wyn full tyme to accomplish his enterpryse, and to have warning ynoughe before they shoulde come at hym. For, furder endes of those endes, and what mighte ensue of this action his Love and Corage (well matched) never looked after, holding for an assured grounde that whosoever in greate thinges will thincke to prevent all objections muste lye still and doo nothinge: This onely, generally hee Remembred that, so longe as *Gynecia* bewrayed not the matter, wch hee thought shee woulde not doo (aswell for her owne honor and savety, as for the hope shee might still have of hym wch ys loathe to dye in a Lovers harte) all the Rest woulde turne to a prety meryment, and enflame his Lover *Basilius*

ageane to a new Casting aboute for the missed favoure. This
Determynacyon thus weyghed this first parte thus performed, up
to *Philocleas* Chamber went *Pyrocles* rapt from hym self with the
excessive forefeeling of his nere Cõmyng Contentment, what
ever paynes hee had taken, what Daungers hee had ronne into:
And specyally those sawcy pages of Love, Doubtes, greeffes
Languisshing hopes and threateninge dispayres, came all nowe
to his mynde in one Ranck, to beutify this after followyng
blisfullnes, and to serve for a moste fitt sauce, whose sowernes
mighte give a kynde of Lyfe to the delightfull chere his
Imaginacyon fedd uppon. All the great estate of his father
seemed unto hym but a tryffling pompe, Whose good standes
in other menns Conceipt, in Comparyson of the true Comforte
hee founde in the depth of his mynde, and the knouledg of any
mysery that mighte ensue this Joyous adventure was recked of,
but as a sleight purchase of possessing the topp of happynes:
And yet well hee founde that extremity of Joy ys not withoute
a certeyne Joyfull payne, by extending the harte beyond his
wonted Limittes, and so forcibly holding all the fancyes to
one object, that yt Confoundes theyre mutuall worckinge
not withoute a Charming kynde of Ravisshing them from
the free use of theyre owne function. Thus greeved onely
with too muche gladnes, beeyng come to the dore whiche
shoulde bee the entrie to his happynes, hee was mett with
the later ende of a Songe: whiche *Philoclea* like a solitary
Nightingale, (bewailing her guyltles punishment and helples
mysfortune) had newly delivered over, meaning none shoulde
bee Judge of her passyon but her owne Conscyence: The
songe having bene accorded to a sweetly played on Lute,
conteyned these verses, whiche shee had lately with some
arte Curyously written, to enwrapp her secrett and resolute
woes.

[1]*Vertue* [2]*Bewty and* [3]*Speeche, did* [1]*stryke,* [2]*wounde,* [3]*Charme,*
    [1]*My Hart,* [2]*Eyes,* [3]*Eares with* [1]*wonder,* [2]*Love,* [3]*Delighte*
[1]*First,* [2]*Second* [3]*Last did* [1]*bynde,* [2]*enforce and* [3]*Arme,*
    [1]*His* [2]*worckes* [3]*Shewes* *Fruites* w[th] [1]*witt,* [2]*grace and* [3]*vowes*
    might.

Thus Honor, lyking, trust, muche, farr and Deepe,
    Held, pearst possest, my Judgment, sence, and will,
Till wronge, Contempt, Deceipt, did growe, steale, creepe,
    Bandes, favoure, faythe, to breake, Defyle, and Kill.

· Then greef, unkyndenes, proof, tooke, kyndled, taughte,
    Wellgrounded, Noble, Dewe, spyte, rage, disdayne,
But, ah, alas, (in vayne) my mynde, sight, thoughte
    Dothe him, his face, his wordes, Leave, shunne, refrayne
    For nothing, tyme, nor place can lewse, quenche, ease,
    Myne owne, embrased, sought, Knott, Fyer, disease.

The force of Love to those pore folcke that feele yt ys many
wayes very straunge, but no way straunger, then that yt dothe
so encharme the Lovers Judgement, uppon her that holdes the
Raynes of his mynde, that what soever shee dothe ys ever in his
eyes best; And that best beeyng by the Continuall motyons of
oure chaunging lyfe turned by her to any other no thing, that
thing ageane becometh best. So that *Nature* in eche kynde
suffering but one Superlatyve, the Lover onely admittes no
positive yf shee sitt still, that ys best, for so ys the Conspiracy
of her severall graces helde best together to make one perfect
figure of Beuty: yf shee walke, no doubt that ys best, for besydes
ye making happy the more places by her steppes the very sturring
addes a pleasaunt lyfe to her naturall perfections. Yf shee bee
sylent that, withoute Comparyson ys best, synce by that meanes
the untrubled eye moste freely may devowre the sweetnes of his
object: But yf shee speake, hee will take yt uppon his deathe
that ys best the quintessence of eche woord beeyng distilled
downe into his affected sowle. Example of this was well to bee
seene in the given over *Pyrocles* who with panting breathe and
sometymes sighes not suche as sorowe (restrayning the inward
partes) dothe make them glad to delyver: But, suche as the
Impacyence of desyer with the unsurety of never so sure hope

217

COUNTESS OF PEMBROOKES

ys wonte to breathe owte. Nowe beeyng at the dore, of the one syde hearinge her voyce whiche hee thought yf the Philosophers sayde true of the heavenly spheared harmony, was by her not onely represented but farr surmounted: And of the other, having his eyes overfilled with her Beuty, (for the *Duke* at his parting had lefte the Chamber open and shee at that tyme lay (as the heate of that Contry did well suffer) uppon the Toppe of her bedd. Having her beutyes eclipsed wth no thinge but with a fayre smock, wroughte all in flames of Ashe culloure silke and golde, lying so uppon her right syde, that the lefte thighe downe to the foote, yeelded his delightfull proportion to the full viewe: whiche was seene by the help of a Riche Lampe whiche (throughe the Curteynes a litle drawne) cast suche a lighte upon her, (as the Moone dothe when yt shynes into a thynn wood) *Pyrocles* I say was stopped with the vyolence of many Dartes cast by *Cupid*, alltogether uppon hym. That quyte forgetting hym self, and thinckinge therein all redy hee was in the best degree of felicity, I thincke hee woulde have lost muche of his tyme and with too muche love omitted greate fruite of his Love, had not *Philocleas* pityfull accusing of hym, forced hym to bringe his spirites ageane to a newe Byas: For shee laying her hande upon her fayre Cheeke, uppon wch there did privyly trickle the sweete droppes of her Delightfull, thoughe sorowfull teares, made these wordes wayte uppon her monefull Songe. And hathe that Crewell *Pyrocles* (sayde shee) deserved somuche of mee, that I shoulde for his sake lifte up my voyce in my best Tunes, and to hym Continually with powering owte my playnte, make a disdaynfull oblation: Shall my Soule still do this honor to his unmercyfull tyranny, by my lamenting his Losse, to shewe his worthynes & my weykenes? Hee heares thee not simple *Philoclea* hee heares thee not, and yf hee did, some hartes growe the harder the more they fynde theyre advantage: Alas what a Miserable Constitution of mynde have I, I disdayn my fortune, and yet reverence hym that disdaynes mee, I accuse his ungratefullnes, and have his vertue in admiracyon? O yee deafe heavens, I woulde eyther his injury, coulde blott oute my affection, or my affection coulde forgett his injury? wth that giving a pityfull but a sweete speeche, shee tooke ageane the Lute, and began to singe this Sonet wch mighte serve as an explayning to the other.

The Love whiche ys imprinted in my sowle,
  With Bewtyes sealle and vertue fayre disguysde,
With Inward Cryes puttes forthe a bitter Rowle,
  Of huge Complayntes, that nowe yt ys despysde,

Thus thus, the more I Love, the wronge the more,
  Monstruous appeares, Long truthe receyved late,
Wrong sturres remorced greef, greefes deadly sore,
  Unkyndenes breedes, unkyndenes fostereth hate.

But ah, the more I hate, the more I thincke,
  Whome I doo hate, the more I thinck on hym,
The more his Matcheles giftes doo deepely sincke,
  Into my Brest, and Loves renewed swym,
    What Medicyn then can suche Disease remoove?
    Where Love drawes hate, and hate engendereth Love.

But, *Pyrocles* that had hearde his name accused & Condemned
(by the mouthe, whiche of all the Worlde and more hee moste
loved) had then Cause enowghe to Calle his mynde to his owne
home: And with the moste haste hee coulde (for true Lovers
feares the accident of an Instant) to matche the excusing of his
faulte, with accomplishment of his arrant thether. And therefore blowne up and downe with asmany contrary passyons
(as *Æolus* sent oute wyndes uppon the *Troyan* Reliques guyded
uppon the Sea by the valyant *Æneas*) hee went' into her
Chamber; And with suche a pace as reverent feare dothe
teache, hee came to her bedd syde: where kneeling downe,
and having prepared a longe Oration for her, his eyes were so
filled with her sighte, that as yf they woulde have robbed all
theyre fellowes of theyre services, bothe his harte faynted, and
his Toungue fayled in suche sorte, that hee coulde not bringe
forthe one worde, but referred her understanding to his eyes
Language. But, shee in extremity amased to see hym there at
so undue a season, and asshamed that her beutyfull body made
so naked a prospect drawing in her dilicate Lymes into the
weyke guarde of the Bedd, & presenting in her face to hym,
suche a kynde of pityfull Anger, as mighte shewe this was onely
a faulte: Therefore, bycause shee had a former grudge unto
hym, turning away her face from hym, shee thus sayde unto
hym. O *Cleophila*, or *Pyrocles*, (for whether Name I use, yt
muche skilles not, synce by the one I was first deceyved and by

the other now betrayed). what straunge motyon ys the guyde of thy Crewell mynde hether? Doest thow not thincke the day tormentes thow haste given mee sufficyent, but, that thow doest envy mee the Nightes quyett? wilt thowe give my Sorowes no truce, but, by making mee see before myne eyes, howe muche I have lost, offer mee due Cause of Confirming my Complaynt? Or ys thy harte so full of Rancoure, that thow doest desyer to feede thyne eyes, with the wretched spectackle of thyne overthrowne enemy? and so to satisfy the full measure of thy undeserved Rage with the receyving into thy sighte the unrelevable Ruyns of my desolate lyfe? O *Pyrocles, Pyrocles,* for thyne owne vertues sake Lett myseryes bee no Musick unto thee, and bee content to take to thy self some Coloure of excuse, that thow diddest not knowe, to what extremity thy Inconstancy or rather fallshoode hathe broughte mee: *Pyrocles,* (to whome every sillable shee pronounced was a Thunderbolt to his harte) egally distracted betuixt amasement and sorowe, abasshed to heare suche a stopp of his desyres, (greeved with her payne but tormented to fynde hym self the Author of yt) with quaking lippes and pale cheare, Alas, Dyvine Lady sayde hee: youre Displeasure ys so Contrary to my desert, and youre wordes so farr from all expectation, that I have leste abillity nowe I have moste neede, to speake in ye Cause, upon wch my self dependeth. For my truthe ys so undoubtedly Constant unto yo^w, my hart ys so assured witness to yt self of his unspotted faythe, That, (having no one thing in mee wherowte any suche Sacriledge mighte aryse) I have nothing like wyse in so direct thinge to say for my self, but sincere and vehement protestatyons: For in truthe there may moste wordes bee spent, where there ys some probabillity to breede on bothe sydes Conjecturall allegacyons. But so perfect a thinge ys my Love in yo^w as yt suffers no questyon, so yt seemes to receyve Injury by any addicyon of wordes unto yt, yf my Soule coulde have beene polluted with Treachery, yt woulde like wyse have provyded for yt self due furniture of Colourable answers: But as yt stoode upon the naked Confidence of his untouched Duty, so I must Confess yt ys alltogether unarmed ageanst so unjust a vyolence as yo^w lay uppon mee. Alas, lett not the paynes I have taken to serve yo^w, bee now accoumpted Injuryous unto yo^w? Let not ye Daungerus Conning I have used to please yo^w, bee

220

deemed a Treason ageāst yow; Synce I have deceyved them, whom yow feare, for youre sake, Do not yow Destroy mee for theyre sake. What can my wordes furder express? I have ridd them bothe oute of the howse, There ys none here to bee eyther hynderers or knowers of the perfecting the mutuall Love wch once my Love wrought in yow towardes mee, but onely the Allmighty powers, whome I Invoke to bee the tryers of my Innocency; And yf ever my thoughtes did receyve somuche as a faynting in theyre true affection, yf they have not continually with more ardoure from tyme to tyme pursewed the possession of youre sweetest favoure, yf ever in that profession they receyved eyther spott or falshoode, then lett theyre most horrible plaigues falle uppon mee. Lett myne eyes bee deprived of theyre Lighte wch did abase ye heavenly Beames that strake them, Lett my falsifyed toungue serve to none use, but to bemone myne owne wickednes? Lett my harte empoysoned wth detestable Treason bee the seate of infernall Sorowe? Let my Soule wth the endless anguish of his Conscience become his owne Tormentor? O false Mankynd, (cryed oute the sweete *Philoclea*) howe can an Impostumed harte, but yeelde forthe evill matter, by his mowthe? Are oathes there to bee beleeved where vowes are broken? No, no, who dothe not feare due recompencing plagues, dothe litle feare, the Invoking of plaigues will make them come ever a whitt the sooner. But alas, what ayleth this newe Conversion? Have yow yet an other sleighte to play? Or do yow thincke to deceyve mee in *Pyrocles* forme, as yow have done in *Cleophilas*? Or rather now yow have betrayed mee in bothe those, ys there some thirde Sexe lefte yow? Into whiche yow can transforme youre self, to enveigle my Simplicity? Enjoy, enjoy the conquestes yow have allredy wonne, and assure youre self yow are come to the furthest poynte of youre Cunning: For my parte unkynde *Pyrocles*, my onely Defence shall bee Beleef of nothinge, My Comfort my faythfull Innocency, and the punishment I desyer of yow shall bee youre owne Conscyence. *Philocleas* hard percevering in this unjust Comdempnacyon of hym did so overthrow all the mighte of *Pyrocles* mynde, (who sawe that tyme woulde not serve to make proof by Deedes, and the better wordes hee used the more they were suspected of deceiptfull Cunninge): That voyde of all Counsell and deprived of all Comforte, fynding best Desertes punisshed, and nerest hopes prevented, hee did abandon the succoure of hym self. And suffered greef so to Close his hart, that his breath fayling hym, with a Deathfull shutting of his eyes hee fell downe by her beddsyde: Having had tyme, to doo no more, but, Oh, whome doest tho^w kill, *Philoclea*? Shee that litle looked for suche an extreme event of her Doynges starting oute of her bed lyke *Venus* rysing from her Mother the sea, not somuche (wth amasemět and greef of her faulte) striken downe, as lifted up with force of Love and desyer to help, shee layde her fayre body over his Brest, and (throwyng no other water in his face but the streame of her teares, nor giving hym no other blowes but the kisses of her well formed mowthe) her onely Cryes were these Lamentacyons: O unfortunate suspicyons (sayde shee) the very meane to lose that, wee moste suspect to lose? O unkyndenes kyndenes of myne wch turnes an Imagined wronge with an effectuall Injury? O folly, to make quarrells my Supplications, or to use hate as the Mediator of Love? Chyldish *Philoclea*? haste thow throwne away the Jewell wherein all thy pryde Consisted? haste thow with too muche haste overronne thy self? Then woulde shee Renewe her kisses and yet not fynding the Lyfe returne Reduble her playntes in this maner: O Devyne Sowle sayde shee, whose vertue can possess no less then the highest place in heaven, yf for my Eternall plaigue thow haste utterly lefte this moste sweete mansyon before I followe thee wth *Thisbyes* punishmět of my Rash unwarynes, Heare this protestacyon of myne, that ys, the wronge to thee, proceeded of a moste syncere but unresistable affection; So ledd with this pityfull example yt shall ende in the mortall hate of my self, and yf yt may bee I will make mee a Tombe of thy memory. But as shee was rysing perchaunce to have begun some suche enterpryse, *Pyrocles* severing his eye Liddes, and having for his firste object her beloved Beuty whiche wrought in hym: Not unlike to those, who lying abrode are so mooved by the Morninge Sunne to pay the tribute of theyre sighte to his fayrenes, hee was allmoste in asmuche daunger of having his Spirittes ageane overpressed with this too excessive Joy. But that shee fynding hym alyve and forgetting naturall bashfullnes, for the late feare of his Losse with her dere embracem^{tes} added strength to his lyfe: So that coming ageane to the use of his feete and lifting the sweete burden of

222

ARCADIA

Philoclea in his Armes, hee layde her on her bedd ageane, having so free scope of his servisable sighte, that there came into his mynde, a Songe the Shepeheard *Philisides* had in his hearing sunge of the beutyes of his unkynde Mistris wch in *Pyrocles* Judgm^t was fully accomplished in *Philoclea*: The Songe was this.

> *What Toungue can her perfections tell?*
> *In whose eche parte all penñs may dwell.*
> *Her hayre fyne Laces made of golde,*
> *In Curled knottes Mans thoughte to holde,*
> *But that her forehead sayes in mee,*
> *A whiter Bewty yow may see,*
> *Whiter in deede, more white then snowe,*
> *Whiche on Colde wynters face dothe growe.*
>
> *That dothe present those prety Browes,*
> *Whose equall Lynes theyre Angles bowes,*
> *Lyke to the Moone when after Change,*
> *Her Horned face in Heaven dothe Range,*
> *And Arches bee to those fayre Lyddes,*
> *Whose wincke eche Bolde attempt forbiddes.*
>
> *As for the Starres, whose spheares contayne*
> *The Matcheles prayse even prayse dothe stayne,*
> *No Lampe whose Lighte by arte ys gott,*
> *No Sunne whiche shynes and seeth nott,*
> *Can Liken them withoute all pere,*
> *Save one asmuche as other Clere.*
>
> *Whiche onely thus unhappy bee,*
> *Bycause them selves they can not see,*
> *Her Cheekes with kyndly Clarett spredd*
> *Like Christall, underlayde with Redd,*
> *Her Nose and Chynñ suche Ivory weares,*
> *No* Elephant *so perfect beares.*
>
> *But who those Ruddy Lippes can mysse,*
> *Whiche Blessed still them selves do kisse,*
> *Rubyes, Cheryes, and Roses newe,*
> *In worthe, in Taste, in perfect Hewe,*
> *Whiche never parte but that they showe,*
> *Of precyous partes the Duble Rowe,*
> *The second sweetely fenced warde,*
> *Her hevenly dewed Toungue to garde.*

Whence never worde in vayne dothe flowe,
Fayre under these dothe stately growe,
The handle of this pleasaunt worcke,
The Neck in whiche strange graces lurcke,
Suche bee I thincke the sumptuous Towers,
Whiche skill dothe make in Princely Bowers.

So true a Taste invites the Eye,
A litle Downeward to espye,
The Lovely Clusters of her Brestes,
Of Venus Babb the wanton Nestes,
Lyke Pummells Rounde of Marble Clere,
Where Azured vaynes well mixte appeare,

With Lycoras stalkes of Porphiry,
Betwixt these Twoo a way dothe lye,
A way, more worthy Beutyes fame,
Then that wch beares the Milcken Name,
These Leades unto the Joyous feelde,
Whiche onely still dothe Lillyes yeelde.
But Lillyes suche, whose Native smell
The Indyan Odoures doo excell.

Waste yt ys callde, for, yt dothe waste,
Menns Lyves untill yt bee embraste,
There may one see, and yet not see,
Her tender Ribbes well armed bee,
Like Whitest Snowe, in silver Brooke,
Fayre, thorow fayre strykes of heedefull Looke.

In these Delightes the Wandering thoughte,
Mighte of eche syde a stray bee broughte,
But, that her Navell dothe unite,
The Curyous Circle buysy sighte,
A Daynty sealle of virgyn waxe,
Where no thing but Impressyon lackes.

The Belly theyre glad sighte dothe fyll,
Justly entituled Cupids Hill.
A Hill moste fitt for suche a Master,
A spottles Myne of Alablaster;

Lyke Alablaster fayre and slyke,
But softe and supple, Sattyn like,
For, suche an use the worlde hathe gotten,
The best thinges still must bee forgotten.

Yet never shall my Songe, omitt,
Those thighes for Ovids *songe more fitt,*
Whiche flancked with twoo sugred flanckes,
Lifte up theyre stately swelling Banckes,
That Albyon Cleeves *in whitenes passe,*
With hanches smoothe as Looking glasse.

But, bowe all knees, now of her knees,
My toungue dothe tell what fancy sees,
The knottes of Joye, the Gynnes *of Love,*
Whose motyon makes all graces moove,
Whose boughte enchaynde dothe yeeld suche sighte,
Like Cunning paynters shadowyng white,
The gartering place dothe Chyldelike signe,
Shewes easy Printe in Mettall fyne.

But, there ageane, the flesh dothe ryse,
In her brave Calves, lyke morning skyes,
That Limittes have in smallest smalle,
Whose eeven descent makes equall falle,
There ofte steales oute that Round cleane foote,
This Noble Cedars *precyous Roote.*

In shewe and sente pale vyolettes
Whose stepp on earthe all Beuty settes,
But, Back unto her Back my Muse,
Where Ledas Swann *his fethers* [mewes],
Alonge whose Ridge suche Bones are mett
Lyke Comfettes Rounde in Marchepane sett.

Her shoulders bee like twoo white Doves,
Pearching uppon square Royall Rooves
Whose gentle rayes suche Luster fynde,
Lyke thynnest Lawne with Tynsell lynde,
And thence those Armes deryved are,
The Phenix *wynges bee not so Rare.*

For faulteles lengthe, and stayneles Hewe,
Ah, woe ys mee, my woes Renewe,
Nowe Course dothe Leade mee to her hande,
Of my first Love, the fatall Band,
Where whitenes dothe for ever sitt,
Nature *her self enameld yt.*

For, there with straunge Compact dothe lye,
Warme snowe, moyste perle, softe Ivory,
There falle those Saphyre *Coloured Brookes,*
Whiche Conduyt like with Curyous Crookes,
Sweete Ilandes makes in that sweete Lande,
As for the fyngers of the Hande,
The Bloody shaftes of Cupids *warr,*
With Amatistes *they headed are.*

Thus hathe eche parte his Bewtyes parte,
But, howe the Graces *doo Imparte,*
To all her Lymmes especiall grace,
Becomming every tyme and place
Whiche dothe even Buty butify,
And moste bewitche the wretched ey.

Howe all this ys but a fayre Inne,
Of fayrer Guest whiche dwelles therein,
Of whose hye prayse, and praysefull Blisse
Goodnes the penn, Heaven Paper ys,
The Incke Immortall fame dothe lende,
As I begãn, so must I ende,
No toungue can her perfections tell,
In whose eche parte all pennes may dwell.

But doo not thincke (Fayre Ladyes) his thoughts had suche Leysure as to ronne over so longe a Ditty: The onely generall fancy of yt came into his mynde fixed upon the sence of the sweet Subject. Where using the benefitt of the Tyme, and fortifying hym self, with the Confessing her late faulte, (to make her nowe the sooner yeelde to penance) turning the passed greeffes and unkyndenes, to the excess of all kynde Joyes (as passyon ys apte to slyde into all Contrary) beginning nowe to envy *Argus* thowsand eyes *Brierius* hundred handes, feighting ageanst a Weyke resistance whiche did stryve to bee overcome; Hee gives mee occasyon to leave hym in so happy a plighte, least my Penn mighte seeme to grudge, at the due Blisse of these pore Lovers, whose Loyalty had but smalle respite of theyre fyery Agonyes. And nowe *Lalus* pype dothe come to my hearing, whiche invites mee to his Mariage that in this Season was celebrated betweene hym & the handsome *Kala*, whome longe hee had loved: whiche, I hope (Fayre Ladyes) youre eares bee not so full of great matters, that yow will disdayne to heare.

Here endes the Thirde Booke or Acte.

THE THIRDE EGLOGUES.

Lalus, not with many paynted wordes nor false harted promyses had wonne the Consent of the beloved *Kala*, but, with a true and simple making her knowe hee loved her, not forcing hym self beyonde his reache to buye her affection: But giving her suche prity presentes as neyther coulde weary hym with the giving, nor shame her with the taking. Thus the first Straweberyes hee coulde fynde were ever in a cleane washt Dishe sent to *Kala*, thus poesyes of the Springe flowers wrapt up in a litle greene silke, and dedicated to *Kalas* Brestes, thus some tymes his sweetest Creame, sometymes ye best Cake bredd his Mother made, were reserved for *Kalas* taste: Neyther woulde hee stick to kill a Lambe, when shee woulde bee Content to come over the way unto hym, but then lo, howe the howse was swept and rather no fyer, then any smooke to truble her, then Love songes were not daynty, when shee woulde heare them, and asmuche manerly sylence when shee woulde not. In goynge to Churche great worship to *Kala*, so that, all the Parrishe sayde, never a Mayde they knewe so well wayted on, and when Dauncyng was aboute the May Powle, no body taken oute but shee, and hee (after a leape or twoo, to shewe her his activity) woulde frame all the Rest of his Dauncing, onely to please her: As for her Fathers sheepe, hee had no less Care of them then his owne, so that shee mighte play her as shee woulde, warranted with honest *Lalus* Carefull-nes. But yf hee spyed *Kala*, favouring any one of the Flock more then his fellowes, then that was Cherysshed, shearing hym so, (when shorne hee must bee) as mighte moste become hym: But while the wolle was on, wrapping within yt some verses, wherein *Lalus* had a speciall guyfte, & making the Innocent Beast his unwitting Messinger. Thus constantly continewyng, thoughe hee were none of the fayrest, at lengthe hee wann *Kalas* harte, the honestest wenche in all those quarters: And so with Consent of bothe Parentes (withoute wch neyther *Lalus* woulde aske, nor *Kala* graunte), Theyre Mariage day was appoynted, whiche because yt fell oute in this tyme, I thincke yt shall not bee Impartinent to remember a litle oure Shepeheardes, while the other greater persons are eyther sleeping or otherwyse occupyed:

228

Lalus Mariage once knowne there needed no Inviting of the Neighboures in that valley, for so well was *Lalus* beloved, that they were all redy to doo hym Creditt. Neyther yet came they like *Harpyes* to devoure hym, butt one broughte a fatt pigg, the other a tender kydd, the third a great goose, asfor Cheese, and Milke and Butter were the *Gossipps* presentes: Thether came of Straungers Shepeheardes, onely the Melancholy *Philisides*, for the vertuous *Coredens* had longe synce lefte all joyfull solempnityes, and as for *Strephon* and *Klaius*, they had lost there *Mistris*, wch putt them into suche extreme sorowes, as they coulde scarsely abyde the lighte of the day, muche less the eyes of men. But of the *Arcadian* borne Shepeheardes thether came good oulde *Geron*, younge *Histor*, thoughe unwilling, and upright *Dicus*, mery *Pas* and Jolly *Nico*: As for *Dametas*, they durst not presume (his Pryde was suche) to invite hym, and *Dorus*, they founde mighte not bee spared, And there under a Bower was made of Boowes (for *Lalus* howse was not able to receyve them) they were enterteyned with harty wellcome, and every one placed according to his Age. The woemen (for suche was the maner of that Contry) kept together to make good Chere amonge themselves, from wch otherwhiles a certeyne paynfull Modesty restraynes them, and there mighte the sadder Matrones give good Counsell to *Kala*, who, pore sowle wept, for feare of that shee desyered: But among the Shepeheardes was all honest liberty, no feare of Telltales who hunt greate prayes, nor in deede myndes in them to give Telltales any occasyon ; But one questioning wth an other of the Manuring of his grounde & governing his flock, the highest poynt they reched to was to talke of holynes of Mariage: To wch purpose assoone as theyre sober Dyner was ended, *Dicus* in steade of thanckes sange this Songe wth a clere voyce and cherefull Countenaunce.

Lett Mother Earthe, *now deck her self in flowers,*
　To see her Offspring seeke a good encrease,
Where justest Love dothe vanquish Cupids *powers,*
　And Warre of thoughtes ys swallowed up in peace,
　　　Whiche never may decrease:
　　　But like the Turtles fayre
　　　Live One in Twoo, a well united payre,
　　　Whiche, that no Chaunce may stayne,
　　　O Hymen *longe theyre Cupled joyes mentayne.*

COUNTESS OF PEMBROOKES

O Heaven *awake, shewe forthe thy stately face,*
  Lett not these slombering Clowdes thy Beutyes hyde,
But *with thy Cherefull presence help to grace,*
   The honest Brydegrome and the basshfull Bryde,
         Whose loves may ever byde.
      Like to the Elme *and* Vyne,
      With mutuall embracementes them to twyne,
      In whiche delightfull payne,
      O *Himen, long theyre Cupled Joyes mentayne.*

Yee Muses *all whiche Chaste effectes allowe,*
  And have to Lalus *shewed youre secrett skill,*
To this Chaste Love your sacred favoures bowe,
  And so to hym and her youre giftes distill,
         That they all Vyce *may kill,*
      And like as Lillyes Pure,
      Do please all eyes and spottles do endure,
      Where, that, all Blisse may Raygne
      O Himen *long theyre Cupled Joyes mentayne.*

Yee Nymphes *whiche in the* Waters *empyres have,*
  Since Lalus *Musick ofte dothe yeelde yo{w} prayse,*
Graunt to the thinge wch we for Lalus *crave*
  Lett one tyme (but longe firste) Close upp theyre dayes,
         One grave theyre bodyes sease
      And like to Rivers *sweete,*
      When they through dyvers do togethers meete,
      One streame bothe streames conteyne,
      O Himen *long theyre Cupled Joyes mentayne.*

Pan, *father* Pan, *the god of silly Sheepe,*
  Whose Care ys Cause that they in nomber growe,
Have muche more Care of them wch them do keepe
  Synce from these good, the others good dothe flowe.
         And make theyre Issue showe,
      In nomber like the hearde,
      Of younglinges wch thy self with love hast reard
      Or like the Droppes of Rayne,
      O Himen *longe theyre Cupled Joyes mentayne.*

ARCADIA

Vertue (*yf not a* God) *yet* Goddes *cheefe parte,*
  Bee thow the Knott of this theyre open vowe,
That still hee bee her heade, shee bee his harte,
  Hee cleave to her, shee unto hym do bowe.
            Eche other still allowe,
        Like Oke *and* Mistelltowe
        Her strength from hym, his prayse from her do growe
        In wch moste Lovely trayne,
        O Himen *long theyre Cupled Joyes mentayne.*

But thow fowle Cupid, *syer, to Lawless lust*
  Bee thow farre hence with thy impoysoned Darte,
Which thoughe of glittering golde shall here take Rust,
  Where simple Love, whiche Chastenes dothe imparte,
           Avoydes the hurtfull Arte
        That needing Charming still,
        Suche myndes wth sweete affections for to kili
        Whiche beeyng pure and playne,
        O Himen *long theyre Cupled Joyes mentayne.*

All Churlish wordes, shrewde answers, Crabbed Lookes,
  All privatenes self seeking Inward spite,
All waywardnes wch nothing kyndely brookes,
  All stryfe for Toyes and Clayming Masters Righte,
           Bee hence ay putt to flighte,
        All sturring Husbandes hate,
        Geanst Neighboures good for womanysh debate
        Bee fledd, as thinges moste vayne,
        O Himen *longe theyre Cupled Joyes mentayne.*

All Peacockes pryde, and frutes of Peacockes pryde,
  Longing to bee with losse of Substance gay,
With Recklessnes what may thy howse betyde,
  So that yowe may on her sure slippers stay
           For ever hence away.
        Yet lett not Sluttery,
        The Sincke of filthe bee Counted huswyfry,
        But keeping wholesome meane,
        O Himen *long theyre Cupled Joyes meyntayne.*

But above all away vyle Jelosy,
  The evill of evills just Cause to bee unjust
Howe can hee Love suspecting Treachery?
    Howe can shee Love where Love can not wynn trust?
            Goo, Snake hyde thee in Dust
            Ne dare once shewe thy face,
            Where open hartes do holde so Constant place,
            That they thy stinge Restrayne,
            O Himen *longe theyre Cupled Joyes mentayne.*

The Earthe *ys deckt with flowers, the* Heavens *displayed,*
  Muses *graunt giftes;* Nymphes *longe and joyned lyfe,*
Pan, *store of Babes,* Vertue *theyre thoughtes well stayde,*
  Cupids *Lust gõn, and, gonn ys bitter stryffe,*
            Happy Man, Happy Wyfe,
            No pryde shall them oppress,
            Nor yet shall yeeld to Lothsome sluttishnes,
            And Jelosy ys slayne,
            For Himen *will theyre Cupled Joyes mentayne.*

Truely *Dicus* (sayde *Nico*) all tho, thow diddest not graunte mee the pryze, the last day, when undoubtedly I wann yt, yet, must I needes say, thow for thy parte, haste sunge well & thriftely : *Pas* streight desyered all the Company they woulde beare witnes, that *Nico* had once in his lyfe spoken wysely, For, saide hee I will tell yt his Father who will bee a glad Man when hee heareth suche Newes. Very trewe sayde *Nico*, but in deede so wolde not thyne in like Case, for hee woulde not thow shouldest live but one hower longer that a discreet worde wandered oute of thy mouthe; And I pray thee (sayde *Pas,*) gentle *Nico*, tell mee what mischaunce yt was that broughte thee to taste so fyne a Meate? Mary goodman Blockhead (sayde *Nico*) bycause hee speakes ageanst Jelosy, the filthy Treytor to true affection, and yet disguysing yt self in the rayment of Love. Sentences Sentences (cryed *Pas*) alas, howe rype witted these younge Folkes bee nowadayes? but, well Counseylled shall that Husband bee, when this Man comes to exhorte hym not to bee Jelous: And so shalle hee, (answered *Nico*) for I have seene a fresh example, though yt bee not very fitt to bee knowne. Come, Come, sayde *Pas*, bee not so sqweymish I knowe thow longest more to tell yt, then wee to heare yt : But, for all his wordes,

232

Nico woulde not bestowe his voyce, till hee was generally in-treated of the Rest, & then with a Mery Mariage Looke hee sange this followynge Discourse, for with a better grace hee coulde singe then tell.

A Neighboure myne, not longe agoo there was,
  (But Nameless hee, for Blameless hee shall bee)
That marryed had a Trick and Bony Lass,
  As in a Somer day a Man mighte see,
    But hee hym self a fowle unhandsome groome,
    And farr unfitt to holde so good a Rowme,

Nowe whether mooved with self unworthynes,
  Or whether Beuty fitt to make a pray,
Fell Jelosy did so his Braynes oppress,
  That yf hee absent were but half a day,
    Hee gest the worst, (yo^w wott what ys the worste)
    And in hym self newe Doubting Causes nurste.

While thus hee fearde, the silly Innocent,
  Who yet, was good, bycause shee knewe none yll,
Unto his Howse a Jolly Shepeheard went,
  To whome oure Prince did beare a great good will,
    Bycause in Wrastling and in Pastorall,
    Hee farr did passe the rest of Shepeherdes all,

And therefore hee a Courtyer was benamed,
  And as a Courtyer was with Chere receyved,
(For they have toungues to make a pore man blamed)
  Yf hee to them his Duety mysconceyved,
    And for this Courtyer shoulde well like this Table,
    The goodman bad his wyfe bee servisable.

And so shee was, and all with good Intent,
  But fewe dayes past, while shee good maners usde,
But that her Husband thought her service bent,
  To suche an ende, as hee mighte bee abusde,
    Yet, like a Coward, fearing Straungers pryde,
    Hee made the simple wenche his worthe abyde.

COUNTESS OF PEMBROOKES

With Clumpish Lookes, harde wordes and secrett Nippes,
  Grumbling at her when shee his kyndenes soughte,
Asking her howe shee tasted Courtyers Lippes,
    Hee forste her thincke, that w*ch* shee never thoughte,
      In fyne yt made her gess there was some sweete,
      In that w*ch* hee so fearde that shee shoulde meete.

When once this entred was in womans harte,
  And that yt had inflamde a newe desyer,
There rested then to play a Womans parte,
    Fwell to seeke, and not to quenche the fyer,
      But, for his Je!ous eye shee well did fynde,
      Shee studyed Cunning, howe the same to blynde.

And thus shee did, one day to hym shee came,
  And (thoughe ageanst his will) on hym shee leande,
And oute gan Crye, ah, well away, for shame,
    Yf yow help not oure Wedlock will bee staynde,
      The goodman starting askte what did her moove,
      She sighed and sayde the bad guest sought her love.

Hee litle looking that shee shoulde Complayne,
  Of that whereto hee fearde shee was enclynde,
Bussing her ofte, and in his harte full fayne,
    Hee did demaunde what Remedy to fynde,
      Howe they might gett that Guest from them to wende,
      And yet the Prince (that loved hym) not offend.

Husband, (quoth shee) goo to hym by and by,
  And tell hym that yow fynde I do hym love,
And therefore pray hym, that of Curtesy,
    Hee will absent hym self least hee shoulde moove,
      A younge Gyrles hart, to that were shame for bothe,
      Whereto, yow knowe, this Honest harte were Lothe,

Thus shall yow shewe, that hym yow doo not Doubte,
  And as for mee, (sweete Husband) I must beare.
Gladd was the Man when hee had hearde her oute,
    And did the same, allthoughe with mickle feare,
      For feare hee did, least hee the young man mighte,
      In Choller putt, with whome hee woulde not feighte.

The Courtly Shepeharde muche agast at this,
   Not seeynge earste suche Token in the wyfe,
Thoughe full of scorne woulde not his Duty miss,
   Knowyng, that evell becomes a Howseholde stryffe
     Did goo his way, but sojournd nere there, by,
     That yet, the grounde therof hee mighte espy,

The wyfe thus having settled Husbandes Brayne,
   Who woulde have sworne his wyfe Diana was,
Watched when shee a furder poynte mighte gayne,
   W^{ch} Litle tyme did fittly bringe to pass,
     For, to the Courte her Man was calde by name,
     Whether hee needes must goo for feare of blame.

Three dayes before that hee must sure departe ;
   Shee written had (but in a hand disguysde)
A Letter suche whiche mighte from eyther parte,
   Seeme to proceede, so well yt was devysde,
     Shee sealled yt first, then shee the sealling brake,
     And to her Jelous husband did yt take.

With weeping eyes, her eyes shee toughte to weepe,
   Shee tolde hym that the Courtyer had yt sent,
Alas (quoth shee) thus woemens shame dothe Creepe.
   The goodman Redd on bothe sydes the Content,
     Yt Tytle had unto my onely Love
     Subscription was youres moste yf yo^w will proove.

The Pistle self suche kynde of wordes yt had,
   My Sweetest Joy the Comfort of my Sprite,
So may thy Flockes encrease, thy deare hart glad,
   So may eche thing (even as thow wisshest) light,
     As thow wilt digne to reede and gently Reede,
     This Mourning Incke in wch my harte dothe bleede.

Longe have I Loved, (alas thow worthy arte,)
   Longe have I Loved (alas Love craveth Love,)
Longe have I Loved thy self (alas my harte)
   Dothe breake, now toungue unto thy Name dothe moove,
     And thincke not that thy answer, answer ys,
     But that yt ys my Doome of Bale or Blisse.

235

COUNTESS OF PEMBROOKES

The Jelous Wretche must nowe to Courte bee gõn,
Ne can hee fayle, for Prince hathe for him sent
Nowe ys the tyme wee may bee here alone,
And give a Longe desyer a sweete Content,
Thus shall yoᵂ bothe rewarde a Lover true,
And eke revenge his wronge suspecting yow.

And this was all and this the Husband Redd,
With Chafe ynoughe, till shee hym pacyfyed,
Desyering that no greefe in hym bee bredd,
Now that hee had her wordes so truely tryed,
But that shee woulde to hym the Letter showe,
That with his faulte hee might her goodnes knowe.

That streight was done, with a many a boysterus threate,
That to the Duke hee woulde his synne declare,
But now the Courtyer gãn to smell the feate,
And with some wordes wᶜʰ shewed litle Care,
Hee stayed untill the goodman was departed,
Then gave hee hym the Blowe wᶜʰ never smarted.

Thus may yow see the Jelous wreche was made,
The Pander of the thinge hee moste did feare,
Take heede therefore, how yoᵂ ensue that trade,
Least that some Marckes of Jelosy yow beare,
For, sure, no Jelosy can that prevent,
Whereto twoo partyes once bee full Content.

Beholde (sayde *Pas*) a whole Dicker of witt, hee hathe pickt
oute suche a Tale, with intention to keepe a husbande frome
Jelosy, (whiche were ynoughe to make a sanctifyed Husbande
Jelous) To see subtiltyes somuche in the feminine gender: But
saide hee, I will stryke *Nico* deade, with the wyse wordes that
flewe oute of my Gorge; and withoute furder Intreaty, thus
sange.

Who, dothe Desyer that Chaste his wyfe shoulde bee,
First, bee hee True, for Truthe, dothe Truthe deserve,
Then suche bee hee, as shee his worthe may see,
And one man still Credit with her preserve,

Not toying kynde, nor Causelesly unkynde,
Not sturring thoughtes, nor yet denying Righte,
Not spying faultes, nor in playne Errors blynde,
Never hard hand, nor never Raynes too lighte.

236

As farr from want, as farr from vayne expense,
  (The one dothe force, the Later dothe entyse)
Allowe good Company, but keeping from thence,
  All filthy Mowthes, that glory in theyre vyce.
    Thus done, thow haste no more, but leave ye Rest,
    To Vertue, Fortune, Tyme *and* Womans *brest.*

Well Concluded, saide *Nico,* when hee hathe done all, hee leaves the Matter to his wyves Discretion ; Nowe when soever thow marryest, let her Deck thy heade with *Acteons* ornament. *Pas* was angry with his Wish, (beeying in deede towardes Maryage) that they mighte perchaunce have fallen to Buffettes. But that *Dicus* (who knew yt was more wisdome to lett a Fraye then parte a Fray), Desyered *Philisides* (who as a Straunger satt amonge them Revollving in his mynde all the Tempestes of evill Fortunes hee had passed) that hee woulde doo somuche grace to all the Company as to singe one of his Contry Songes : *Philisides* knewe yt no good Manners to bee sqweymish of his Cunning, having putt hym self in theyre Company, and yet loathe eyther in tyme of Mariage to singe his Sorowes more fitt for funeralles, or by any owtewarde matter to bee drawne to suche Myrthe, as to betray as yt were that passyon, to wch hee had given over hym self : Hee tooke a meane waye betweene bothe, and sange this Songe hee had learned before, hee had ever subjected his thoughtes to acknowledge no Master but a Mistrys.

As I my litle Flock on Ister Bancke,
  (A Litle Flock, but well my Pype they couthe)
Did pyping Leade, the Sunne allredy sancke,
  Beyonde oure Worlde, and ere I gatt my Boothe,
  Eche thinge with Mantle black, the Night did soothe.
    Saving the Glowe worme *whiche woulde Curteous bee,*
    Of that smalle Lighte ofte watching Sheepeherdes see.

The Wellkyn had full nigardly inclosde,
  In Coffer of Dymme Clowdes his sillver groates,
(Yclipped Starres) eche thing to Rest disposde,
  The Caves were full, the Mountaynes voyde of Goates,
  The Byrdes eyes closde, closde up theyre Chirping Notes,
    As for the Nightingale, wood Musick Kinge,
    (Yt August was) hee daynde not then to singe.

Amydd my Sheepe, thoughe I sawe noughte to feare,
 Yet, (for I no thing sawe) I feared sore,
Then founde I whiche thinge ys a charge to beare,
 For, for my Sheepe I feared mickle more,
 Then ever for my self, synce I was bore,
  I satt mee downe, (for so to goo ne coulde)
  And sange unto my Sheepe, least stray they shoulde.

The Songe I sange oulde Languette *had mee taughte,*
 Languette *the Shepehearde best swifte* Ister *knewe,*
For Clerckly reade, and hating what ys naughte,
 His faythfull harte, Cleane mowthe and handes as trewe,
 With his sweete skill, my skilless youthe hee drewe,
  To have a feeling Taste of hym that sittes,
  Beyonde the Heaven, farre more beyonde oure wittes.

Hee sayde the Musick best thilke Powers pleasde,
 Was Jumpp Concorde betweene oure witt and will,
Where Highest notes to godlynes are Raysde,
 And Lowest sinck not downe to Jott of yll,
 With oulde true Tales hee wonte my eares to fille,
  Howe Shepeherdes did of yore, howe nowe they thryve,
  Spoylling theyre Flock, or while tuixt them they stryve.

Hee lyked mee, butt pittyed Lustfull yowthe,
 His good stronge Staffe my slippery yeares up bore,
Hee still hopte well, bycause I Loved truthe,
 Till forste to parte, with harte and eyes even sore,
 The worthy Coredens *hee gave mee ore,*
  But thus in Okes trewe shade recoumpted hee,
  Whiche now in Nightes deepe shade Sheepe, hearde of mee,

Suche maner tyme there was, what tyme I nott,
 When all this Earthe this Dãm or Moulde of oures,
Was onely won'de with suche as Beastes begott
 Unknowne as then were they that buylden Towers,
 The Cattell wylde or tame in natures Bowers,
  Might freely Ronne, or Rest as seemed them.
  Man was not Man theyre Dwellinges in to hemm,

ARCADIA

The Beastes had sure some Beastly pollicy,
   For, no thinge can Indure where order nys;
For once the Lyon by the Lambe did lye,
   The fearefull Hynde the Leoperd did kisse,
   Hurtles was Tygers pawe, and Serpentes hisse,
     This thincke I well the Beastes with Corage cladd,
     Lyke Senators a harmeles Empire had.

At whiche whether the others did repyne,
   (For Envye harboureth moste in feeblest hartes)
Or that they all to Chaunging did enclyne,
   (As even in Beastes theyre Dāmes leave Chaunging partes)
The Multitude to Jove a Sute impartes,
     With Naying, Blaying, Braying and Barking,
     Roaring and Howling, for to have a Kinge.

A Kinge, in Language theyres they sayde they woulde,
   (For then theyre Language was a perfect speeche)
The Byrdes likewyse with Chirpes and pyinge coulde,
   Chackling and Chattering that of Jove beseeche,
   Onely the Owle warnde them not to seeche
     So hastely that, whiche they woulde Repent
     But, sawe they woulde, and hee to Dezertes went.

Jove, wysely sayde, (For wysdome wysely sayes)
   O Beastes take heede what yow of mee desyer,
Rulers will thincke all thinges made them to please,
   And soone forgett the Swincke Due to theyre hyer,
   But, (synce yow will) parte of my Heavenly fyer,
     I will yow lende, The Rest youre selves must give,
     That yt bothe seene and felt may with yow live.

Full glad they were, and tooke the Naked Sprite,
   Whiche streight the earthe yclothed in his Clay,
The Lyon, Harte, the Ounce gave active Mighte,
   The Horse good shape, The Sparrow Lust to play,
   Nightingale voyce, entysing Songes to say,
     Elephant gave a perfect memory,
     And Parret redy toungue that to apply.

COUNTESS OF PEMBROOKES

The Foxe gave Crafte, the Dogg gave flattery,
  Asse, patience, the Moulle a worcking thoughte,
Ægle hye Looke, Wolffe secrett Crewelty,
  Monkye sweete Breathe, the Cowe her fayre eyes broughte,
  The Ermion whitest skynne spotted with noughte.
    The Sheepe mylde seeming face, Clyming the Beare,
    The Stagg did give the harme eschewing feare.

The Beare her sleightes the Catt his Melancholy,
  Ante Industry, and Cony skill to buylde,
Cranes Order, Storckes to bee apearing Holy,
  Cameleon ease to Chaunge, Duck ease to yeelde,
  Crockadile teares whiche mighte bee falsly speelde,
    Ape greate thinge gave, thoughe hee did mooving stand,
    The Instrument of Instrumentes the hand.

Eche other Beast lykewyse his present bringes,
  And (but they Drad theyre Prince they ofte should want,)
They all Consented were to give hym winges,
  And ay more Awe towardes hym for to plante,
  To theyre owne Worcke this priviledg they graunte,
    That from thence forthe to all eternity,
    No Beaste shoulde freely speake, but onely hee.

Thus Man was made, thus Man theyre Lorde became,
  Who at the first wanting or hyding pryde,
Hee did to Beastes best use his Cunning frame,
  With water, Drincke, herbes, meate, and naked hyde,
  And Fellowlyke lett his Dominyon slyde,
    Not in his sayinge (saying I.) but Wee.
    As yf hee ment his Lordshipp Comõn bee.

But when his seate so Rooted hee had founde,
  That they now skilde not, howe from hym to wende,
Then gan in giltles Earthe full many a wounde,
  Iron to seeke, whiche ageanst yt self shoulde bende,
  To teare the Bowells that good Corne should sende,
    But yet the Comõn Damñ none did bemone,
    Bycause (thoughe hurt) they never heard her grone.

240

Then gañ hee factions in the Beastes to breede,
  Where helping weyker sorte, the Nobler Beastes,
As Tygres, Leoperdes, Beares and Lyons seede,
  Disdaynd with this in Dezertes soughte theyre Restes,
  Where famyn, Raven, toughte theyre hongry Chestes,
    Thus Craftely hee forced them to do yll,
    Whiche beeyng done hee afterwardes woulde kill.

For Murder done, whiche never earst was seene,
  By those greate Beastes, as for the weykers good,
Hee Chose them selves his Guarders for to bee,
  Geanst those of mighte of whome in feare they stood,
  As Horse and Dogg not greate but gentle blood,
    Blythe were the Comõns Cattle of the Feelde,
    Tho, when they sawe theyre Foen of greatnes kilde.

But, they or spent, or made of sclender mighte,
  Then quickly did theyre meaner Cattell fynde,
The greate Beames goñ the Howse on shoulders lighte,
  For by and by, the Horse fayre Bittes did bynde,
  The Dogg was in a Collar toughte his kynde,
    As for the gentle Byrdes like Case mighte Rewe,
    When Faulcon they and Gosshauke sawe in Mewe.

Worste fell to smallest Byrdes, and meanest Hearde,
  Who now his owne full like his owne hee usde,
Yet first but woolle, or Fethers of hee tearde,
  And when they were well usde to bee abusde,
  For hongry Throate theyre flessh with Teethe hee brusde
    At Lengthe for glutton taste hee did them kill,
    At last for sporte theyre silly Lyves did spill.

But, yet, O Man, Rage not beyond thy neede,
  Deeme yt no prayse to swell in Tyranny,
Thow arte of Blood, Joye not to make thinges bleede.
  Thow fearest Deathe, thincke they are loathe to dye
  A Playnte of guiltles Hurte dothe pearse the skye,
    And yow pore Beastes in pacyence byde youre hell,
    Or know youre strengthes and then yow shall doo well.

241

Thus did I singe and pype Eighte solempne howers,
  To Sheepe whome Love, not knowledge made to heare,
Now Fancyes Fittes, now Fortunes balefull stowers.
  But then I homeward Calde my Lambkyns Dere,
  For to my Dymmed Eyes began to appeare,
    The Night, growne oulde, her Black heade waxen graye
    Sure Sheepeheardes signe, that Morne woulde soone fetch day.

Finis.

According to the Nature of dyvers Eares, dyvers Judgmentes streight followed, some praysing his voyce, others the wordes, Fitt, to frame a Pastorall style, others the straungenes of the Tale, and scanning what hee shoulde meane by yt: But oulde *Geron* who had borne hym a grudge, eeven synce in one of theyre *Eglogues* hee had taken hym upp over bitterly, tooke holde of this occasyon to make his Revenge. And sayde hee never sawe thing worse proportioned, then to bringe in a Tale of hee knewe not what Beastes at suche a Banquett when rather some Songe of Love or matter for Joyfull melody was to bee broughte forthe: But (sayde hee) this ys the Right Conceypt of a younge Man, thincke then they speake wyselyest when they can not understand them selves: Then invited hee *Histor* to answer hym in Eglogue wyse, who in deede having beene longe in Love wth the fayre Bryde *Kala*, and nowe prevented, was growen into a Detestation of Mariage, but thus yt was.

              Geron.   Histor.

Geron.   *In faythe good* Histor, *Longe ys youre delay,*
              Frome Holly Mariage, sweete and surest meane,
          Oure Foolish Lustes in Honest Rules to stay,
              I pray thee doo to Lalus *sample leane,*
              Thow seest how friske and Jolly nowe hee ys,
              That last day seemd hee coulde not chewe a Beane.

          Beleeve mee, Man, there ys no greater Blisse,
              Then ys the quyet Joy of Loving wyffe,
          Whiche who so wantes, half of hym self dothe mysse
              Frende withoute Change, Playfellow withoute stryfe,
              Foode withoute fullnes, Counsell withoute stryfe,
              Ys this sweete Dubling of oure single Lyfe.

Histor.   *No Doubte to whome so good Chance did betyde,*
    As for to fynde a Pasture strewde with golde,
  Hee were a Foole yf there hee did not byde,
    Who woulde not have a Phenix *yf hee coulde,*
  The Humming Wasp yf yt had not a Stinge,
    Before all Flees the Wasp accept I woulde,
  But this Bad worlde fewe golden Feeldes dothe bringe,
    Phenix *but one, of* Crowes *wee Millyons fynde,*
  The Wasp seemes gay, but ys a Comberus thinge.

Yf many Kalas *oure* Arcadia *gave,*
  Lalus *example I woulde soone ensue,*
And thincke I did my self from sorowe save,
  But of suche wyves wee fynde a sclender Crewe,
  Shrewdnes so sturres, Pryde *so puffes up theyre hart*
  They syldome ponder what to them ys due.

With Maigre Lookes, as yf they still did smarte,
  Pewling and whimpering or else scoulding flatt
Make home more payne then following of the Carte
  Eyther dull sylence, or Eternall Chatt.
Still Contrary to what her Husband sayes,
  Yf hee do prayse the Dogg, shee likes the Catt,
  Auster shee ys when hee woulde honest playes.
And gamesome then when hee thinckes on his Sheepe,
  She biddes hym goo, and yet from Journey stayes,
Shee warre dothe ever with his kinsfolke keepe,
  And makes them fremd, who frendes by Nature are,
Envying shallowe Toyes with Mallys Deepe,
  And yf forsoothe there come some newfounde ware,
  The Litle Coyne his sweating browes hathe gott,
Must goo for that, yf for her Love hee Care,
  Or else, nay faythe, myne ys the Luckless Lott,
That ever fell to honest woman, yett,
  No wyfe but I have suche a Man god wott,
Suche ys theyre speeche, who bee of sober witt,
  But who dothe lett theyre toungues shew well theyre
    Rage,
Lorde what by wordes they speake, what spyte they
  spitt.

The howse ys made a very loathsome Cage,
   Wherein the Byrde dothe never singe but Crye,
With suche a Will that no thinge can asswage,
   Dearely the Servauntes do theyre wages bwye
Revylde for eche smalle faulte, some tyme for none,
   They better Live, that in a Gayle doo lye,
Lett other fowler spottes away bee blowne,
   For I seeke not theyre shame, but still mee thinckes
   A better Lyfe yt ys to live alone.

[Geron.] Who for eche fickle feare from vertue shrinckes,
   Shalle in this lyfe embrace no worthy thinge,
No mortall Man the Cupp of Surety drinckes,
   The Heavens doo not good happes in Handfulles
   bringe,
But let us pick oute good from oute muche badd,
   That still oure litle worlde may knowe his kinge,
But certenly so longe wee may bee glad,
   While that wee doo what nature dothe requyer,
And for the event wee never oughte bee sadd,
   Man ofte ys plaigued wth ayer, ys burnte wth fyer,
In water Drownde, in earthe his Buryall ys,
   And shall wee not therefore theyre use desyer,
Nature above all thinges requyreth this,
   That wee oure kynde do Laboure to meyntayne
Whiche drawne oute Lyne, dothe holde all humane
   blisse.

Thy Father justly may of thee Complayne,
   Yf thow doo not repay his deedes for thee,
In graunting unto hym a Graundsyers gayne,
   Thy Comon wealthe may Rightly greeved bee
Whiche must by this Immortall bee preserved,
   Yf thus thow murder thy posterity,
His very beeyng hee hathe not deserved,
   Who for a self Conceipt will that forbeare,
Whereby that beeyng ay must bee Conserved,
   And God forbidd woemen suche Cattell were,
As yow paynte them. But, well in yow I fynde,
   No man dothe speake arighte, who speakes in feare,

Who onely sees the evill ys worse then blynde,
These Fifty winters marryed I have beene,
And yet fynde no suche faultes in Womankynde,
I have a Wyfe worthy to bee a Queene,
So well shee can Comaunde, and yet, obay,
In Ruling of a Howse so well shee ys seene,
And yet in all this tyme betwixt us Tway,
Wee beare oure Duble yock with suche Consent
There never past fowle worde, I dare well say,
But these are youre Love toyes wch still are spent
In Lawless games, and Love not as yo^w shoulde,
But with muche study learne late to Repent,
Howe well last day before youre Prince yo^w coulde,
Blynde Cupids *worckes with wonder testify,*
Yet nowe the Roote of hym abase yo^w woulde,
Goo too Goo too and Cupid *now applye,*
To that where thow thy Cupid *mayste avowe,*
And thow shalte fynde in woemen vertues lye,
Sweete supple myndes wch soone to wisdome bowe,
Where they by wisdomes Rules directed are;
And yet not forst fonde Thraldome to allowe,
As wee to gett are framed, so they to spare,
Wee made for paynes, they made oure paynes to cherish,
Wee care abroade, and they of home have Care,
O Histor, *seeke within thy self to Florishe,*
Thy Howse by thee must Live or else bee gone,
And then who shall the name of Histor *norishe?*
Riches of Children passe a Princes *throane,*
Whiche touche the Fathers harte with secrett Joy,
When withowte shame hee saythe these bee myne owne.
Marry therefore, for Marryage will Destroy,
Those passyons wch to youthfull hedd do Clyme,
Mothers and Nurses of all vayne Annoy.

Histor.   *Perchaunce, I will, but, nowe mee thinckes yt tyme,*
Wee goo unto the Bryde, and use this day,
To speake with her, while freely speake wee may.

Hee spake these last wordes with suche affection, as a
Curyous eye mighte easely have perceyved hee liked *Lalus*
fortune better then hee Loved his person; But then in deede

did all aryse and went to the woemen, where spending all the Daye and good parte of the nighte in Daunsing, Carrolling, and Wassalling, lastly they left *Lalus* where hee longe desyered to bee lefte, and with many unfayned thankes returned every Man to his home: But some of them having to Crosse the way of the twoo Lodges, mighte see a Lady making dolefull Lamentatyon over a Body seemed Deade unto them. But mee thinckes *Dametas* cryes unto mee, yf I come not the sooner to Comfort hym, hee will Leave of his golden worcke, hathe allredy Cost hym somuche Laboure and Longing.

Here ende The Thirde Booke
and Thirde Eglogues.

The Fourthe Booke or Acte.

THE Everlasting Justice (using oure selves to bee the punisshers of oure faultes, and making oure owne actions the beginninge of oure Chastisement, that oure shame may bee the more manifest, and oure Repentance followe the sooner,) tooke *Dametas* at this present (by whose folly the others wysdome mighte receyve the greater overthrowe) to bee the instrument of reveyling the secrettst Connyng: So evill a grounde dothe evell stande uppon, and so manifest yt ys, that no thing Remaynes strongly, but that whiche hathe the good foundacyon of goodnes. For, so yt fell oute, that *Dametas* having spent the whole day in breaking up the Combersome worcke of the Pastor *Dorus*, and feeling in all his Laboure no payne somuche as that his hongry hope receyved any stay: Having with the pryce of muche sweate and wearynes gotten upp the huge Stone, whiche hee thoughte shoulde have suche a golden lyning, the good man (in the greate Bedd that stone had made) founde no thinge but these twoo verses written uppon a broade peece of velume,

Who hathe hys Hyer, hathe Well his Laboure plaste,
Earthe thow doste seeke and store of Earthe thow haste.

What an Inward Discountenance yt was to Master *Dametas*, to fynde his hope of wealthe turned into pore verses (for wᶜʰ hee never Cared muche) no thing can describe, but eyther the Feeling in ones self, the state of suche a mynde as *Dametas* had, or at least the thinckyng what was *Mydas* fancy, when (after the greate pryde hee conceyved to bee made Judge betuixt Goddes) hee was rewarded wᵗʰ the Ornament of an Asse eares: Yet the Deepe apprehension hee had receyved of suche Riches, coulde not sodenly lose the Cullor, that had so throwly dyed his thick brayne, but that hee turned and tossed the pore Bowells of the Innocent earthe, till the farr passing of the Night, and the tedyousnes of his fruitles Laboure made hym content, rather to exercyse his Discontentacyon at home, then there. Yet forced hee was, (his horse beeyng otherwyse burdened) with digging Instrumentes to returne, as hee came, moste parte of the way, on Foote: with suche grudging Lamentacyons, as a Nobler Mynde woulde (but more nobly) make for the Losse of his Mistris: For so farr hee had his foolish sowle, with the expectatyon of that whiche hee reputed felicity, that hee no less accompted hym self miserable then yf hee had falne from suche an estate his fancy had embrased. So then home ageane went *Dametas* punished in Conceipt, as in Conceipt hee had erred, till hee had founde hym self there from a fancyed Losse falne into an essentiall misery: For entering into his howse three howers wthin nighte, (in steade of the Lightsome Countenance of *Pamela* wch gave suche an Inward decking to that lodge, as proudest pallaces mighte have cause to envy yt, and of the gratefull Conversation of *Dorus*, whose witty behavyour made that Lonelynes seeme full of good Company) in steade of the lowde scoulding of *Miso* and the buysy tumbling up and downe of *Mopsa* (whiche thoughe they were so shorte as quyte Contrary to the others prayse worthynes, yet were they farr before them in filling of a howse) hee founde no thinge but a solitary Darckenes (whiche as naturally yt breedes a kynde of yrcksome gastfullnes, so yt was to him a moste present terror) remembring the Charge hee had lefte behynde, whiche hee well knewe imported no less then his Lyfe unto hym. Therefore Lighting a Candle there was no place a Mouse coulde have dwelled in, but, that hee with quaking diligence soughte into, but when hee sawe, (hee coulde see no thing of that hee moste Cared for) then became hee the Right Paterne of a wretche dejected, with feare, for Crying and howling, knocking his heade to ye walles hee began to make pittyfull Complayntes where no body coulde heare hym: And with too muche Dread hee shoulde not recover her leave all Consideracyons howe to recover her. But at lengthe looking lyke a Shee gote, when shee castes her Kydd for very sorowe hee tooke in his owne behalf, oute of the Lodge hee went ronning as fast as hee coulde having now Receyved the very forme of hanging into his Consideracyon: Thus ronning as a man that woulde have ronne from hym self, yt was his foolish fortune, to espy by the glimmering Lighte the Moone did then yeelde hym, one standing alofte amonge the Bowghes of a fayre Ashe. Hee that woulde at that tyme have asked Counsell of a Dogg, Cast up his face, as yf his toothe had beene Drawyng oute, and wth muche bending his sighte, hee perceyved

248

yt was Mistris *Mopsa*, fittly seated there for her witt and dignity: There, (I will not say wth Joy, for howe coulde hee taste of Joy, whose Imaginacyon was fallen from a Pallace to a gallowes) but yet with some Refresshing of Comforte in hope hee shoulde learne better tydinges over, hee began to Crye oute, O *Mopsa* my beloved Chickyn here am I thyne owne Father *Dametas*, never in suche a towardnes to hanging, yf thow can not help mee. But never a worde coulde his Eloquence procure of *Mopsa*, who in deede was there attending for greate matters: This was yet a newe Burden to *Dametas* who thought all the worlde was conspired ageanst hym, and therefore with a silly Choller hee began an other Tune. Thow vyle *Mopsa* saide hee now the vengeance of my Fatherly Curse light overthwart thee yf thow doo not streighte answer mee: But neyther blessing nor Cursing coulde prevayle with *Mopsa*, who was nowe greate with Chylde wth thexpectation of her May game hopes, and did longe to bee delivered, with the thirde tyme beeyng named, wch by and by followed. For *Dametas* rubbing his ellbowe, stampping, and whyning, seeying neither of these take place began to throwe stones at her, and with all to Conjure her by the Name of Hellish *Mopsa*: But, when hee had named her the thirde tyme, No Chyme can more sodenly follow the stryking of a Clock, then shee (verily thinckking yt was the God that used her Fathers voyce, throwyng her armes abrode, and not Considering shee was muffled uppon so hye a Tree) came fluttering downe like a hooded Hawke, like enough to have broken her neck, but that the Tree full of Bowghes, tost her from one Boughe to an other, and lastly well bruysed brought her to receyve an unffrendly salutatyon of the Earthe.

Dametas, assoone, as shee was Downe came Ronning unto her, and fynding her so Close wrapt pulde of the scarlett Cloake in good tyme for her, for with the sorenes of the Falle, yf shee had not had breathe given her, shee had delivered a Foolish sowle to *Pluto*; But then *Dametas* began a fressh to desyer his Daughter, not to forgett the paynes hee had taken for her in her Chyldehoode (wch hee was sure shee coulde not remember) and to tell hym where *Pamela* was. O good *Appollo* sayde *Mopsa*, yf ever thow didst beare Love to *Phaetons* Mother, Lett mee have a kinge to my husband? Alas, what speakest thow of *Phaeton* sayde *Dametas*, yf by thy Circumspect meanes I fynde not oute *Pamela*, thy Father will bee hanged to morowe: It ys no matter thoughe hee bee hanged sayde *Mopsa*, doo but thow make *Dorus* a Kinge and lett hym bee my husband, good *Appollo*, for my Corage dothe muche prick mee towardes hym. Ah *Mopsa* cryed oute *Dametas* where ys thy witt doest thow not knowe thy Father? haste thow forgotten thy self? I do not aske witt of thee myne owne good *Appollo* sayde shee, but I see thow wouldest have mee Remember my Father, and in deede forgett my self; No, no, a good husband. Thow shalte have thy fill of Husbandes saide *Dametas*, and do but answer mee my questyon. O I thancke thee sayde *Mopsa* with all my hart hartely, but lett them bee all Kinges. *Dametas* seeyng no other way prevayle, fell downe on his knees, *Mopsa*, *Mopsa* sayde hee doo not thus cruelly torment mee? I am allredy wretched ynoughe, alas eyther help mee, or tell mee thow canst not: Shee that woulde [not] bee behynde *Appollo* in Curtisy, kneeled downe on the other syde, I will never leave tormenting thee (sayde *Mopsa*) untill thow haste satisfyed my Longing, but I will proclayme thee a promyse breaker: that even *Jupiter* shall heare yt. Nowe, by the Fostering thow haste receyved in this place, save my Lyfe saide *Dametas*: Nowe by this fayre Ashe (answered *Mopsa*) where thow didest receyve so greate a good turne, graunte poste haste to my burning fancy? O where ys *Pamela*, sayde *Dametas*? O a Lusty husband sayde *Mopsa*: *Dametas* that now verely assured hym self his Daughter was madd, began utterly to dispayre of his Lyfe, and therefore amazed, catching her in his Armes, to see whether hee coulde bringe her to her self, Hee mighte feele the weighte of a great Cudgell light uppon his shoulders: And for his first greeting hee knewe his wyfe *Misos* voyce, by the Calling hym Ribalde, villayne, and asking hym whether shee coulde not serve his turne aswell as *Charita*. For, *Miso* having according to *Dorus* Counsell goñ to *Mantinea*, and there harboured her self in an olde acqueyntance howse of hers assoone as Tenñ of the Clock was striken where shee had remayned Cloasely all that while, I thinck with suche an amiable Chere as when Jelous *Juno* satt Crosslegged to hynder the Chyldesbirth of her Husbandes Love: with open mowthe shee went to the Magistrate appoynted over suche matters, and there withe the moste scoulding Invective her Rage rather then Eloquence coulde bringe forthe, shee requyred his ayde to take *Dametas*. Who had lefte his Duty to the *Duke* and Daughter, to Committ adultery in ye howse of *Charitas* unckle in the *Oudemaine* streete: But neyther was the name of *Charita* remembred, nor any suche streete knowne, yet suche was the generall myslike all men had of *Dametas* unworthy advauncement, that every man was glad to make hym self a Minister of that wch mighte redounde to his shame. Therefore with *Panns* Cryes and Laughters there was no suspected place in all the City but was searched for under the Tytle of *Dametas*; *Miso* ever Foremoste encoraging them wth all the shamefull blasinges of his Demeynor, encreasing the sporte of hunting her Husband with her diligent barcking. Till at lengthe, having done bothe hym and her self asmuche infamus shame, as suche a toungue in suche an action mighte performe, in the ende (not beeyng able to fynde the thinge that was not) to her Mare ageane shee went, having neyther suspicyon nor Rage any thing mitigated. But, (Leaving behynde her a sufficyent Comedy of her Tragicall Fancyes) away homewarde shee came, Imputing the not fynding her Husband rather to any Chaunce, then to his Innocency. For her hart beyng apt to receyve and norish a bitter thoughte, yt had so swallowed up a determeyned Condempnatyon, that in the very Anatomy of her Spirites one shoulde have founde no thing but Develish disdayne, and hatefull Jelosy: In this sorte grunting at her Mischeevous spyte, shee came by the Tree, even as *Dametas* was making that evill understood intercession to his foolish *Mopsa*. Assoone as shee hearde her husbandes voyce, shee verily thoughte shee had her pray, and therefore stealling from her Mare as softly as shee coulde, shee came creeping and halting behynde hym; Eeven as hee (thincking his Daughters litle wittes had quyte lefte her greate Nowle) begañ to take her in his Armes, thincking perchaunce her feeling sence mighte calle her mynde partes unto her. But *Miso*, who sawe no thing but thorow the Choller of Revengefull anger established uppon the forejudgment of his trespas (undoutedly Resolving that *Mopsa* was *Charita*) *Dorus* had tould her of, mamping oute her hoarse voyce, shee gave hym the wooden salutatyon yow hearde of: *Dametas*, that was not so sensible in any thinge, as in Blowes, turned up his blubberd face like a Lowte new whipte, Alas, thow woman (sayde hee) what hathe thy pore Husband deserved, to have his owne yll Luck loaden with thy Displeasure? *Pamela*, ys lost, *Pamela* ys lost. *Miso* (still holding on the Course of her former fancy) what tellest thow mee, naughty varlett (sayde shee) of *Pamela*? Doest thow thincke that dothe answer mee for abusing the Lawes of Maryage? Have I brought thee Children? have I beene a true wyfe to thee, to bee despysed in myne owlde age? And ever amonge shee woulde sawse her speeches with suche Bastynades, that pore *Dametas* begañ now to thincke, that eyther a generall Madding was fallen, or else that all this was but a vision: But, as for visyons the smarte of the Cudgell, putt those oute of his fancy. And therefore, ageane turning to his wyffe, not knowyng in the worlde, what shee mente, *Miso*, (sayde hee) Hereafter thow mayest examen mee, Doo but now tell mee, what ys become of *Pamela*? I will first examen this Drabbe (sayde shee) and withall lett fall her staff as hard as shee coulde uppon *Mopsa*, still taking her for *Charita*: But *Mopsa*, that was all redy angry (thincking shee had hyndered her from *Appollo*) lepte up and caughte her by the throate, like to have strangled her, but that *Dametas* from a Condempned man was fayne to become a Judge and parte this Fray, suche a picture of a Rude Discorde, where eche was oute with the other twoo. And getting the oportunity of theyre falling oute, to houlde hym self in surety (who was in deede the veryest Coward of the three) hee Renewed his earnest demaunde of them. But yt was a sporte to see, howe the former Conceiptes *Dorus* had imprinted in theyre Imaginacyons kept still suche a Dominion in them, that *Miso* (thoughe shee now founde and felt yt was her Daughter *Mopsa*) yet did *Charita* continually pass throughe her thoughtes: wch shee uttered with suche Crabbed questyons to *Dametas*, that, hee (not possible conceyving any parte of her doubte) remayned astonisshed, and the astonishment encreased her Doubte. And as for *Mopsa*, as shee had first assuredly taken hym to bee *Appollo*, and thought her Mothers Coming did marre ye bargayne, so nowe (thoughe muche talking to and fro had delyvered somuche Lighte into the mysty moulde of her Capacity, as to knowe hym to bee her Father) yet, remayned there suche footestepps of the fore taken oppinyon, that shee thought verily her Father and her Mother were hasted thether to gett the first wissh: And therefore to what soever they asked of her, shee woulde never answer, but, embrasinge the Tree, as yf shee feared yt had beene ronning away; Nay sayes shee, I will have the first wish, for, I was firste here. Whiche they understoode no more then *Dametas* did what *Miso* ment by *Charita*. Till at lengthe with muche urging them (beeyng in deede better able to perswade bothe, then to meete hande to hande with eyther) hee prevayled somuche with them, as to bringe them into the Lodge, to see what losse theyre negligence had suffered. Then in deede, the nere Neighbourehed they bare to them selves, made them leave theyre Toyes and looke into what Daungerus plighte they were falne, as soone as the *Duke* shoulde knowe his Daughters escape: And as for yᵉ woemen they began to enter a Fresh into theyre brawling, whether were in the faulte, But *Dametas* who did feare that (amonge his other evills, the thunderbolte of that storme woulde falle upon his shoulders) slipte away from them, and with so maigre a chere as mighte muche sooner engender laughter then pitty, O true *Arcadia* woulde hee say, (tearing his hayer and berde, and some tyme for too muche woo making unwyldy somersaultes) how darest thow beare upon thee suche a fellonyous Traytor as I am? And yoʷ falseharted Trees, why woulde yow make no Noyse, to make her ungracyous departure knowne? O *Pamela*, *Pamela*, howe often, (When I broughte thee in fyne Poesyes of all Coloured flowers) wouldst thow clapp mee on the Cheeke and say, thow wouldest bee one day eeven with mee? Was this thy meaning to bringe mee to an eeven payre of gallowes? Ah yll toughte *Dorus* that came hether, to learne good manners of mee, did I ever teache thee to make thy Master sweate oute his harte for nothinge? and in the meane tyme ronne away with thy Mistris? O my Dunn Cowe I did thincke some evill was towardes mee ever synce the last day thow didst ronne away from mee, and holde up thy tayle so pityously: Did not I see an Egle kill a Cuckowe whiche was a playne foretoken unto mee *Pamela* shoulde bee my destruction? O wyfe *Miso*, yf I durst say yt to thy face, why diddest thow suspect thy husband that loves a peece of Cheese better then a woman? And, thow litle *Mopsa* that shalte inherite the shame of thy Fathers Deathe, was yt tyme for thee to clyme Trees, wᶜʰ shoulde so shortly bee my best buryall? O that I coulde live withoute Deathe, or dye, before I were aware? O harte, why haste thow no handes at Comaundement to dispatche mee? O handes why want yoᵂ a hart to kill this villayne? In this sorte did hee Invey ageanst every thing some tymes thincking to ronne away, whyle yt was yet nighte: But hee that had included all the worlde within his Sheepehooke, thought that worse then any Deathe, some tymes for Dreade of hanging, hee went to hange hym self, (fynding (as in Deede yt ys) that feare ys farr more paynfull to Cowardes, then Deathe to a true Corage.) But his fingers were no thing nimble in that action, and any thinge was lett ynoughe thereunto, hee beeyng a true Lover of hym self withoute any Ryvall: But lastly guyded by a farr greater Constellatyon then his owne, hee remembred to searche the other Lodge where yt mighte bee, *Pamela* that nighte had retyred her self. So thether with trembling hammes hee Carrying hym self, but (employing his Duble key wᶜʰ the *Duke* for speciall Credit had unworthely bestowed uppon hym) hee founde all the Gates so barred that his key woulde not prevayle: Saving onely one Trapp dore whiche went downe into a vaulte by the seller, whiche as yt was lefte unknowne of *Pyrocles*, so had hee lefte yt ungarded. But, *Dametas* that ever knewe the Buttery better then any place, gott in that way, and pasing softely to *Philocleas* Chamber (where hee thoughte moste likely to fynde *Pamela*) the Dore beeyng lefte open, hee entered in, and by the Lighte of the Lampe hee mighte discerne one a bedd with her: whiche (allthoughe hee tooke to bee *Pamela*) yet, thincking no surety enoughe in a matter tuching his neck, hee went hard to the Bedsyde of those twoo unfortunate Lovers. Who at that tyme, beeyng not muche before the Breake of day (whether yt were, they were so by fore apoyntment surprysed to bringe theyre faulte to open punishment, or that the too hye degree of theyre Joyes had overthrowne yᵉ wakefull use of theyre sences, or that theyre sowle lifted up wᵗʰ extremity of Love after mutuall satisfaction had lefte theyre bodyes derely joyned; to unite them selves together, so muche more freely as they were freer of that earthly prison, or what so ever other Cause mighte bee Imagined of yt) but, so yt was, that they were, as then possessed with a mutuall sleepe, yet not forgetting with vyny embrasementes to give any eye a perfect modell of affection. But, *Dametas* looking with the Lampe in his hande (but neyther with suche a face nor mynde) uppon these excellent Creatures (as *Psiche* did uppon her unknowne Lover) and giving every way freedome to his fearefull eyes, did not onely perceyve yt was *Cleophila*, (and therefore muche different from the Lady hee soughte) but that this same *Cleophila* did more differ from the *Cleophila* hee and others had ever taken her for : Satisfyed with that, and not thincking yt good to awake ye sleeping Lyon, hee went downe ageane, taking with hym *Pyrocles* sworde (wherewith uppon his shirte *Pyrocles* came onely apparelled thether) beeyng sure to leave no weapon in the Chamber (and so making the Dore as fast as hee coulde on the owtesyde) Hoping with the Reveyling of this faulte, to make his owne ye less or at least that this Injury woulde so fill the *Dukes* heade, y^t hee shoulde not have Leysure to chastize his negligence ; Lyke a Foole, (not Considering that the more Rage breedes the Crueller punishment) hee went first into the *Dukes* Chamber, and not fynding hym there, hee rañn downe crying with open mowthe the *Duke* was betrayed, and that *Cleophila* did abuse his Daughter: The noyse hee made (beeyng a man of no fewe wordes) joyned with the yelping sounde of *Miso* and his unpleasant Inheritrixe, broughte together some nomber of the Shepeheardes. To whome hee (withoute any Regarde of first Reserving yt for the *Dukes* knowledge) spattered oute the Bottome of his stomack, swearing by hym hee never knewe y^t *Cleophila* (whome they had taken all that while to bee a Woman) was as arrant a Man as hym self was, whereof hee had seene sufficyent signes and tokens, and that hee was as Close as a Butter Flee with the Lady *Philoclea*. The pore men Jelous of theyre Princes Honoure, were redy with weapons to have entred the Lodge, standing yet in some pawse, whether yt were not best to heare some newes of the *Duke* hym self : when by the sodayne Coming of other Shepeheardes, whiche with astonisshed lookes rann from one Crye to the other, theyre greefes were surcharged with the evell tydinges of the *Dukes* deathe. Turning therefore all theyre eyes & myndes that way, they rañn to the Cave where they sayde hee lay deade: The Sunne beginning now to sende some promyse of his Cominge Lighte, making haste (as I thinke) to bee *Spectator* of the followyng tragedyes. But of *Basilius*, thus yt had fallen oute, the *Duke* having past over the nighte more happy in Contemplacyon then action, (having had his spirites sublimed with the sweete Imagination of embracing the moste desyered

Cleophila) Doubting least the Caves Darcknes mighte deceyve hym in the dayes approche, thought yt now season to returne to his wedlock bedd, remembring ye promyse hee had made *Cleophila* to observe true order towardes *Gynecia*. Therefore departing, but not departing withoute bequeathing by a will, of wordes sealled with many kisses (a full gifte of all his Love and Lyfe to his mysconceyved Bedfellowe) hee went to ye mouthe of the Cave, there to apparrell hym self, in whiche doynge, the motyon of his Joye coulde not bee brydeled, from uttering suche like wordes. Blessed bee thow O Nighte sayde hee that haste with thy sweete winges shrowded mee in the vale of blisse? Yt ys thow that arte the first begotten Chylde of tyme, the day hathe beene but an usurper upon thy delightfull inheritance? Thow invitest all Living things to Comfortable Rest, thow arte the stopp of stryfe, and the necessary Truce of approching Battells: And therewith hee sange these verses, to Confirme his former prayses.

> *O Nighte the ease of Care the pledge of pleasure,*
> *Desyers best meane, Harvest of Hartes affected,*
> *The seate of peace, the Throne whiche ys erected,*
> *Of humane Lyfe to bee the quyett Measure.*
> *Bee Victor still of* Phebus *golden Treasure.*
> *Who hathe oure sighte, with too muche sight infected,*
> *Whose Lighte ys Cause wee have oure Lyves neglected,*
> *Turning all* Natures *Course to self displeasure.*
> *These stately starres in theyre now shyning faces,*
> *With slyly sleepe and Silence Wisdomes Mother,*
> *Witness his wronge whiche by thy help ys eased,*
> *Thow arte therefore of these oure Dezert places,*
> *The sure Refuge by thee, and by none other.*
> *My sowle ys blist, sence joyed, and fortune raysed.*

And yet, furder woulde his Joy needes breake forthe; O *Basilius* saide hee the rest of thy lyfe tyme hathe bene but a Dreame unto thee, yt ys now onely thow begynnes to live, nowe onely thow haste entered into the way of blisfullnes? Shoulde fancy of Mariage keepe mee from this Paradyse, or opinion of I knowe not what promyse bynde mee from paying the righte Dutyes of nature and affection? O who woulde have thoughte there coulde have bene suche difference betwixt women? Bee not

Jelous no more, good *Gynecia*? but yeelde to the preheminence of more excellent giftes? support thy self uppon suche marble pillers as shee dothe? Deck thy brest with those Alablaster bowells that *Cleophila* dothe: Then accompanyed with suche a litle perhapps thow mayste recover the possession of my other-wyse included Love. But alas *Gynecia*, thow canst not shewe suche evidence, therefore thy Plea ys vayne. *Gynecia* hearde all this hee sayde, who had Cast aboute her *Cleophilas* garment, (wherein shee came thether, and had followed *Basilius* even to the Caves entry) full of Inward vexation betuixt the Deadly accusation of her owne guyltynes, and dispitefull doubte shee had *Cleophila* had abused her: But (bycause of the one syde fynding the *Duke*, did thincke her to bee *Cleophila*) shee had libèrty to imagyn yt mighte rather bee the *Dukes* owne unbrydeled enterpryse wch had barred *Cleophila*, then *Cleophilas* conning Deceyving of her. And that of the other syde, yf shee shoulde heddely seeke a vyolent Revenge her owne honor mighte bee as-muche interessed, as *Cleophila* endaungered: Shee fell to this Determeynacyon: First with fyne handling of the *Duke*, to settle in hym a perfect good opinion of her, and then, as shee shoulde learne howe thinges had passed, so to take into her self newe devysed Counsells: But this beeyng her first actyon having given unloked for attendance to the *Duke*, shee hearde with what parcialitie hee did preferr her self to her self. Shee sawe in hym how muche fancy dothe [not] onely darcken reason, but be-guyled sence, shee founde opinyon Mistris of the Lovers Judgm^t, wch serving as good Lesson to her wyse Conceypte shee went oute to *Basilius*, setting her self in a grave behavyour and stately silence before hym. Untill hee (who at the first thinking her by somuche shadow as hee coulde see to bee *Cleophila* was beginning his loving Ceremonyes) did now (beeyng helped by the peeping lighte where with the morning did overcome the Nightes darckenes) knowe her face, and his error: Whiche acknoulledging in hym self (with starting back from her) shee thus with a modest bitternes spake unto hym. Alas my Lorde, well did youre wordes discypher youre mynde, and well bee those wordes Confirmed with this gesture? Very Loathsome must that wooman bee from whome a Man hathe Cause to goo back? and litle better liked ys that wyfe before whome the husband preferres them hee never knewe? Alas hathe my faythfull observing my parte of Duty made yo{w} thincke youre self ever a whitt the more exempted? hathe that wch shoulde Clayme gratefullnes beene a Cause of Contempt? ys the beeyng a Mother of *Pamela* become an odyous name unto yo{w}? Yf my lyfe hetherto ledd, have not avoyded suspicyon? yf my vyolated truthe to yo{w} bee deserving of any punishment? I refuse not to bee Chastized with the moste Crewell torment of youre Displeasure, I Refuse not misery purchased by my owne meryt. Hard I must needes say (allthoughe till nowe) I thoughte I shoulde never have Cause to say, ys the Desteny of Womankynde, the tryall of whose vertue must stande uppon the Loving them, that employ all theyre industry not to bee beloved. Yf *Cleophilas* younge yeares had not had asmuche gravity hidden under youthfull face, as youre gray heayres have beene but the vizor of a farr unfitting youthfullnes, youre vicyous mynde had broughte some fruites of late repentance, and *Gynecia* mighte then have beene wth muche more righte despysed. *Basilius* that was more asshamed to see hym self so overtaken (then *Vulcan* was when wth muche Cunning hee prooved hym self Cuckolde) began to make certeyne extravagant excuses: But the matter in yt self hardly brooking any purgation with the sodeñes of the tyme wch barred any good conjoyned inventyon, made hym some tymes alledge one thinge, to whiche by and by hee would bringe in a contrary, one tyme with flatt denyall, (an other tyme with miti- gating the faulte, now brave then humble) use suche a stamering defensive, that *Gynecia* (the vyolence of whose feare in deede rañn an other way) was content thus to fasten up the last stiche of her anger. Well, well, my Lord saide shee yt shall well be- come yo{w} so to govern youre self, as yo{w} may bee fitt rather to direct mee, then to bee judged of mee, and rather bee a wyse Master of mee, then an unskillfull pleader before mee: Re- member the wronge yo{w} doo to mee, yt ys not onely to mee but to youre Children, whome yow had of mee, to youre Contrey, when they shall fynde they are commaunded by hym that can not commaund his owne undecent appetites. Lastly to youre self, since with these paynes, yo{w} doo but buylde up a howse of shame to dwell in, yf frome these moveable goodes of nature (where- with in my first yowthe my Royall Parentes bestowed mee uppon yow) Bearing of Children and increase of yeares have withdrawne mee. Consider I pray yo{w}, that as yow are the

258

Cause of the one, so in the other, tyme hathe not lefte to worcke his never fayling effectes in yow: Truely, truely very untymely are these fyers in yow, yt ys hye season for us bothe, to lett Reason enjoy his due Soveraignty, Let us not plante a newe those weedes, wch by *Natures* course are content to fade? *Basilius* that woulde rather then his lyfe the matter had beene ended, the best Rethorick that hee had was Flatt demaunding pardon of her, swearing yt was the very force of *Appollos* destiny, wch had Carryed hym thus from his owne *Byas*, but that now lyke farre Travellers were tought to love theyre owne Contry, had had suche a Lesson withoute Booke of affection unto her, as hee woulde repay the Debt of this Error with the Interest of a greate deale more true honor, then ever before hee had borne her. Neyther am I to give Pardon to yo^w my Lorde sayde shee, nor yo^w to beare honor to mee, I have taken this boldenes for the unfayned Love I owe yo^w to delyver my sorowe unto yo^w, muche more I have for the Care of youre well doynge, then for any other self fancy: For, well I knowe, that by youre good estate my lyfe ys meyntayned, neyther yf I woulde can I seperate my self from youre fortune. For my parte therefore I clayme no thinge, but that wch may bee safest for youre self my lyfe will honor, and what soever else shall bee but a shadow of that body. How muche *Basilius* owne shame had founde hym Culpable and had all redy even in sowle redd his owne Con-dempnacyon somuche did this unexpected myldenes of *Gynecia* captive his harte unto her, wch other wyse perchaunse woulde have growne to a desperate Carelesnes: Therefore, embracing her, and Confessing that her vertue shyned in his vyce, hee did even with a true Resolved mynde vowe unto her, that, so longe as hee unworthy of her did live shee shoulde bee the furdest, and onely limittes of his affection. Hee thancked the Destinyes that had wroughte her Honor oute of his shame, and, that had made his owne fynding to goo amiss, to bee the best meane ever after to holde hym in the Right pathe. Thus Reconcyled to *Basilius* greate Contentation who began some thinge to marcke hym self in his doynges his harder happe guyded his eye to the Cupp of golde wherein *Gynecia* had putt the liquor ment for *Cleophila*, and having fayled of that guest, was now carrying yt home ageane: But, hee (whome perchaunce sorowe perchaunce some long disaccustomed paynes had made extreamely thirsty) tooke yt oute of her handes: Allthoughe shee directly toulde hym, bothe of whome shee had yt, what the effect of yt was, and the litle proof shee had seene therof, hyding no thinge from hym, but that shee mente to minister yt to an other Patient. But *Basilius*, whose belly had no eares & muche Droughte kept hym from the desyering a Taster, fynding yt not unpleasant to his palett, drancke yt all moste of, Leaving very litle to cover the Cuppes bottom: But within a while, that from his stomack the drincke had delivered to his principall vaynes his noysome vapoures, first with a paynefull stretching and forced yawning, then, with a darcke yeallownes dying his skynñ and a Coulde deadly sweate, Principally aboute his temples, his Body by naturall course longing to deliver the heavy burden to his eartheley Dame (wanting force in his knees wch utterly abandoned hym with hevy fall soone gave proof) whether the operation of that unknowne potion tended. For with panglike grones, and gastly turning of his eyes, ymediately all his lymẽs stiffened and his eyes fixed, hee having had tyme to declare his Case, onely in these wordes O *Gynecia*, I dye, have care, of what or howe muche furder hee woulde have spoken, no man can tell: For *Gynecia* having well perceyved the chaunging of his Coloure, & those other evell signes, yet had not looked for suche a sodayne overthrowe, but rather had bethought her self what was best for hym. When shee sodenly sawe the matter come to that *Peryod*, coming to hym, and neyther wth any Cryes getting a worde of hym nor with any other possible meanes able to bringe any Living action from hym, the heighte of all ugly sorowes, did so horribly appeare before her amased mynde, that at the first yt did not onely distract all power of speeche from her, but allmoste witt, to Consider, Remayning as yt were quickly buryed in a grave of miseryes. Her paynefull memory had streighte filled her with the true shapes of all the fore past myscheefes, her Reason began to crye oute ageanst the Rebellyon of synfull sence, and to teare yt self with anguish: For, having made so weyke a resistance her Conscyence, (a terrible witnes of ye Inward wickednes) still norisshing this debatefull fyer, her Complaynte now not having an ende directed unto yt something to disburden sorowe, but as an unnecessary downefalle of Inward wretchednes, shee sawe the rigor of the Lawes was like to lay a shamefull deathe upon her. Whiche beeyng for that action undeserved, made yt the more

Insupportable, and yet in depthe of her sowle moste deserved, made yt seeme the more myserable. At lengthe letting her toungue goo as her dolorus thoughtes guyded yt, shee thus with Lamentable demeanor spake; O bottomles pitt of sorowe in whiche I can not conteyne my self having the fyer brandes of all furyes within mee still falling, and yet by the infinitnes of yt never fallen: Neyther can I ridd my self beeyng fettered with the everlasting Consideracyon of yt, for, whether shall I Recomend the protection of my dishonored fall? To the earthe? yt hathe no lyfe, and waytes to bee encreased by the Reliques of my shamed Carckas. To men? who are allwayes Crewell in theyre Neighboures faultes, and make others overthrowe become ye Badge of their evill masked vertue. To the heavens? O Inspeakable torment of Conscyence wch dare not looke uppon them? No synne can enter there: O, there ys no Receipt for polluted myndes, whether then wilte thow leade this Captive of thyne O snaky dispayer? Alas, Alas, was this the freeholding power that accursed poyson hathe graunted unto mee, that to bee helde the surer yt shoulde deprive lyfe? was this the folding in myne Armes promysed, that I shoulde foulde no thing, but a Deade body? O Mother of myne what a deathfull snake have yo^w given mee? O *Philoclea*, well hathe my Mother Revenged uppon mee my unmotherly hating of thee? O *Cleophila*? to whome yet least any misery shoulde faile mee, remayne some sparckes of my detestable Love, yf thow haste (as now alas my mynde assures mee thow haste) deceyved mee? There ys a fayrer Scene prepared for thee, to see the Tragicall ende of thy hated Lover? With that worde, there flowed owte twoo Rivers of teares oute of her fayre eyes whiche before were drye, the Remembrance of her other myscheefes beeyng dryed up in a furyous fyer of self detestation, Love onely according to the Temper of yt melting yt self into those bryne tokens of passyon: Then turning her eyes ageane unto the body, shee Remembred a dreame shee had had some dayes before, wherein thinckcing her self called by *Cleophila* passing a trublesome passage shee founde a Deade body, whiche tolde her, there shoulde bee her onely rest. This, no sooner caughte holde of her Remembrance, then that shee determining with her self yt was a direct vision of her fore appoynted ende, tooke a certeyn Resolution, to embrace Deathe: Assoone as yt shoulde bee offered unto her,

and no way to seeke the prolonging of her annoyed lyffe. And
therefore kissing the colde face of *Basilius* and even so will I
rest sayde shee, and joyne this faulty sowle of myne to thee yf
so muche the Angry goddes will graunt mee : As shee was in
this plighte, the Sunne now glyming over oure horyzon, the
first Shepeheardes came by, who seeyng the *Duke* in yᵗ Case
(and hearing the noyse *Dametas* made of the Lady *Philoclea*)
Rañ with the dolefull tydinges of *Basilius* deathe unto hym.
Who presently with all his Company came to the Caves entry
where the *Dukes* body lay; *Dametas* for his parte more glad,
for the hope hee had of his private escape, then sory for the
publique losse his Contry receyved of a Prince not to bee mislyked. But in *Gynecia* nature prevayled above Judgement, and
yᵉ shame shee conceyved to bee taken in that order, overcame
for that Instant, the former resolution, so that assoone as shee
sawe the foremoste of the Pastorall troupe, the wretched Princes
rañ to have hid her face in the next woodes: But with suche
a mynde that shee knewe not allmoste her self what shee coulde
wish to bee the grounde of her savety. *Dametas* that sawe her
ronne away in *Cleophilas* upper Rayment, and judging her to
bee so, thoughte certeynly all the Spirittes in hell were come to
play a Tragedy, in those woodes; suche straunge Chaunge hee
saw every way: The *Duke* deade at the Caves mouthe the
Duchess, (as hee thought) absent, *Pamela* fled away wᵗʰ *Dorus*,
his wyffe, and *Mopsa* in dyvers franzies. But of all other thinges
Cleophila conquered his capacity, sodeynly from a woman growne
a man, and from a lockt chamber gotten before hym into the
Feeldes, whiche hee gave the rest quickly to understand: For
in steade of doyng any thing as the exigent requyred, hee began
to make Circles and all those fantasticall defences hee had ever
hearde were fortifications ageanst Devells. But the other
Shepeheardes who had bothe better wittes, and more faythe,
forthewith devyded them selves, some of them ronning after
Gynecia, taking her to bee *Cleophila*, & esteeming her ronning
away to bee a greate Condempnation of her owne guyltynes :
Others goynge to theyre Prince, to see what service was best for
them, eyther in recovery of his lyfe or honoring his deathe they
that went after the *Duchess* had soone overtaken her in whome
now the first feares were stayed and the Resolution to dye, had
possessed his place in her mynde. But, when they sawe yt was

the *Duchess* to whome (besydes the obeydient duety they owed
to her state) they had allwayes carryed, a singuler love for her
Curteous Liberalityes, and other wyse and vertuous partes w^ch
had filled all that people with affection and admiration : They
were all sodeynly stopped, beginning to aske pardon for theyre
followyng her in that sorte, and desyering her to bee theyre
good Lady as shee had ever bene : But the *Duchess* who now
thirsted to bee Ridd of her self, whome shee hated above all
thinges, with suche an assured Countenaunce as they have,
(who allredy have dispensed with shame and digested the sorowes
of deathe) shee thus sayde unto them, Continew, Continew my
Frendes, youre doynge ys better then youre excusing, the one
argues assured faythe, the other want of assurance : Yf yo^w
loved youre *Prince*, when hee was able and willing to doo yo^w
muche good, wch yow coolde not then requyte unto hym, doo
yo^w now publish youre gratefullnes, when yt shall bee seene to
the worlde, there are no hopes left to leade yow unto yt.
Remember, remember yo^w have lost *Basilius* a Prince to defend
yo^w, a Father to care for yo^w, a Companyon in youre Joyes,
a frende in youre wantes, and yf yo^w loved hym shewe yow hate
the author of his Losse ? It ys I, faythfull *Arcadians* that have
spoyled this Contry of theyre Protector, I, none but I was the
Minister of his unnaturall ende, Carrye therefore my blood in
youre handes to testify youre owne Innocency, neyther spare
for my Titles sake, but Consider yt was hee that so entitled mee.
And yf yow thincke of any benefites receyved by my meanes,
thinck with yt that I was but the instrument, and hee the
Springe ? what stay yee Shepeheardes, whose greate Shepeheard
ys goñ ? yow neede not feare a womañ, nor reverence youre
Lordes Murderer, nor take pitty of her, who hathe not pitty of
her self ? with this shee presented her fayre neck to some by
name, to others by signes, desyering them to doo Justice to the
worlde, Duty to theyre good *Duke*, honor to them selves and
favoure to her. The pore men looking one upon an other unused to bee Arbitrers in Princes Matters, and beeynge nowe
fallen into a greate perplexity betweene a Prince Deade, and
a Princess alyve, but once for them shee mighte have goñ
whether shee woulde, thinckyng yt a sacriledge to tuche her
person : when, shee fynding shee was not a sufficyent Orator to
perswade her owne deathe by theyre handes, well sayde sheè, yt

ys but somuche more tyme of mysery for my parte. I will not give my lyfe somuche pleasure, from henceforwarde, as to yeelde to his desyer of his owne Choyse of deathe, synce all the rest ys taken of mee, yet lett mee excell in misery? Leade mee therefore whether yo^w will, onely happy because I can not bee more wretched. But neyther somuche woulde the honest Shepeardes doo, but rather with many teares bemoned this encrease of theyre former losse: Till shee was fayne to leade them with a very straunge spectacle, eyther that a Princes shoulde bee in the handes of Shepeheardes, or a Prisoner shoulde direct her gardyans, Lastly before eyther witnes or accuser a Lady condempne her self to deathe. But in suche moanefull Marche they went towardes the other Shepeheardes, who in ye meane tyme had lefte nothing unassayed to revive the *Duke*, but all was booteles and theyre Sorowes had encreased, the more they had suffered any hopes vaynely to aryse: Amonge other tryalls they made at least to knowe the Cause of his ende, having espyed the unhappy Cupp, they gave the litle Licoure that was lefte in yt to a Dogge of *Dametas*, in wch within short space yt wroughte the same effect allthoughe *Dametas* did somuche to recover hym, that for very Love of his lyfe, hee dasht oute his Braynes. Now, alltogether & having *Gynecia* among them, (who to make her self the more odyous did continually recorde to theyre myndes the excess of theyre Losse) they yeelded them selves over to all those formes of Lamentation that Dolefull Images do imprint in the honest, but over tender hartes, especially when they thincke the Rebounde of the evills falles to theyre owne smartes: Therefore after the auncyent great maner, some of them Remembringe the Nobility of his byrthe, others his shape, (wch though not excellent) yet, favoure and pitty drewe all thinges nowe to the highest poynte, others his peaceable governement (the thing wch moste pleaseth men resolved to live of theyre owne): Others his Liberality, wch thoughe yt can not lighte uppon all men, (yet all men naturally hoping yt may bee they) makes yt a moste amiable vertue. Some calling in question the greatenes of his power, wch encreased the Compassion, to see the present Chaunge (having a dolefull memory how hee had tempered yt with suche familier Curtesy among them, that they did more feele the fruites then see the Pompes of his greatnes) all with one Consent giving hym the sacred Tytles of good, just, mercyfull the Father of the people, the lyfe of his Contrey. They rañ aboute his body, tearing theyre beardes and garmentes, some sending theyre Cryes to heaven, others inventing particuler howling Musickes many vowyng to kill them selves, at the day of his funeralles : Generally giving a true testimony, that Men are Loving Creatures when Injuryes putt them not from theyre naturall Course, and how easy a thing yt ys for a Prince by succession deepely to sincke into the sowles of his Subjectes, a more lyvely monument, then *Mausolus* tombe. Lastly having one after the other cryingly songe the *Dukes* praise, and his owne Lamentation they did all desyer *Agelastus* (one notably noted amonge them) as well for his skill in theyre *Poetry* as for an austerely meyntayned sorowfullnes (wherewith hee seemed to despise the worckes of nature) to make an universall Complaynte for them in this universall mischeef. Who did yt in this sestine.

Synce wayling ys a budd of Causefull Sorrowe,
Synce sorrowe ys the follower of yll Fortune,
Synce no yll Fortune equalles publique Damage,
Nowe Princess Losse hathe made oure Damage publique,
    Sorrowe pay wee unto the Rightes of Nature,
    And Inward greeffe seale up with outeward waylinge.

Why shoulde wee spare oure voyce from endles waylinge?
Who Justly make oure hartes the seates of Sorowe,
In suche a Case, where yt apeares that Nature,
Dothe add her force unto the stinge of Fortune,
    Chosing alas, this oure Theater publique,
    Where they woulde Leave Tropheys *of cruell Damage.*

Then since suche powers conspire unto oure Damage,
Whiche may bee knowne, but never helpt wth wailing,
Yet let us leave a Monument *in publique,*
Of willing teares, torne here, and Cryes of Sorrowe.
    For lost, lost, ys by Blowe of Crewell Fortune,
    Arcadias *gemme the Noblest Chylde of* Nature.

O Nature *Doting olde, O blynded* Nature *?*
Howe haste thow torne thy self, soughte thyne owne Damage ?
In graunting suche a Scope to filthy Fortune.
By thy Impes *loss, to fill the worlde with wayling?*
    Cast thy Stepp mother eyes uppon oure Sorowe,
    Publique oure Loss, to see thy shame ys publick.

O that wee had, (to make oure woes more publique)
Seays in oure eyes, and brazen Toungues by Nature,
A yelling voyce, and Hartes compost of Sorowe,
Breathe made of flames with knowing noughte but Damage.
    Oure Sportes murdering oure selves, oure Musickes wayling
    Oure studyes fixte uppon the falles of Fortune.

No, no, oure myscheef growes in this vyle Fortune,
That private panges, can not breathe oute in publique,
The furyous Inward greeffes with hellish wayling.
But forced are to burden feeble Nature
With secrett sence of oure eternall Damage,
And sorowe feede feeding oure Sowles with sorowe.
    Synce Sorowe then concludeth all oure Fortune,
    With all oure deathes, shewe wee this Damage publique
    His Nature *feares to dye who lives still* Wayling.

They did with suche harty Lamentation disperse amonge those woodes theyre resounding Shreekes, that the Sunne the perfectest marck of Tyme having gotten up twoo howers Jorney in his dayly chaunging Circle: Theyre voyce helped with the onely answering *Eccho,* came to the eares of the faythfull & worthy gentleman *Philanax,* who at that tyme was comming accompanyed with dyvers of the Principall *Arcadian* Lordes, to vizitt the *Duke* upon this occasyon. Fame the Charge of many Eares and governor of many Toungues had delivered to the attentive eares of *Philanax* the late Droncken Commotion of the *Phagonians,* with so large an encrease, that hee (who too well knewe, that too muche provision mighte well loose some Charge, but to little might well loose all) had speedely assembled in the Frontyers where hee lay V. C Horse, and came with all diligence giving order, more should bee in redynes yf more needed: But beeyng come to the very Towne yt self of *Phagonia* (as yt was oute of his way) hee there understoode how farr the vertue of *Cleophila* had made *Basilius* fortunate, and that those dangers feared were utterly passed: yet to avoyde any other disturbance to his Masters quyett (whom hee loved with incomparable Loyalty) suffering those that were pardoned to enjoy the fruites of a Princes worde, hee placed guarrysons in all the Townes and villages any thing nere the Lodges: Over whome hee appoynted Capteynes of suche wisdome and vertue,

266

as might not onely with the force of the Souldyors keepe the
Inhabitantes frome outerage, but mighte unparcyally looke to the
Discipline bothe of the Men of warr, and of the people. That
done thinckyng yt aswell his Duety to see the *Duke*, as of good
purpose (beeyng so neare) to receyve his further direction (accompanyed as above sayde) hee was this Morning coming unto
hym, when those unpleasant voyces gave his mynde an uncerteyne presage of his neare aproching sorowe : For, by and
by hee sawe the body of his Derely beloved *Prince*, & hearde
Gynecias waymenting, not suche as the *Turtle* like *Dove* ys wonte
to make for the ever oversoone Losse of her onely loved Make,
but with Cursinges of her lyfe, Detesting of her owne wickednes, seeming therefore onely not to desyer deathe bycause shee
woulde not shewe a Love of any thinge. The Shepeheardes,
especially *Dametas* (knowyng hym to bee the second person in
authority,) gave forthe with relacyon unto hym what they knewe
& had prooved of this Dolorus spectacle, besydes the other accidentes of his Children : But hee principally touched with his
Masters losse lighting from his horse with a heavy Cheare,
kneeled downe by hym, where fynding hee coulde doo no more
then yᵉ Shepeheardes had for his Recovery, the Constancy of
his mynde surprisde before hee mighte calle together his best
Rules, coulde not refrayne suche like wordes. Ah dere Master
sayde hee, what Chaunge yt hathe pleased the Allmighty Justice
to worcke in this place? How soone, (not to youre Losse who
have lived longe to nature and now live longer by youre deserved
glory) but longest of all in the eternall Mansyon yoᵂ now possesse : But, howe soone I say, to youre Rewyn have yoᵂ lefte
the frayle Barcke of youre estate? O that the wordes my moste
faythfull Duty delivered unto yoᵂ, when yoᵂ first entred this
solitary Course, mighte have wroughte asmuche perswasion
in yoᵂ, as they sprange from Truthe in mee? Perchaunce
youre Servaunte *Philanax* shoulde not now have had Cause in
youre Losse to bevayle his owne overthrawe : And therewith
(taking hym self) And in deede, evill fitteth yt mee (saythe
hee) to lett goo my harte to womanish Complayntes, (synce my
Prince beeyng undoubtedly well) yt rather shewes Love of my
self wᶜʰ makes mee bewayle my owne losse. No, the true Love
must bee procured in the honor of youre memory, and that
must bee shewed with seeking just Revenge uppon youre unjust

and unnaturall Enimyes: And farr more honorable yt will bee for youre Tombe to have the blood of youre Murderers sprinkled uppon yt, then the teares of youre Frendes? And yf youre Sowle looke downe uppon this miserable earthe, I Doubte not, yt had muche rather youre Deathe were accompanyed with well deserved punishmet of the Causers of yt, then with the heaping on yt more Sorowes with the ende of them to whome yo^w vouchsafed youre affection. Lett them Lament that have woven this webb of Lamentacyon? Lett theyre owne Deathes make them Crye oute of youre Deathe, that were the Aucthors of yt? Therewth carrying manfull sorow and vindicatyve resolucyon in his face, hee rase up looking uppon the pore guyltles Princes, transported with an unjust Justice, that his eyes were sufficyent Herauldes for hym to denounce a Mortall hatred: Shee, (whome furyes of Love fyrebrandes of her Conscyence, shame of the worlde, with the miserable Losse of her husband, towardes whome nowe the Disdayne of her self bredd more Love with the remembraunce of her vision, wherewith shee resolved assuredly the Goddes had appoynted that shamefull ende to bee her Resting place had sett her mynde in no other way but to deathe) used suche like speeches to *Philanax* as shee had doone before to the Shepeheardes: Willing hym not to looke uppon her as a Woeman, but a Monster, not as a Princess but as a Traytor to his Prince, not as *Basilius* wyfe, but as *Basilius* Murderer. Shee toulde hym howe the worlde requyred at his handes, the just Demonstration of his Frendship, yf hee now forgott his Prince, hee shoulde shewe hee never loved but his Fortune. But like the vermyn wch sucke of ye Living blood, and leave the body so soone as yt ys deade: Pore Princess needlesly seeking to kyndell hym whoo did moste deadly detest her, whiche hee uttered in this bytter answer. Madame (saide hee) yo^w doo well to hate youre self, for yo^w can not hate a worse Creature, and thoughe wee feele ynough youre hellish disposicyon, yet, wee neede not Doubte yo^w are a Counsell to youre self of muche worse then wee knowe: But now feare not, yo^w shall not longe bee Combered wth beeyng guyded with so evell a Sowle, therefore prepare youre self, that yf yt bee possible yo^w may deliver up youre Spirite so muche purer, as yo^w washe youre wickednes with Repentance.

Then having presently given order, for the bringing from

Mantinea a greate nomber of Tentes for the receipt of the Principall *Arcadians*, the maner of that Contry beeyng that where
the Prynce dyed, there shoulde bee order taken for the Contryes
governement: And in the place any Murder was committed, the
Judgment shoulde bee given there before the body were buryed,
bothe Concurring in this Matter, and allredy greate parte of the
Nobility beeyng aryved hee delyvered the *Duchess* to a gentleman of greate Trust. And as for *Dametas*, taking from hym
the keyes of bothe ye Lodges calling hym the Moathe of the
Princes estate, and onely spott of his Judgment, hee Caused
hym with his wyffe and Daughter to bee fettered upp in as
many Cheynes and Clogges as they coulde beare; And every
thirde hower to bee cruelly whipte, till the determyned Judgm^t
shoulde bee given of all those matters, that done, having sent
allredy at his first comming to all the quarters of the Contry to
seeke *Pamela*, allthoughe with smalle hope of overtaking them,
hee hym self went, well accompanyed to the Lodge, where the
twoo unfortunate Lovers were attending a crewell Conclusion of
theyre longe paynefull late pleasaunt affection. *Dametas* Clownish
eyes having beene onely the Discoverers of *Pyrocles* Stratagem,
hee had no sooner taken a full view of them (whiche in some
sightes woulde rather have any thinge then an accusing mynde),
and locked the Dore uppon those twoo younge folckes, nowe
made Prisoners for Love, as before they had beene Prisoners to
Love: But that, ymediately upon his goyng downe whether
with noyse that *Dametas* made, or with the Creeping in of the
Lighte, or rather as I thincke that hee had but litle slept that
Nighte, so, the sweete embracement hee enjoyed gave his sences
a very easy salve to come to them selves. But, so yt was y^t *Pyrocles*
awaked, grudging in hym self, that sleepe (though very shorte)
had robbed hym, of any parte of those his highest Contentmentes,
especially Considering that hee was then to prepare hym self to
returne to the *Dukes* bedd, and at his Coming, to sett suche a
Comicall face of the Matter, as hee shoulde fynde by ye speeches of
Basilius and *Gynecia* shoulde bee moste Convenyent: But beeyng
now fully awaked, hee mighte heare a greate noyse under the
Lodge, whiche (as affection ys full of Doubtes) made hym leape
oute of his Bedd. Having first with earnest kissing the Pereles
Philoclea, (who then soundly sleeping) was the naturall Image of
exact Beuty receyved into his sence, a full proportion of the

greatest delighte hee coulde imagyn under the Moone: But looking up, the first evell handsell hee had of the evell Case wherein
hee was was the seeyng of hym self deprived of his sworde
from wch hee had never separated hym self in any occasyon, and
even, in that Nighte first, by the *Dukes* bedd, and then there
had layde yt, as hee thoughte safe. Putting greate parte of the
Trust of his well doynge in his owne Corage, so armed, for
in deede the Confidence in ones self ys the Cheef Nurse of
true Magnanimity, wch Confidence notwithstanding dothe not
leave the Care of necessary furnitures for yt: And therefore, of
all the *Grecians Homer* dothe ever make *Achilles* the best armed.
But that I say, was his firste yll token but by and by hee perceyved hee was a Prisoner, before any arrest for the Dore w^ch
hee had lefte open, was made so fast of ye owtesyde that, for
all the force hee coulde employ unto yt coulde not undooe
Dametas Doynge: Then went hee to the wyndowe to see, yf y^t
way, there were any escape for hym, and his dere Lady, but as
vayne hee founde all his employment there. Not having mighte
to breake oute but onely one Barre, wherein notwithstanding
hee strayned his synewes to the uttermoste, and that hee rather
tooke oute to use for other services, then for any possibility hee
founde of escape: For even then yt was that *Dametas* having
gathered together ye first coming Shepeheardes, did blabber oute
what hee had seene in *Philocleas* Chamber. *Pyrocles* marckingly
harckened to all that *Dametas* sayde, whose voyce and mynde
acquayntance had taughte hym sufficyently to knowe, but when
hee assuredly perceyved all his action with the Lady *Philoclea*
was fully discovered: Remembring with all the Crewelty of the
Arcadian Lawes, whiche withoute exception did Condempne
all to deathe who were founde in acte of Mariage withoute
solempnity of Mariage. Assuring hym self besydes the Lawe,
that the *Duke* and *Duchess* would use so muche more hate ageanst
theyre Daughter, as they had founde them selves sotted by hym
in the pursuite of theyre Love: Lastly seeyng, they were not
onely in the way of Deathe but fitly encaged for deathe, Looking
with a harty greef upon the honor of Love, the felowless *Philoclea* (whose Innocent sowle now enjoying his owne goodnes did
litle knowe the daunger of his ever fayre then sleeping harboure)
his excellent witt strengthened with vertue, but guyded by Love,
had soone described to hym self a perfect vision of theyre present

Condicion, wherein having presently cast a resolute reconing of his owne parte of the misery, not onely the cheef but sole Burden of his anguish consisted in the unworthy Case wch was like to falle upon the best Deserving *Philoclea.* Hee sawe the mysfortune, not the mysmeaning of his worcke, was like to bring that Creature to ende in whome the worlde (as hee thought) did begyn to receyve honor: Hee sawe, the weyke judgment of Man woulde condempne that as a deathe deserving vice in her, whiche had in truthe never broken ye bandes of a true Living vertue. And howe often his eye turned to his attractive *Adamant,* so often did an unspeakeable horror stryke his noble harte to Consyder so unrype yeares, so faultles a Beuty, the Mansyon of so pure goodnes shoulde have her youthe so untymely Cutt of, her naturall perfections unnaturally consumed her vertue rewarded wth shame: Some tymes hee would accuse hym self of negligence, that had not more Curyously looked to all the howse entryes, and yet coulde hee not ymagyn the way *Dametas* was gotten in. And to Calle back what might have beene, (to a man of wisdome and Corage, carryes but a vayne shadowe of Discourse, some tymes hee coulde not Choose, but wth a Dissolution of his Inwarde mighte) lamentably Consider with what face hee myght looke uppon his (till then) Joy *Philoclea,* when the next light waking shoulde deliver her, shoulde perchaunce bee the last of her hurtless lyfe: And that the first tyme shee shoulde bende her excellent eyes uppon hym, shee shoulde see the accursed Author of her dreadfull ende. And even this Consideracyon more then any other did so settle yt self in his well disposed mynde, that dispersing his thoughtes to all the wayes that mighte bee of her savety fynding a very smalle discourse in so narrow limittes of tyme and place, at lengthe in many difficultyes, hee sawe none beare any Likelyood for her lyfe, but his deathe: For then hee thought yt woulde falle oute when they founde his body deade (having no accuser but *Dametas,* as by his speeche there were not), that then yt might justly appeare, that eyther *Philoclea* in defending her honor, or ellse hee hym self in dispayre of atcheeving had lefte his Carckas proof of his fact, but witnes of her Clearenes. Having a small while stayed uppon the greatnes of this Resolution, and looked to ye furdest of yt, (Bee yt so sayde) the valyant *Pyrocles* never lyfe for better Cause nor to better ende was bestowed: For, yf deathe bee to followe this facte, whiche no Deathe of myne shall ever make repent, who ys to dye so justly as my self, and yf I must dye, who can bee so fitt executors as myne owne handes, wch as the were accessaryes to the fact, so in killing mee they shall suffer theyre owne punishmĕt. But then arose there a newe Impediment, for *Dametas* havinge carryed away any thinge wch hee thoughte mighte hurte as tender a Man as hym self, hee coulde fynde no fitt instrument wch might give hym a finall Dispatche: At lengthe making the more haste least his Lady shoulde awake, taking the Iron barr (whiche beeyng sharper some thing at the one ende then at ye other) hee hoped joyned to his willing strengthe mighte breake of the sclender thridd of mortallity, Truely (saide hee) Fortune, tho^w haste well persevered myne enimy, that will graunte mee no Fortune to bee unfortunate, nor lett mee have an easy passage, nowe I am to truble thee no more. But, sayde hee, O barre blessed in that thow haste done service to the Chamber of the Peragon of lyfe, since thow couldest not serve mee to make a perfect escape, yet, serve my turne I pray thee that I may escape from my self? Therewithall yet, once looking to fetche the last repast of his eyes, and newe ageane trãsported wth the pityfull Case hee lefte her in, kneeling downe, hee thus prayed unto *Jupiter*. O greate maker and greate Ruler of the worlde, (sayde hee) to thee doo I sacrifice this bloode of myne, and suffer (O *Jove*) the errors of my youthe to passe away therein, and lett not ye sowle by thee made, and ever bending unto thee bee ever rejected of thee: Neither bee offended, that I do abandon this body, to the government of whiche thow haddest placed mee withowte thy Leave. Synce howe can I knowe, but that thy unsearcheable mynde ys I shoulde so doo, synce thow haste taken from mee all meane longer to abyde in yt: And synce the Difference standes, but in a shorte tyme of dyinge (thow that haste framed myne harte enclyned to doo good) How can I in this small space of myne benefit somuche all the Humane kynde, as in preserving thy perfectest worckmanship, thy Cheefest honor? O Justice yt self, howe soever thow determeynest of mee, Lett this excellent Innocency not bee oppressed? Lett my Lyfe pay her losse? O *Jove* give mee some signe, that I may dye with this Comfort. And pawsing a litle (as yf hee had hoped for some token) And when soever, to the eternall Darknes of the earthe shee dothe followe mee, Lett oure Spirites possess one place, and lett them bee more happy in that uniting: with that stryking the Barr uppon his harte syde, with all the force hee had, (and falling withall uppon, to give yt the more throwgher passage) the Barre in truthe was too blunt, to doo the facte, allthoughe yt persed his skynñ, and bruysed his Ribbes very sore, so that, his breathe was allmoste past hym. But the noyse of the Falle drave away sleepe from the quyett sences of the dere *Philoclea*, whose sweete sowle had an earthly salutation of a Deadly spectacle unto her with so muche more astonishment, as the falling a sleepe but a litle before had lefte her self in the uttermoste poynte of Contentment: And sawe nowe before her eyes the moste Cruell enterpryse that Humane nature can undertake, withoute discerning any Cause therof, but the lyvely printe of her affection had soone toughte her not to stay longe uppon deliberation in so urgent a necessity. Therefore getting with speede her well accorded Lymmes oute of her sweetened bedd, as when Jewells are hastily pulde oute of some Riche Coffer, shee spared not the nakednes of her tender feete: But (I thinck) borne as fast with desyer, as fayre carryed *Daphne*, shee came ronning to *Pyrocles*, and fynding his spirites trubled wth the falle, shee putt by the barre that lay close to hym, and strayning hym in her moste Loving embracement, My Comfort, my Joy, my Lyfe, sayde shee, what haste have yo^w to kill youre *Philoclea* with the moste cruell torment that ever Lady suffered. Doo yow not yet perswade youre self, yet y^t any hurte of youres ys deathe unto mee, and that youre deathe shoulde bee my hell? Alas, yf any sodayne myslike of mee (for other Cause I see none) have Caused yow to loathe youre self, yf any faulte or Desert of myne hathe bred this terriblest rage in yow, rather lett mee suffer the bitternes of yt, for so shall the Deserver bee punished, Mankynde preserved from suche a Rwyn, and I for my parte shall have that Comforte that I dye by the noblest hand, that ever drewe sworde: *Pyrocles* greeved with his Fortune, that hee had not in one instant Cutt of all suche deliberacyon, thincking his lyfe onely reserved to bee bounde to bee the unhappy newes teller, Alas sayde hee, my onely Starre, why do yo^w this wronge to god youre self and mee, to speake of faultes in yo^w? No, No, moste faultles moste perfect Lady, yt ys youre excellency that makes mee hasten my desyered ende? yt ys the Righte I owe to the generall nature that (thoughe ageanst private nature) makes mee seeke the preservation of all that shee had done in this age, Lett mee, Lett mee dye? There ys no way to save youre lyfe, (moste worthy to bee Conserved) then that my deathe be youre Clearing: Then did hee with farr more payne and backwarde loathnes then the so nere killing hym self was (but yet driven with necessity to make her yeelde to that hee thought was her savety) made her a short butt Pithy discourse, what hee had hearde by *Dametas* speeches, confirming the rest with a playne Demonstration of theyre Imprisonment. And then sought hee newe meanes of stopping his breathe, but y^t by *Philocleas* laboure above her force hee was stayed to heare her, in whome a man mighte perceyve, what smalle difference in the worcking there ys, betuixt a symple voydenes of evell, and a Judiciall habite of vertue: For shee not with an unshaked magnanimity, wherewith *Pyrocles* wayed and despysed deathe but with an Innocent guyltlesnes, not knowyng why shee shoulde feare to deliver her unstayned sowle to god (helped with ye true Loving of *Pyrocles*, wch made her thincke no lyfe withoute hym) did allmoste bringe her mynde, to as quyett attending all accidentes as ye unmastered vertue of *Pyrocles*. Yet having with a prity palenes (wch did leave milcken Lynes uppon her Rosy Cheekes) payde a litle Duety to humane feare, taking the Prince by the hande, & kissing the wounde hee had given hym self, O the onely Lyfe, of my Lyfe, (and yf yt falle oute so) the Comforte of my Deathe (sayde shee) farr farr, from yo^w bee the Doyng of mee suche wronge, as to thinck I will receyve my lyfe as a purchase of youre Deathe? But well may yo^w make my deathe somuche more myserable, as yt shall any thinge bee delayed after myne onely felicity? Do yo^w thincke I can accoumpte of the moment of Deathe like the unspeakeable afflictions my sowle shoulde suffer, so ofte, as I calle *Pyrocles* to my mynde wch shoulde bee as ofte as I breathed: Shoulde these eyes guyde my steppes that had seene youre murder? shoulde these handes feede mee, that had not hyndered suche a myscheef? shoulde this harte remayne within mee at every pant, to Counte the Contynuall Clock of my myseryes? O, No, yf dye wee must, Lett us thanck deathe hee hathe not denyed so true an unyon; And truely my *Pyrocles* I have hearde my Father and other wyse men say, that the

Killing ones self ys but a false Coloure of true Corage proceeding rather of feare of a further evell eyther of torment or shame.
For yf yt were not respecting the harme, that woulde likewyse
make hym not respect what mighte bee done unto hym, and
hope beeyng of all other the moste Contrary thinge to feare, this
beeyng an utter banishment of hope, yt seemes to receyve his
grounde in feare: What soever (woulde they say) comes oute
of despayre can not beare the tytle of valeure, wch shoulde bee
lifted up to suche a heighte that holding all thinges under yt
self, yt shoulde bee able to meyntayne his greatenes even in y^e
midst of his myseryes. Lastly, they woulde say god had appoynted us Capteynes of these oure bodily fortes, wch without
treason to that Matie were never to bee delyverd over, till they
were redemaunded: *Pyrocles* who had that for a Lawe unto
hym not to leave *Philoclea* in any thinge unsatisfyed, allthoughe
hee still remayned in his former purpose, and knewe the tyme
woulde growe shorte for yt, yet (hearing no noyse the Shepeheardes beeyng as then ronñ to *Basilius*) with setled and humbled
Countenaunce, as a Man that shoulde have spoken of a thinge
y^t did not concerne hym self, bearing even in his eyes sufficyent shewes, that yt was no thinge but *Philocleas* daunger w^ch
did any thinge burden his harte far stronger then Fortune,
Having with vehement embracing of her, gott yet some fruite
of his delayed ende hee thus answered the wyse Innocency of
Philoclea. Lady, moste worthy not onely of lyfe, but to bee
the very lyfe of all thinges, the more notable Demonstratyons
yow make of the Love, so farr beyonde my Desertes? with w^ch
yt pleaseth yow to overcome fortune in making mee happy, the
more am I even in Course of humanity (to leave that Loves
force, wch I neyther can nor will leave) bounde to seeke re-
quytalles, witnes, that I am not ungratefull to doo, wch the infi-
nitenes of youre goodnes, beeyng suche as yt can not reche unto
yt, yet Doynge all I can, and payinge my lyfe wch ys all I have,
thoughe yt bee farr (withowte measure) shorte of youre Desert,
yet, shall I not Dye in Debt to myne owne Duety. And
truely, the more excellent argumentes yow made to keepe mee
from this passage ymagined farr more terrible then yt ys, the
more playnely yt makes mee see, what reason I have to prevent
the Losse, not onely *Arcadia* but all the face of the earthe
shoulde receyve, yf suche a Tree (wch eeven in his first springe

dothe not onely beare moste beutyfull blossomes, but moste rare Fruites) shoulde bee so untymely cutt of: Therefore, O moste truly beloved Lady to whome I desyer, for bothe oure goodes, that these may bee my last wordes give mee youre Consent even oute of that wysdome, wch must needes see that (besydes youre unmatched betternes wch perchaunce yo^{w} will not see) yt ys fitter one dye then bothe. And synce yo^{w} have sufficyĕtly shewed yo^{w} Love mee, lett mee clayme by that Love yo^{w} will bee content rather to lett mee dye contented, then wretchedly rather with a clere and joyfull Conscyence, then with desperate Condempnation, that I accursed villayne shoulde bee the meane of banishing from the sighte of men the true example of vertue: And bycause there ys no thinge lefte mee to bee imagined, wch I somuche desyer, as that the memory of *Pyrocles* may even have an allowed place in youre Judgment, I am content to drawe somuche breath longer, as by answering the sweete objections yo^{w} alledged may bequeathe (as I thincke) a righte Conceypte unto yo^{w} that this my doynge ys oute of judgment, and not spronge of passyon. Youre Father yo^{w} say was wonte to say, that this like action dothe rather proceede of feare of furder evell or shame, then of a true Corage: Truly first they putt a very guessinge Case, speaking of them who can never come after to tell wth what mynde they did yt. And as for my parte I call the Immortall truthe to witnes, that no feare of torment can appall mee, who knowes yt ys but dyvers maners of apparelling deathe, and have longe learned, to sett bodily payne, but in the seconde forme of my beeyñg: And as for shame, howe can I bee ashamed of that, for wch my well meaning Conscyence will answer for mee to god, and youre unresistable beuty to the worlde: But, to make that Argument in his owne force, and graunt yt done for the avoyding of a furder payne or dishonor, for, as for ye name of feare, yt ys but an odyous tytle of a passyon (given to that wch true judgment performeth) graunte I say, yt ys to shunñ a worse Case. And truely I doo not see but that true fortitude looking into all humane thinges with a persisting Resolution carryed away neyther with wonder of pleasing thinges nor astonishment of unpleasing thinges dothe not yet deprive yt self of the discerning the Difference of evills: But rather ys ye onely vertue wch with an assured tranquility shunnes the greater by valyaunt entering into the less. Thus for his Contryes savety hee will spend his lyfe, for the saving of a Lym̃ hee will not nigardly spare his goodes, for the saving of all his body hee will not spare the Cutting of a Lym: Where in deede the weyke harted man will rather dye then see the face of a Surgeon who mighte with as good reason say that the Constant man abydes the paynefull surgery for feare of a furder evill, but hee ys Content to wayte for deathe yt self. But neyther ys true, for neyther hathe the one any feare, but a well chosing Judgment, nor the other hathe any Contentment but onely feare, not having a harte actively to performe a Matter of payne ys forced passively to abyde a greater Damage. For, to doo, requyers a whole harte, to suffer falleth easelyest in the broken myndes, and yf in bodily tormentes muche more in shame, wherein synce valeure ys a vertue ys ever limitted, wee must not ronñ so infinitely as to thincke the valyant man ys willingly to suffer any thinge: synce the very suffering of some thinges ys a certeyne proof of want of Corage, and yf any thinge among the Cheefest may shame goo for yf honor bee to bee helde dere, his Contrary ys to bee abhorred. And that not for feare, but of a true election wch ys the less inconvenyence, eyther the Losse of some yeares more or lesse (For once wee knowe oure Lyves bee not immortall) or the submitting oure selves to eche unworthy mysery wch the folish worlde may lay uppon us: As for theyre Reason that feare ys contrary to hope, neither doo I Defend feare nor muche yeelde to the authority of hope, to either of wch great inclyning shewes but a feeble reason, wch must bee guyded by his Servauntes. And, who buyldes not uppon hope, shall feele no earthquake of Dispayre. Theyre last alledging of the heavenly powers as yt beares the greatest name, so ys yt the onely thinge that at all bredd any Combat in my mynde: And yet I Do not see, but yf that god have made us Masters of any thing, yt ys of oure owne Lyves, oute of wch withoute doyng wronge to any body, wee are to issue at oure owne pleasure. And the same argument would asmuche prevayle to say wee shoulde for no necessity lay away from us any of oure Joyntes, synce they beeing made of hym, withoute his warraunt wee shall not departe from them. Or yf that may bee for a greater Cause, wee may passe to a greater degree, and yf wee bee Lyfe Tenauntes to god in this litle Castle doo yow not thinke wee must take warning of hym to give over oure Charge when hee leaves us unprovyded of good myndes to tarry in yt. No certeynly doo I not answered the sorowfull *Philoclea*, synce yt ys not for us to appoynt that mighty Matie what tyme hee will help us, the uttermoste Instant ys scope ynough for hym to revoke every thinge to ones owne desyer: And therefore to prejudicate ones owne determinacyon ys but a doubte of goodnes in hym, who ys no thinge but goodnes. But when in deede hee dothe eyther by sicknes or outeward force lay deathe uppon us, then are wee to take knowledg, that suche ys his pleasure, and to knowe, that all ys well that hee dothe: And that wee shoulde bee Masters of oure selves, wee can shewe at all no title nor Clayme, since neyther wee made oure selves, nor boughte oure selves, wee can stand uppon no other Right but his gifte, wch wee must limitt as yt pleaseth hym. Neyther ys there any proportion betuixt the losse of any other Lymm̃, and that synce the one bendes to the preserving all, the other to the Destruction of all, the one takes not away the mynde from the actions, for wch yt ys placed in the worlde, the other cuttes of all possibility of his worcking: And truely my moste dere *Pyrocles* I must needes protest unto yo^w, that I can not thincke youre Defence even in Rule of vertue sufficyent, sufficyent, and excellent yt were yf the question were not of twoo owteward thinges wherein a Man mighte by *Natures* freedome determeyn whether hee woulde preferr shame to payne present, smaller torment to greater followyng, or no. But to this (besydes the Comparysons of the Matters vallewes) there ys added of the one parte a direct evell doyng wch maketh the ballance of that syde too muche unequall synce a vertuous Man withoute any respect, whether the greef bee less or more, ys never to doo that wch hee can not assure hym self ys allowable before the ever living Rightfullnes: But rather to think Honors or shames wch stande in other mens true or false Judgmentes paynes or not paynes wch yet never approche oure sowles, to bee no thing in regard of an unspotted Conscyence. And these Reasons doo I remember I have hearde good men bringe in, that synce yt hathe not his grounde in an assured vertue, yt proceedes rather of some other disguysed passion: *Pyrocles* was not so muche perswaded as delighted by her well conceyved and sweetely pronounced speeches: But when shee had closed up her pityfull discourse,

278

and as yt were sealled up her delightfull Lippes with the moyst-
nes of her teares wch followed still one an other lyke a precyous
Rope of perle (Nowe thinckring yt highe tyme) Bee yt as yow
say (sayde hee moste vertuous bewty) in all the rest: But never
can god hym self perswade mee y^t *Pyrocles* lyfe ys not well
lost for to preserve ye moste admirable *Philoclea*, Lett that bee
yf yt bee possible, written in my Tombe, and I will not envy
Codrus honor. With that hee woulde ageane have used the
barre, meaning yf that fayled, to leave his braynes uppon the
walle. When *Philoclea*, nowe broughte to that shee moste
feared, kneeled downe unto hym, and embracing so his Legges
that withoute hurting her (whiche for no thing hee woulde have
done) hee coulde not ridd hym self from her shee did with all
the Conjuring wordes wch ye authority of Love may lay beseeche hym hee woulde not nowe so Crewelly abandon her, hee
woulde not leave her Comfortles in y^t misery, to wch hee had
brought her: That then in deede shee woulde even in her sowle
accuse hym to have moste fowlly betrayed her, that then shee
shoulde have Cause to Curse the tyme that ever the name of
Pyrocles came to her eares, wch otherwyse no deathe coulde make
her doo. Will yo^w leave mee saide shee not only dishonoured as
unchaste with yo^w, but as a Murderer of yo^w? will yow give
my eyes suche a picture of hell before my nere approching
deathe, as to see the Murdered body of hym I love more then
all the Lyves y^t nature can give? With that shee sware by the
hyghest Cause of all devotions, that yf hee did persever in that
crewell Resolucyon, shee woulde not onely Confess to her Father,
that wth her Consent this acte had beene committed: But yf
that woulde not serve (after shee had pulde oute her owne eyes
made accursed by suche a sighte) shee woulde give her self so
terrible a deathe, as shee might thinck the payne of yt woulde
Counterveyle the never dying payne of her mynde. Nowe
therefore kyll youre self, to make mee (whome yow say yo^w
love) as longe as I after live yo^w chaunge my loving admiration
of yo^w, to a detestable abhorring of youre name: And, so in
deede yow shall have the ende yo^w shoote at, for in steade of one
deathe yow shall give mee a thowsand, and yet in the meane
tyme deprive mee of the help god may send mee. *Pyrocles* even
overwayed wth her so wysely uttered affection, fynding her
determinacyon so fixed, that his Ende shoulde but deprive them

bothe of a present Contentment, and not avoyde a comming evell (as a Man that rañ not into yt by a sodayn qualme, but by a true use of reason preferring her lyfe to his owne, now that wisdome did manifest unto hym, that way woulde not prevayle) hee retyred hym self with as muche tranquillity from yt as before hee had gon unto yt: Lyke a Man that had sett the keeping or leaving of the body as a thing wth oute hym self and so thereof had a freed & untrubled Consideracyon. Therefore throwyng away the barr from hym, (and taking her up from the place, where hee thoughte the Consummating of all beutyes very unworthely lay) suffering all his sences to devoure up theyre cheefest foode wch hee assured hym self they shoulde shortly after for ever bee deprived of, Well saide hee moste dearely Lady whose Contentment I preferr before myne owne, and judgment esteeme more then myne owne I yeelde unto youre pleasure: The goddes send yow have not wonne youre owne Losse, for my parte they are my witnesses, that I thinck I do more at youre Comaundement in delaying my deathe, then an other woulde in bestowing his lyffe. But now, sayde hee, as thus farr I have yeelded unto yow, so graunte mee in recompence thus muche ageane, that I may fynde youre Love in graunting, as yo^w have founde youre authority in obtayninge: My humble sute ys yo^w will say, I came in by force into youre Chamber, for so I am resolved to affirme, and that will bee the best for us bothe, but in no case name my name, that whatsoever come of mee my howse bee not Dishonored. *Philoclea* fearing least refusall woulde turne hym back ageane, to his vyolent refuge gave hym a certeyne Countenaunce, that might shewe shee did yelde to his request: The later parte wherof in deede shee ment for his sake to performe neyther coulde they spend more wordes together. For *Philanax* with Twenty of the Noblest personages of *Arcadia* after hym, were come into the Lodge, *Philanax* making the rest stay belowe: For the Reverence hee bare to woman hood, as stilly as hee coulde came to the dore and opening yt, drewe the eyes of those twoo Dolefull Lovers upon hym, *Philoclea* closing ageane for modesty sake the Riches of her beutyes, but *Pyrocles* tooke holde of his Barr mynding at least to dye before the excellent *Philoclea* shoulde receyve any outerage. But *Philanax* rested a while upon hym self, striken wth admiration at the excellent shape of *Pyrocles*, whome before hee had never seene, and withall remembring the notable acte hee had done, (when with his Corage and eloquence hee had saved *Basilius* perchaunce the whole State from utter Ruyñ,) hee felt a kynde of Relenting towardes hym : But when the same thought came wayted on with the Remembrance of his Masters deathe, (wch hee by all probabilityes thoughte hee had beene of Counsell unto with the *Duchess*) Compassyon turned into hatefull passyon, and lefte in *Philanax* a straunge Medley betuixt pity and Revenge betwixt liking and abhorring. O Lorde sayde hee to hym self what wonders dothe *Nature* in oure tyme, to sett wickednes so beutyfully garnisshed ? and that whiche ys straungest, oute of one spring to make wonderfull effectes bothe of vertue and vyce to issue ? *Pyrocles* seeyng hym in suche a Muse, neyther knowyng ye Man nor the cause of his Coming, but assuring hym self yt was not for his good, yet thoughte best to begin wth hym in this sorte: Gentleman sayde hee, what ys the Cause of youre Coming to my Lady *Philocleas* Chamber ? ys yt to defend her from suche vyolence, as I mighte goo aboute to offer unto her ? yf yt bee so, truely youre Coming ys in vayne : For her owne vertue hathe beene a sufficient resistance, there needes no strength to bee added to so invyolate Chastity. The exellency of her mynde makes her body ympugnable, whiche for my owne parte I had soone yeelded to Confess by goyng oute of this place (where I founde but litle Comfort beeyng so disdaynefully receyved) had I not beene I knowe not by whome presently uppon my coming hether so locked into this Chamber that I coulde never escape hence : where I was fettered in the moste guilty shame that ever Man was, seeyng what a Paradyse of unspotted goodnes my filthy thoughtes soughte to defyle, Yf for that therefore yo^w come, all redy I assure yo^w youre arrant ys performed : But yf yt bee to bring me, to any punishment whatsoever for having undertaken so unexcusable presumption, truely, I beare suche an Accuser aboute mee of myne owne Conscyence, that I willingly submitt my self unto yt. Onely thus muche lett mee demaunde of yo^w that yo^w will bee a witness unto the *Duke* what yow heare mee say, and oppose youre self y^t neyther his sodayne fury nor any other occasyon may offer any hurte to this Lady in whome yo^w see nature hathe accomplisshed so muche, that I am fayne to lay myne owne faultynes as a foyle

of her purest excellency; I can say no more, but look upon her
Beuty, Remember her blood, consider her yeares, and Judge
rightly of her vertues, and I doubte not a Gentlemans mynde
will then bee a sufficyent instructer unto yo^w in this (I may
terme yt miserable) Chaunce hapned unto her by my unbrydeled
audacity. *Philanax* was content to heare hym oute, not for
any favoure hee owed hym, but to see whether hee woulde
reveyle any thing of the originall Cause, and purpose of the
Dukes deathe: But fynding yt so farr from that, that hee named
Basilius unto hym (as supposing hym alyve) thincking yt rather
Cunning then ignorance, Younge man saide hee whome I have
cause to hate before I have meane to knowe, yow use but a
poynte of skill by Confessing the manifest smaller faulte to bee
beleved hereafter in the Denyall of the greater. But for that
matter all passeth to one ende, & hereafter we shall have leysure
to seeke by tormentes the truthe yf the love of truthe yt self
will not bringe yo^w unto yt. As for my Lady *Philoclea* yf yt so
falle oute as yo^w say yt shall bee the more fitt for her yeares
and comely for the greate howse shee came of, that an yll
governed beaty hathe not Cancelled the Rules of vertue: But,
howsoever yt bee yt ys not for yo^w to teache an *Arcadian* what
reverent Duty wee owe to any of that progeny, But, sayde
hee come yow with mee withoute resistance for the one can
not avayle, and the other may procure pitty. Pitty (sayde *Pyrocles*
with a bitter smyling, disdayned wth so currish an answer) No,
No *Arcadian* I can quickly have pitty of my self, and I wolde
thinck my lyfe moste miserable whiche shoulde bee a gifte of
thyne? Onely I demaunde this Innocent Ladyes security, w^ch
untill thow haste confirmed unto mee by an oathe, assure thy
self the first that layes handes on her shall leave his lyfe for a
Testimony of his sacriledge. *Philanax* with an Inward scorne,
thincking yt moste manifest, they were bothe (hee at least)
Counsell of the *Dukes* deathe, well (sayde hee) yow speake muche
to mee of the *Duke* I do heare sweare unto yo^w by the Love I
have ever borne hym shee shall have no worse (howesoever yt
falle oute) then her owne Parentes. And uppon that worde ot
youres I yeelde, sayde the pore *Pyrocles*, deceyved by hym that
ment not to deceyve hym. Then did *Philanax* sende for apparrell for hym, and having arrayed hym delyvered hym into
the handes of a noble man in the Company, every one desyerus

to have hym in his charge: Somuche did his goodly presence (in whome true valure shyned) bredd a delightfull admiration in all the beholders. *Philanax* hym self stayed wth *Philoclea* to see, whether of her hee mighte learne any disclosing of this former Confusion: But shee sweete Lady whome first a kyndly shamefastnes had seperated from *Pyrocles* (they beeyng bothe lefte in a more open viewe then her modesty woulde well beare) Then, the attending her Fathers Comyng and studying howe to behave her self towardes hym for bothe theyre savetyes had called her spirites unto her, now that *Pyrocles* uppon a sodeyn was delivered oute of the Chamber from her. At the first shee was so surprised with the extreme strokes of the wooful sighte that like those that in theyre Dreame are taken with some ugly vision, they woulde fayne crye for help, but have no force, so remayned a while quite deprived not onely of speeche but allmoste of every other lyvely action. But when in deede *Pyrocles* was quite drawne from her eyes, and that her vitall strength began to returne unto her, now not knowing what they did unto *Pyrocles* (but according to the nature of Love fearing the worste) wringing her handes and letting abundance of Teares bee the first parte of her eloquence bending her amber crowned hed over her bedsyde to the hard harted *Philanax*: O *Philanax*, *Philanax* sayde shee I knowe howmuche authority yo^w have with my Father, there ys no Man whose wysdome hee somuche esteemes, nor whose faythe hee somuche reposeth uppon. Remember how ofte yo^w have promysed youre service unto mee? How often yow have given mee occasion to beleeve that there was no Lady in whose favour yow desyerd more to remayne: Nowe my Chaunce ys turned, lett not youre trothe turne, I present my self unto yo^w the moste miserable & humble supplyant Living. Neyther shall my desyer bee greate, I seeke for no more lyfe, then I shall bee thought worthy of, yf my bloode may wassh away the Dishonor of *Arcadia*, spare yt not, allthoughe through mee yt hathe never bene willingly dishonored. My onely suite ys yo^w will bee a meane for mee, that while I am suffered to enjoy this lyfe I may not bee separated from hym, to whome the gods have joyned mee: And that yo^w determeyn no thing more cruelly of hym then yo^w do of mee And yf yo^w rightly judge of oure vertuous Mariage whereto oure Innocencyes were the solempnityes, and the goddes

them selves ye witnesses, then procure wee may live together:
But yf my Father will not so conceyve of us, as the faulte
(yf any were) was united, so lett the punishment bee united
allso: There was no Man that ever loved his Prince or any
thing pertayning unto hym wth a truer harte then *Philanax* did,
this made eeven to the depthe of his harte receyve a moste
vehement greef to see his Master made as yt were more miserable after deathe: And for hym self there was nothing coulde
have kept hym from falling to all tender pitty, but the perfect
perswasion hee had that all this was joyned to the pack of ‚his
Masters deathe, wch the speeche of Maryage made hym the
more beleeve. Therefore muttering to hym self suche like wordes,
the vyolence the Gentleman spake of ys now turned to Mariage,
hee alledged *Mars* but shee spake of *Venus*: O unfortunate
Master this hathe beene that fayre Devell *Gynecia*, hathe sent
away one of her Daughters prostituted the other, empoysoned
thee to overthrow ye Dyadem of *Arcadia*? But at lengthe, thus
unto her self hee sayde, Yf youre Father (Madame) were now to
speake unto, truly there shoulde no body bee founde a more
Redy Advocate for yo^w then my self: For I woulde suffer this
faulte, thoughe very greate to bee blotted oute of my mynde by
youre former ledd lyfe, and beeyng Daughter to suche a Father:
But, synce amonge youre selves yo^w have taken hym away, in
whome was the onely power to have mercy, yow must nowe bee
Cloathed in youre owne worcking, and looke for no other then
that wch Deade pityles Lawes may allott unto yo^w. For my
parte, I loved yo^w for youre vertue, but nowe where ys that I
loved yo^w for? Youre Father? unhappy folkes yo^w have robbed
the worlde of hym? These wordes of her Father were so litle
understoode of the onely well understanding *Philoclea*, that shee
desyerd hym to tell her what hee ment to speake in suche darcke
sorte unto her of her Lorde and Father? whose displeasure was
more dreadfull unto her, then her punishment, that shee was free
in her owne Conscyence, shee had never deserved evell of hym,
but in this last facte: Wherein notwithstanding yf yt pleased
hym to proceede with pacyence, hee shoulde fynde her Choyse
had not beene unfortunate. Hee that sawe her wordes written
in ye playne table of her fayre face, thoughte yt impossible
there shoulde bee therein conteyned deceypte, and therefore so
muche the more abasshed: Why saide hee Madame, woulde yow

284

have mee thinck that yow are not of Conspiracy with Princess *Pamelas* flighte & youre Fathers deathe? with that worde the sweete Lady gave a pityfull Crye, having streighte in her face and brest abundance of witnesses that her harte was farr from any suche abhominable Consent: Ah, of all sydes utterly ruyned *Philoclea* sayde shee, now in deede I may suffer all Consent of hope to dye, in mee? Dere Father where was I that might not doo yo^w my last service? before? soone after miserably followyng yo^w. *Philanax* perceyved the Demonstration so lyvely and true in her, that hee easily acquyted her in his harte of that facte, and the more was mooved to joyne with her in moste harty Lamentation: But Remembring hym that the burden of the State and punishment of his Masters Murders lay all uppon hym, well (sayde hee) Madame I can doo no thinge withoute all the States of *Arcadia*. What they will determyn of yo^w I knowe not, For my parte youre speeches woulde muche prevayle with mee but that I fynde not howe to excuse youre giving over youre body to hym, that for the last proofe of his Treason lent his garmentes to disguyse youre miserable Mother in ye moste vyle facte shee hathe committed: Hardd surely yt will bee, to seperate youre Causes, wth whome yo^w have so nerely joyned youre self. Neyther do I Desyer yt, sayde the sweetely weeping *Philoclea*, what soever yo^w do determyñ of hym, Do that like wyse to mee for I knowe from the fountayne of vertue, nothing but vertue coulde ever proceede. *Philanax* feeling his harte more and more mollifying to her renewed the ymage of his Deade Master in his fancy and using that for the spurres of his Revengefull Choller, went sodenly withoute any speeche from the Desolate Lady, to whome now fortune seemed to threaten unrype Deathe, and undeserved shame among her least evells: But *Philanax* leaving good guarde uppon the Lodge, went hym self to see the order of his other Prisoners, whome even then as hee issewed hee founde encreased with unhoped meanes, the order of wch shall bee from the beginninge therof declared.

Longe mee thinckes yt ys, since any thinge hathe beene spoken of ye Noble Prince *Musidorus* especially having beene lefte in so impacyent a Case, as hee shoulde hardly brooke a tedyous Respite: But so soveraigne a possessyon the Charming *Philoclea* had stolne into that her Eldest Sister was allmoste forgotten. Who having delyverd over the Burden of her fearefull Cares to the naturall ease of a well refresshing sleepe, reposing bothe her body and mynde uppon the trusted supporte of her Princely Shepehearde was with the braying Cryes of a Rascall Company robbed of her quyett: At what tyme shee was in a shrewde lykelyood, to have had greate parte of her trust in *Musidorus* deceyved, and founde her self robbed of that shee had layed in store, as her dearest Jewell, so did her owne beutyes enforce a force ageanst her self. But a greate perill preserved her from the Lesse, and the Coming of her Enimyes defended her from the vyolence of a Frende, so that shee at one instant opened her eyes whiche (in so duble a daunger) had greate neede to looke to them selves: And the every way enraged *Musidorus* rase from her enraged, betuixt the repentant shame of his promyse breaking attempt, and the tyrannicall fyer of Lust, whiche (having all redy caughte holde of so sweete and fitt a fewell) was past the Calling back of Reasons counsell, and nowe betwixt the Doubte hee had what these men woulde goo aboute and the spyte hee conceyved ageanst theyre Combersome presence. But the Clownes having with theyre hidyous noyse broughte them bothe to theyre feete, had soone knowledge what guests they had founde: For in deede these were the skoñy Remnaunte of those *Phagonian* Rebells, whose noughty myndes coulde not trust so muche to ye goodnes of theyre Prince as to lay theyre hangeworthy neckes uppon the Constancy of his promysed pardon. Therefore, when the rest (who as sheepe had but followed theyre fellowes) so sheepishly had submitted them selves, these onely committed theyre safety to the thickest parte of the Dezart woodes: who as they were in the Constitution of theyre myndes litle better then Beastes so were they apte to degenerate to a beastly kynde having these fewe dayes all redy framed theyre gluttonish stomackes, to have for foode the wylde benefittes of Nature, the uttermoste ende they had beeyng but to drawe oute asmuche as they coulde the Lyne of a tedyous lyffe. In this sorte vagabunding in those untrodden places, they were guyded by the everlasting Justice to bee Chastizers of *Musidorus* broken vowe: whome assoone as they sawe turned towardes them, they full well remembred yt was hee that (accompanyed with some other honest Shepeherdes) had come to the succoure of *Cleophila*, and had lefte among

286

some of them bloody tokens of his valeure, As for *Pamela*, they had many tymes seene her. Thus first styrred up wth a Rusticall revenge ageanst hym, and then desyer of spoyle, to help theyre miserable wantes, butt cheefly thinckyng yt was the way to Confirme theyre owne pardon, to bring the Princess back ageane unto her owne Father, whome (they were sure) hee woulde never have sent so farr sleyghtly accompanyed: They did (without any other Denounsing of warre) sett alltogether uppon the worthy *Musidorus*, who (beeynge before hand, asmuche inflamed ageanst them for the interrupting his vehement pursuite) gave them so brave a wellcome, that the smarte of some made the Rest stand farder of Crying, and prating ageanst hym, but like badd Curres rather barking then closing. Hee in the meane tyme placyng his trembling Lady to one of the fayre Pyne trees, and so setting hym self before her, as mighte shewe the Cause of his Corage grewe in hym self but ye effect was onely employed in her defence: The villaynes that nowe had a second prooffe, howe yll wardes they had for suche a sworde turned all theyre vyolence into throwyng Dartes and stones, in deede the onely way to overmaster the valeure of *Musidorus*. Who fyndyng them some allredy touche, some falle so nere his Cheefest Lady *Pamela*, that in the ende some other might happ to do an incurable myscheef, (setting all his hope in dispayre) ranne oute from his Lady amonge them: who streighte, lyke so many swyne, (when a hardy Mastiff settes uppon them,) dispersed them selves, but the first hee overtooke, as hee ranne, carrying his heade as farr before hym (as those maner of Ronninges are wonte to doo) wth one blowe strake yt cleare of, that (yt falling betuixt the handes and the body and the body falling uppon yt) yt made a shewe as thoughe the fellow had had greate haste to gather up his heade ageane: Another the speede hee made to ronne for ye best game, bare hym full butt ageanst a Tree, so that tumbling back with a brused face and a Dreadfull expectation *Musidorus* was streight uppon hym, and parting with his sworde one of his Legges from hym, lefte hym to make a roaring Lamentation that his morter treading was marred for ever. A thirde, fyndyng his feete to slowe aswell as his handes too weyke, sodenly turned back beginning to open his lippes for mercy, But before hee had well entered a Rudely Compyled oration, *Musidorus* blade was come betuixt his Jawes into his throate, and so the pore man rested there for ever wth a very yll mouthe-full of an answer: *Musidorus* in this furyous chafe woulde have followed some other of those hatefull wretches, but that hee hearde his Lady crye for help. Whome 3 of that villaynous Crewe had (whilest *Musidorus* followed theyre fellowes) compassing aboute some Trees sodenly come uppon and surprysed, threatning to kill her, yf shee cryed, and meaning to Convey her oute of sighte while the Prince was making his blood thirsty Chase: But shee y^t was resolved no worse thinge coulde falle unto her then the beeyng deprived of hym, (on whom shee had establisshed all her Comfort) wth a pityfull Crye fetched his eyes unto her. Who then thinckinge so many weapons thrust into his eyes as wth his eyes hee saw bent ageanst her, made all harty speede to succoure her: But one of them wyser then his Companyons, sett his Dagger to her Alablaster throate, swearing yf hee threwe not away his sworde hee woulde presently kill her. There was never pore Scholler that having in steade of his Booke some playing Toy aboute hym did more sodenly Cast yt from hym, as the Chylde feared presence of a Crewell Schoole Master, then the valourus *Musidorus* dischardged hym self of his onely Defence when hee sawe yt stoode uppon the instant poynte of his Ladyes Lyfe: And, holding up his noble handes to so unworthy audyence, O *Arcadians*? yt ys I, yt ys I that have done yo^w the wronge, shee ys youre Princess (sayde hee) shee never had will to hurte yow, and yo^w see shee hathe no power, use youre Choller uppon mee that have better deserved yt, Doo not youre selves the wronge to do her any hurte, wch in no tyme or place will ever bee forgiven yo^w: They that yet trusted to his Curtesy bad hym stande furder of from his sworde, whiche hee obaydyently dyd, so farr was Love above all other thoughtes in hym. Then did they calle together the rest of theyre fellowes, who thoughe they were fewe yet according to theyre number possessed many places, and then begãn those Savage Senators to make a Consultatyon what they should doo: Some wisshing to spoile them of theyre Jewells, and lett them goo on theyre Journey (for that yf they carryed them back, they were sure they shoulde have least parte of the pray) others preferring theyre owne homes to any thinge desyering to bringe them to *Basilius* as pledges of theyre surety, and there wanted not, wch cryed, the safest way was to kille them bothe. To suche an unwoi thy thraldome were these greate and excellent personages broughte, but the moste parte resisted to the killing of the Princess, foreseeyng theyre Lyves coulde never bee safe after suche a facte committed, and began to wishe rather the spoyle then Deathe of *Musidorus*: when the villayne that had his legg cutt of, came scrawling towardes them, and beeyng helped to them by one of the Company began wth a groning voyce and wth a disfigured face to demaunde the revenge of his blood, wch synce hee had spent wth them in theyre defence, yt were no reason hee shoulde bee suffered by them to dye discontented. The onely contentment hee requyred was that by theyre help wth his owne handes hee might putt his Murderer to some Crewell deathe: Hee woulde fayne have cryed more ageanst *Musidorus*, but that muche loss of blood helped on wch with this vehemency choked up the spirites of his lyfe leaving hym to make betwixt his body and his sowle an evill favoured partition. But they seeyng theyre fellowe in that sorte dye before theyre faces did swell in newe mortall Rages, all resolved to kill hym, but nowe onely Considering what maner of terrible Deathe they shoulde invent for hym. Thus was a while the agreemēt of his slaying broken by the Disagreement of the maner of yt, and extremity of cruelty grewe for a tyme to bee ye stopp of Cruelty: At lengthe they were resolved every one to have a peece of hym and to beecome all aswell hangemen as Judges. When, *Pamela*, tearing her hayre, and falling downe among them, some tymes with all the sorte of humble prayers mixt with promyses of greate good turnes, (wch they knewe her state was able to performe): Sometyme threatning them that yf they killed hym and not her, shee woulde not onely revenge yt uppon them, but uppon all theyre wyves and Children. Bidding them Consider that thoughe they mighte thincke shee was come away in her fathers Displeasure, yet they mighte bee sure hee woulde ever shewe hym self a Father that the goddes woulde never yf shee lived putt her in so base estate but that shee shoulde ever have abillity to plague suche as they were: Returning afressh to prayers and promyses, and mixing the same ageane with threatninges broughte them (who were nowe growne Colder in theyre fellowes Cause who was past aggravating the matter wth his Cryes) to determeyn with them selves there was no way, but eyther to kill them bothe or save them bothe. As for ye killing,

allredy they having answered them selves, that that was a way
to make them Citizens of the woodes for ever, they did in fyne
Conclude they woulde returne them back ageane to the *Duke*,
wch they did not doubte woulde bee a Cause of a greate Rewarde
besydes theyre saftye from theyre foredeserved punishment:
Thus having eyther by fortune or the force of these twoo Lovers
inward working Vertue settled theyre Crewell hartes to this
genteler Course, they tooke theyre twoo horses and having sett
uppon them theyre Princely prisoners, they returned towardes
the Lodge. The villaynes having decked all theyre heades with
Lawrell Braunches as thincking they had done a notable acte,
singing and showtinge, ranne by them in hope to have broughte
them the same day to the *Duke*: But the tyme was so farr
spent that they were forced to take up that Nightes Lodging
in ye midest of the woodes. Where while the Clownes continewed theyre watche aboute them now that the nighte according to his darck nature did adde a kynde of desolation to
the pensive hartes of the twoo afflicted Lovers: yt ys sayde
that *Musidorus* taking the tender hande of *Pamela* and bedew-
yng yt with his teares, in this sorte gave an Issue to ye swelling of his hartes greef. Moste excellent Lady saide hee, in what
Case thincke yo^w I am with my self, how unmercyfull Judgmentes do I lay uppon my sowle? Now that I knowe not what
god hathe reserved my well meaning enterpryse, as in steade of
doyng yo^w that honoure wch I hoped (and not withoute reason I
hoped) *Thessalia* shoulde have yeelded unto yo^w, am nowe like
to beecome a wretched instrumẽt of youre Discomfort: Alas,
howe Contrary an ende have all the Inclinacyons of my mynde
taken? my faythe falles oute a Treason unto yo^w, and the true
honor I beare yo^w ys the Feelde wherein youre Dishonor ys
like to bee sowne? But I Invoke that universall and onely
wysdome (wch examening the depthe of hartes hathe not his
judgement fixed upon ye event) to beare testimony with mee,
that my desyer (thoughe in extremest vehemency) yet did not
so overgoo my Remembraunce, but that as farr, as mans witt
mighte bee extended I soughte to prevent all thinges y^t mighte
falle to youre hurte: But nowe that all evill fortunes of evill
fortune have crossed my best framed intent, I am moste miserable in y^t that I can not onely not give yow help, but (wch ys
worste of all) am barred from giving yo^w Counseill; For howe

shoulde I open my mowthe to Counsell yo^w in that wherein
yo^w are by my Counseyll moste unworthely falne. The fayre
and wyse *Pamela* (alltho full of Cares of the unhappy turning
of his matter) yet seeyng the greef of *Musidorus* onely sturred
for her, did so treade downe all other motions with the true
force of vertue, that shee thus answered hym, having first
kissed hym (whiche before shee had never done) eyther Love so
comaunding her wch doubted howe longe they shoulde enjoy
one an other, or of a lyvely sparcke of noblenes to descend in
moste favour when hee ys Lowest in affliction. My Dere and
ever Dere *Musidorus* sayde shee, a greate wronge yo^w doo to
youre self that will torment yo^w thus with greef for the faulte
of fortune, synce a Man ys bounde no further to hym self, then
to doo wysely: The Chaunce ys onely to truble them that
stande uppon chaunce, but greater ys ye wrong (at least yf any
thing comes from yo^w may beare the name of wronge) yow doo
unto mee to thincke mee eyther so Chyldish as not to perceyve
youre faythfull faultlessnes or perceyving yt so basely disposed, as
to lett my harte bee overthrowne, standing uppon yt self in so
unspotted a purenes. Holde for certeyne, moste worthy *Musidorus*
yt ys youre self I love, wch can no more bee diminished by these
flowers of evell happ, then flowers are marred wth the tymely
Raynes of Aprill: For howe can I want Comfort, that have the
true and Living Comfort of my unblemisshed vertue? And how
can I wante honor, as longe as *Musidorus* (in whome in deede
honor ys) dothe honor mee? Nothinges bredd from my self can
discomfort mee? and fooles opinyons I will not recoñ as Dishonor. *Musidorus*, looking up to the starres, O mynde of myndes
(sayde hee) the Living power of all thinges wch doest with all
those eyes beholde oure ever varying actions, accept into thy
favourable eares this prayer of myne: Yf I may any Longer
holde oute this dwelling on the earthe, wch ys called a Lyfe,
graunte mee abillity to deserve at this Ladyes handes the grace
shee hathe shewed unto mee; Graunte mee wysdome to knowe
her wysdome and goodnes, so to encrease my Love of her goodnes, that all myne owne chosen desyers bee to my self, but
second to her Determynacyon, what soever I bee, lett yt bee
to her service. Lett mee herein bee satisfyed, that for suche
infinite favoures of vertue I have someway wroughte her satisfaction, but yf my last tyme approcheth, and that I am no longer

to bee among mortall Creatures, make yet my deathe serve her to some purpose? That hereafter shee may not have Cause to repent her self that shee bestowed so excellent a mynde uppon *Musidorus*. *Pamela* coulde not chose but accorde the Conceypte of theyre fortune to these passionate prayers, in somuche, that her Constant eyes yeelded some teares wch wyping from her fayre face with *Musidorus* hande, speakinge softely unto hym, as yf shee had feared more that any body shoulde bee a witnes of her weykenes, then of any thinge else shee had sayde: Yow see, saide shee my Prince, and onely Lorde, what yo^w worcke in mee by youre too muche greeving for mee? I pray yo^w thinck I have no joy but in yo^w, and yf yo^w fill that with sorowe, what doo yo^w for mee? What ys prepared for us wee knowe not, but what with sorowe wee can prevent yt wee knowe: Now lett us turne from these thinges, and thincke yo^w howe yow will have mee behave myself towardes yo^w in this matter. *Musidorus* fynding the authority of her speeche confirmed with direct necessity, the first care came into his mynde was of his dere frende and Cossen the Prince *Pyrocles*, with whome at his parting hee had Concluded what names they shoulde beare, yf upon any occasyon they were forced to give them selves oute for greate men, and yet not make them selves fully knowne: Nowe, fearing least yf ye Princess shoulde name hym for *Musidorus*, the fame of theyre twoo beeynge together woulde discover *Pyrocles*. Holding her hand betuixt his handes a good while together, I did not thincke moste excellent Princess sayde hee to have made any further Request unto yo^w, for, having bene allredy to yow so unfortunate a Suiter, I knowe not what modesty can beare any further Demaunde: But, the estate of one younge Man whome (next to yow farr before myself) I Love more then all the worlde, one bothe worthy of all well beeyng for the noble Constitution of his mynde, and moste unworthy to receyve hurte by mee whome hee dothe in all faythe and Constancy love, the pitty of hym onely goes beyonde all Resolution to the Contrary. Then did hee (to the Princess greate admiratyon) tell her the whole story as farre, as hee knewe of yt; and that when they made the grievous disjunction of theyre longe Company, they had Concluded, *Musidorus* shoulde entitle hym self *Palladius* Prince of *Caria*, and *Pyrocles* shoulde bee *Tymophorus* of *Licia*: Nowe saide *Musidorus* hee keeping a womans habit, ys to use none other name then *Cleo-phila*. But I that fynde yt best of the one syde for youre Honor yt bee knowne yow went away with the *Prince*, and not with a Shepehearde, Of the other syde (accoumpting any deathe less evill, then ye betraying that sweete frende of myne) will take this meane betuixt bothe, and using the name of *Palladius*, (yf the respect of a Prince will stopp youre Fathers fury) that will serve as well as *Musidorus*, untill *Pyrocles* fortune beeyng some way establisshed, I may freely give good prooffes, that the Noble Contry of *Thessalia* ys myne. And yf that will not mitigate youre Fathers opinyon to mee wardes, *Nature* I hope worcking in youre excellencyes will make hym deale well by yow, for my parte the Image of deathe ys nothing fearefull unto mee: And this good I shall have reaped by yt that I leave my moste esteemed frende in no Daunger to bee disclosed by mee. And besydes, (synce I must Confess I am not withoute a Re-morse of her Case) my vertuous Mother shall not knowe her Sonnes vyolent Deathe hid under the fame will goo of *Pal-ladius*: But as Long as her yeares now of good nomber bee coumpted among the Living, shee may joy her self with some possibility of my Returne. *Pamela* promysing hym uppon no occasyon ever to name hym, fell into extremity of weepinge as yf her eyes had beene content to spend all theyre seeyng moyste-nes; Now that there was speeche of the Losse of that wch they helde for theyre cheefest Lighte: So that *Musidorus* was forced to repay her good Counsells wth sweete Consolatyons, wch con-tinewed betuixt them untill yt was aboute Midnighte that theyre thoughtes eeven weary of theyre owne Burdens fell into a strayinge kynde of uncerteynty. And the mynde standing onely uppon the nature of theyre Inward Intelligences, lefte theyre bodyes to give a sleeping respitt to theyre vitall Spirittes: whiche they according to the quality of sorowe receyved with greeter greedynes then ever in theyre Lyves before. According to the nature of sorowe I say that whiche ys past Cares, Remedy, for care stirring ye brayne and making thyn the spirites breaketh rest. But those greeffes wherein one ys determyned there ys no preventing do breede a dull hevynes wch easely clothes yt self in sleepe: As yt fell oute in these persons who dilicately wounde up one in an others Armes layde a plott in y^t picture of deathe, how gladly, yf Deathe came, theyre sowles woulde goo together.

But, assoone as the Morning appeared to play her parte, wch as yow have hearde was laden wth so many well occasioned Lamentacyons, theyre Lobbish guarde (who had all nighte kept them selves awake with prating how valyant actes they had done when they rañ away and howe fayre a deathe theyre fellowe dyed who at his last gaspe sewed to bee a Hangeman) awaked them and sett them uppon theyre horses: To whome the very shyning sorte of excellent vertue thoughe in a very harrish subject had wrought a kynde of reverence in them. *Musidorus* as hee ridd among them of whome they had no other holde` but the holde of *Pamela*, thincking yt wante of a well squared judgment to leave any meane unassayed of saving Lyves, to this purpose spake to his unseemely guardyans, using a playne kynde of phrase, to make his speeche the more Credible. My Masters sayde hee there ys no man that ys wyse but hathe, in whatsoever hee dothe some purpose whereto hee directeth his Doynge: wch so longe hee followes till hee see, that eyther that purpose ys not worthe the paynes, or that an other Doynge carryes with yt a better purpose. That yow are wyse in what yo^w take in hande I have to my Coste learned, that makes mee Desyer yow to tell mee what ys the ende in Carrying the *Princess* and mee back ageane to her Father? Pardon sayde one, Rewarde cryed an other; well sayde hee take bothe, alltho I knowe yow are wyse to Remember that hardly they bothe together, beeing of so contrary a making, for the grounde of pardon ys an evill, neyther any man pardons but remembers an evill done: The Cause of Rewarde ys the opinion of some good acte, and who so rewardeth that holdes the cheef place of his fancy. Nowe one Man of one Company to have the same Consideracyon bothe of good and evell, but that the Conceipt of pardoning (yf yt bee pardoned) will take away the mynde of Rewarding, ys very hard, yf not impossible; for eyther even in Justice will hee punish the faulte aswell as Reward ye Desert or else in mercy ballance the one wth the other, so that the not Chastizing shall bee a sufficyent satisfying. Thus then yo^w may see that in youre owne purpose restes greate uncerteynty: But I will graunte that by this youre Deede yo^w shall obtayne youre Duble purpose. Yet Consider I pray yo^w whether by an other meane, that may not better bee obtayned, and then I doubt not youre wisdomes will teache yo^w to take holde of the better: I am

sure yow knowe any body were better have no neede of a
pardon then enjoy a pardon, for as yt carryes with yt the surety
of a preserved lyfe, so beares yt a Continuall note of a deserved
Deathe. This therefore besydes the Daunger yow may Ronne
into, my Lady *Pamela* beeying the undoubted Inheritrix of this
State, (yf shee shall seeke to revenge youre wronge done unto
her) shall bee continually Cast in youre teethe as Deade Men
by the Lawe: The honester sorte will disdayne youre Company
and youre Children shall bee the more basely reputed of and
youre selves in every slight faulte hereafter, as Men once Condempned aptest to bee overthrowne. Now yf yow will, as I
Doubt not yow will (for yow are wyse) turne youre Course,
and guarde my Lady *Pamela* thetherward, whether shee was
goyng, first yow neede not doubt to adventure youre Fortunes
whether shee goes, and there shall yow bee assured in a Contrey
as good and Riche as this yt of the same Manners and Language,
to bee so farr from the Conceipte of a pardon as wee bothe
shall bee forced to acknouledge wee have receyved by youre
meanes, what soever wee holde deare in this lyfe: And so for
Rewarde judge yow, whether yt bee not more likely yow shall
there receyve yt, where yow have done no evill, but singuler &
undeserved goodnes, or heare where this service of youres shall
bee Diminished by youre Duety and blemisshed by youre
former faulte. Yes I protest and sweare to yow by the fayre
eyes of that Lady there shall no gentlemã in all that Contry
bee preferred, yow shall have Riches, pleasure, ease and that
wch ys best to suche worthy myndes, yow shall not bee forced
to cry mercy for a good fact, yow onely of all the *Arcadians*
shall have the prayse; in continewyng youre late valyant Attempt: These wordes in theyre myndes (who did no thing for
any love of goodnes but onely as theyre sences presented greater
shewes of proffett) began to make them waver, and some to
Clapp theyre handes and stretch theyre heades and sweare yt
was the best way. Others, that wolde seeme wyser then the
rest, to Capitulate what Tenementes they shoulde have, what
subsidyes they should pay, others to talke of theyre wyves, in
Doubte whether yt were best to sende for them or take newe,
where they went: Moste like Fooles not thinking redily what
was next to bee done, but imagening what theare they woulde
make when they came there. One or twoo onely of the least

Discoursers beginning to turne theyre faces towardes the woodes whiche they had lefte, and Comming within the playne nere to the Lodges when unhappily they espyed a Troupe of Horsemen: But then theyre false hartes had quickly for the present feare forsaken theyre last hopes. And therefore keeping on theyre way towardes the Lodge with Songes and Cryes of Joy, these Horsemen who were some of them *Philanax* had sent out to the searche of *Pamela*, came gallowping unto them: Merveyling who they were that in suche a generall mourning durst singe joyfull tunes and in so publique a Ruyn weare the Lawrell tokens of victory, and that wch seemed straungest, they mighte see Twoo among them unarmed like prisoners, but ryding like Capteynes. But when they came nearer they perceyved the one was a Lady, & the Lady *Pamela*: Then gladd they had by happe founde that wch they so litle hoped to meete with all taking these Clownes (who firste resisted them for the Desyer they had to bee the Deliverers of the twoo excellent Prisoners) learning that they were of those *Phagonyans* wch had made the Daungerus uprore. Aswell under Colour to punish that, as this theyre last withstanding them, but in Deede theyre principall Cause beeyng (bycause they them selves woulde have the onely prayse of theyre owne quest) they suffered not one of them to Live: Mary three of the stubbernest of them, they lefte theyre bodyes hanging uppon the Trees, bycause theyre doyng might carry the likelyer forme of judgement, suche an unloked for ende did the lyfe of Justice worcke for the naughty wretches by subjectes to bee executed, that woulde have executed Princes, and to suffer that withoute a Lawe, whiche by Lawe they had deserved. And thus these younge folckes, twyce Prisoners before any due arrest, delyvered of theyre Jaylors, but not of theyre Jayle, had rather chaunge, then respitt of misery: These Souldyors that tooke them wth very fewe wordes of intertaynement hasting to Carry them to theyre Lorde *Philanax*, to whome they came, even as hee (goynge owte of the Lady *Philocleas* Chamber) had overtaken *Pyrocles*, whome before hee had delivered to the Custody of a Noble Man of y^t Contry. When *Pyrocles* ledd towardes his prison sawe his frende *Musidorus* with the noble Lady *Pamela* in that inexpected sorte returned his greef (yf any greef were in a mynde wch had placed every thing according to his naturall worthe) was very muche augmented: For besydes some smalle hope hee had yf *Musidorus* had once bene clere of *Arcadia*, by his Dealing and aucthority to have broughte his onely gladsome desyers to good issue, The hard estate of his frend did no less, nay rather more vexe hym then his owne. For so in deede yt ys ever founde, where valor and frendship are perfectly Coopled in one harte, the reason beeyng that the resolute man having once disgested in his judgment the worste extremity of his owne Case, and having eyther quite repelled or at least excelled all passyon wch ordenarily followeth an over-throwne fortune, not knowyng his frendes mynde so well as his owne, not withoute pacyence hee brookes his Case: (whiche ys as yt were the materiall Cause of making a man happy or unhappy) doubtes whether his frende accoumptes not hym self more myserable and so in deede bee more lamentable. But assoone as *Musidorus* was brought by the Souldyors nere unto *Philanax, Pyrocles* (not knowyng whether ever after hee shoulde bee suffered to see his frende, and determeninge there coulde bee no advauntage by dissembling a not knowing of hym) lepte sodenly from theyre handes that helde hym: And passing wth a strengthe strengthened with a true affection thorowe them that encompassed *Musidorus* hee embrased hym as fast as hee coulde in his armes (and kissing his Cheeke) O my *Palladius*, sayde hee lett not oure vertue now abandon us? Let us proove oure myndes are no slaves to fortune? but in adversity can try-umphe over adversity? Dere *Tymophorus* answered *Musidorus* (seeyng by his apparell his beeyng a Man was revealed) I thancke yo^w for this best Care of my best parte, but feare not, I have kept too longe Company wth yo^w to want now a thorow Determi-nation of these thinges: I well knowe there ys no thing evell but within us, the rest ys eyther naturall or accidentall. *Philanax* fynding them of so nere acquayntance, began presently to ex-amen them a parte, but suche Resolution hee mett within them, that by no suche meanes hee coulde learne further, then yt pleased them to delyver: So that hee thoughte best to putt them bothe in one place, with espyall of theyre wordes and behavyour, that way to sifte oute the more of those forepassed myscheefes. And for that purpose gave them bothe unto the noble Man, who before had the Custody of *Pyrocles*, by name *Sympatus*, leavinge a trusty servaunt of his owne to give diligent watche to what might passe betwixt them. No man that had ever passed thorow the Schoole of affection needes doubte what a tormenting greefe yt was to the Noble *Pamela*, to have the Company of him taken from her to whose vertuous Company shee had bounde her lyfe: But waying with her self yt was fitt for her Honor till her Dooyng were clerely manifested, that they shoulde remayne seperate, kept downe yᵉ rysing tokens of greef shewyng passion in nothing but her eyes wᶜʰ accompanyed *Musidorus* even unto the Tent whether hee & *Pyrocles* were ledd. Then with a Countenaunce more Princely then shee was wonte according to the wonte of highest hartes (Lyke the Palme tree stryving moste upward when hee ys moste burdened) shee Comaunded *Philanax* to bring her to her father & her mother that shee might render them accoumpt of her doynges *Philanax* shewyng a sullen kynde of Reverence unto her: As a Man yᵗ honored her as his Masters heyre, but muche mislyked her (for her in his conceypt) Dishonorable proceedinges, tolde her what was past rather to answer her, then that hee thought shee was ignorant of yt. But her good spirit did presently suffer a true Compassionate Affliction of those hard adventures, wᶜʰ with Crossing her Armes looking a great whyle on the grounde wᵗʰ those eyes wᶜʰ lett falle many teares shee well declared: But in the ende Remembring howe necessary yt was for her not to loose her self in suche an extremity shee strengthened her well created harte, and stowtly demaunded *Philanax* what authority then they had to lay handes of her person who beeyinge the undoubted heyre, was then the Lawfull Princess of that *Dukedome*. *Philanax* answered her grace knew yᵉ auncyent Lawes of *Arcadia* bare shee was to have no sway of government till shee came to xxiᵗⁱ yeares of age or were marryed: And marryed I am (replyed the wyse *Princess*) therefore I Demaund youre Due allegiaunce? The goddes forbid (sayde *Philanax*) *Arcadia* shoulde bee a Dowery of suche Marryages? Besydes hee toulde her, all the States of her contry were evell satisfyed touching her Fathers Deathe: whiche lykewyse according to the Statutes of *Arcadia*, was even that day to bee judged of, before the body were remooved to receyve his Princely funeralles, After that past shee shoulde have suche obaydyence as by the Lawes was due unto her: Desyering god shee woulde shewe her self better in publique government, then shee had done in private. Shee woulde have spoken to the gentleman, but *Philanax* fearing least there

298

by some Commotyon might aryse, or at least a hynderance of executing his Masters Murderers, wch hee longed more after then any thing, hasted her up to the Lodge where her Sister was; And there with a Chosen Company of Soldyoures to guarde the place lefte her with *Philoclea*, *Pamela* protesting they layde vyolent handes uppon her, and that they entered into Rebellious attemptes ageanst her. But hye tyme yt was for *Philanax* so to doo, for all redy was the whole multitude falne into Confused and Daungerus Dimissions, there was a notable example how greate Dissipations Monarchiall governmentes are subject unto: For nowe theyre Prince and guyde had lefte them, they had not experyence to Rule, and had not whome to obay, Publique matters had ever beene privatly governed, so that they had no lyvely taste what was good for them selves, but every thing was eyther vehemently Desyrefull, or extremely terrible. Neighboures Invasions, Civill Discention, Crewelty of the Cominge Prince, & what so ever in Comon sence carryes a Dreadfull shewe was in all mens heades, but in fewe howe to prevent: Harckening on every Rumor, suspecting every thinge, Condempning them, whome before they had honoured, making straunge and impossible tales of the *Dukes* deathe, while they thoughte them selves in Daunger wisshing no thinge but safety assoone as perswasion of savety tooke them, Desyering further benefites as amendment of forepassed faultes (wch faultes notwithstanding none coulde tell eyther the grounde or effectes of) all agreeyng in the universall names of lyking or mysliking: But of what, in especyall poyntes, infinitely disagreeynge. Alltogether like a Falling steeple the partes wherof as wyndowes Stones and Pynacles were well but the whole Mass Ruynous: And this was the generall Case of all, wherein notwithstanding was an extreme medley of dyvers thoughtes. The great men, looking to make them selves stronge by factions, the Gentlemen some bending to them, some standing uppon them selves, some desyerus to overthrowe those fewe wch were over them: The Souldyoures desyerus of trubles as the Nurse of spoile, and not muche unlike to them (thoughe in an other way) were all the Needy sorte, The Riche fearefull the wyse Carefull. This Composicion of Conceyptes broughte forthe a Daungerus tumult, whiche yet, woulde have bene more daungerus, but that yt had so many partes, that no body well knewe ageanst whome to oppose them selves: For some there were that cryed to have the State altered and governed no more by a Prince, Mary in the alteration many woulde have the *Lacedemonian* government of fewe Chosen Senators, others the *Athenian* where the Peoples voyce helde the Cheef authority, but these were rather the Discoursing sorte of men, then the active; beeyng a matter more in Imaginacyon then practize. But they that went nere to the present Case (as in a Contry that knewe no governm^t withoute a Prince) were they that strave whome they should make: Wherof a greate Number there were, that woulde have the Princess *Pamela* presently to enjoy yt: Some disdayning that shee had as yt were abandoned her owne Contry, enclyning more to *Philoclea*: And there wanted not wch wisshed *Gynecia* were delivered and made *Regent* till *Pamela* were worthely marryed. But great Multitudes there were wch having bene acquaynted wth the Just government of *Philanax*, went to establish hym as Livetenaunt of the State, and these were the moste populer sorte, who judged by the Comodityes they felt. But the Principall men in honor and mighte who had longe before envyed his greatenes with *Basilius*, did muche more spurne ageanst any suche preferment of hym: For, yet, before theyre Envy had some kynde of breathing oute of his Rancor by laying his greatnes as a faulte to the *Princes* Judgment, who shewed in *Dametas* hee mighte easely bee deceyved in mens valew. But now yf the Princes choyse by so many mowthes shoulde bee Confirmed, what coulde they object to so Rightly esteemed an excellency? They therefore were disposed sooner to yeelde to any thing then to his raysing, and were content (to Crosse *Philanax*) to stopp those actions wch otherwyse they coulde nott. But thincke good *Philanax* hym self asmuche hyndered by those y^t did ymmoderately honour hym (wch brought bothe more envy and suspicyon uppon hym) as by them that did manifestly resist hym, (but standing onely uppon a Constant desyer of Justice, & a Clere Conscyence) went forward stowtly in the action of his Masters Revenge wch hee thoughte hym self particulerly bounde to: For ye Rest as the ordering of the government, hee accoumpted hym self but as one, wherein not withstanding hee would employ all his Loyall Indevoure. But amonge all the Noble men hee that moste sett hym self ageanst hym, was named *Tymantus* a Man of Middle age, but of extreme Ambition, as one that had placed his utter-

300

moste good in greatnes (thincking smalle difference by what
meanes hee came by yt): Of Comendable witt (yf hee had not
made yt a Servaunt to unbrydeled desyers), Conning to creepe
into Menns favour (wch hee prysed onely as they were servisable
unto hym), hee had bene brought upp in some Souldyery, w^{ch}
hee knewe howe to sett oute wth more then deserved ostentation,
servile, (thoughe envyous) to his betters. And no less tyranni-
cally mynded to them hee had advantage of, coumpted Revengefull, but in deede measuring bothe Revenge and Rewarde, as
the party might eyther help or hurt hym, rather shameles then
boulde: And yet more bolde in practizes then in personall
adventures, in Sum̃a a man that coulde bee as evell as hee listed,
and listed asmuche as any advauntage mighte thereby bee gotten,
as for vertue hee coumpted yt but a Schoolename. Hee even
at the first assembling together fynding the greate stroke *Philanax* carryed among the People, thought his redyest way of
Ambition to joyne with hym, wch thoughe his pryde did hardly
brooke, yet the other vyce carrying with yt a more apparaunt
object, preveyled over the weyker: So that with those Liberall
protestacyons of frendship (wch men that care not for theyre
worde are wonte to bestowe) hee offered unto hym the Choyse
in Mariage of eyther the Sisters, so hee woulde lyke wyse help
hym to the other, and make suche a partition of the *Arcadian*
estate. Wisshing hym that synce hee loved his Master bycause
hee was his Master wch shewed the Love begañ in hym self, hee
shoulde rather, (now occasion was presented) seeke his owne
good substancyally then affect the smoke of a glory by shewing
untymely fidelity to hym self that coulde not rewarde yt, and
have all the fruite hee should gett in Mennes opinyons, w^{ch}
woulde bee as dyvers as many, fewe agreeyng to yeelde to hym
due prayse of his true harte: But *Philanax* who had limitted his
thoughtes in that hee esteemed good, to wch hee was neither
carryed by the vayne tickling of uncerteyne fame, nor from
wch hee woulde bee trãsported by enjoying any thinge where
to the Ignorant worlde gives the excellent name of goodes, with
greate myslike of his offer, hee made hym so peremptory an
answer (not withoute threatning yf hee founde hym foster any
suche fancy) that *Tymantus* went with an Inward spyte from
hym whome before hee had never loved. And mesuring all
Mens Marches by his owne pace, rather thoughte yt some Further

fetche of *Philanax* (as that hee woulde have all to hym self
alone) then was any way taken with the Lovely beuty of his
vertue, whose Image hee had so quyte defaced in his owne sowle
that hee had lefte hym self no eyes to beholde yt. But stayed
wayting fitt oportunity to execute his desyers bothe for hym
self and ageanst *Philanax*, when by the bringing back of *Pamela*,
the People beeyng devyded into many motyons w^ch (bothe w^th
murmering Noyses and putting them selves in severall troupes)
they well shewed hee thought apte tyme was layde before hym
(the waters beeyng as the Proverb saythe trubled) and so the
better for his fisshing: Therefore, goyng among the Cheeffest
Lordes whome hee knewe Principally to repyne at *Philanax*,
and making a kynde of Convocation of them hee Inveyed
ageanst his proceeding, Drawyng every thinge to the moste
malicyous interpretation that Malice hym self coulde instruct
hym to doo. Hee sayde yt was season for them to looke to
suche a weede, that else woulde overgrowe them all, yt was not
now tyme to Consult of the Deade, but of ye Living, since
suche a slye wolffe was entered among them, that coulde make
Justice the Cloake of Tyranny, and Love of his late Master the
Distruction of his now beeyng Children: Do yow not see
saide hee how farr his Corruption hathe stretched, that hee
hathe suche a Nomber of Rascalles voyces to declare hym Lief-
tenaunt, redy to make hym Prince? But that hee instructes
them Matters are not yet rype for yt. As for us, bycause wee
are to Riche to bee boughte, hee thinckes us the fitter to bee
kylde: Hathe *Arcadia* bredd no man but *Philanax*? ys shee
become Steppmother to all ye Rest? and hathe given all her
blessinges to *Philanax*? Or yf there bee men among us, Lett
us shewe wee disdayne to bee Servauntes to a servaunte: Let
us make hym knowe, wee are farr worthyer not to bee Slaves
then hee to bee a Master. Thinck yo^w hee hathe made suche
haste in these matters to give them over to an other mans hande?
Thincke yow hee durst become the Jaylor of his Princess but
eyther meaning to bee her Master or her Murderer? And all
this for the dere good will hee beares to the *Dukes* memory whose
authority as hee abused in his lyfe, so hee woulde now persever,
to abuse his Name after his Deathe? O notable affection for
the Love of the Father to kill the wyfe, and disherite the
Children? O single mynded modesty, to aspyer to no lesse then

302

ARCADIA

the Princely Dyadem? No, No hee hathe viewed all this while,
but to rome the sooner to his affected ende. But let us Remember, what wee bee? in quality his equalles, in nomber farr
before hym, Lett us deliver the *Duchess*, and oure naturall
Princesses and leave them no longer under his aucthority; whose
proceedinges woulde rather shewe, that hee hym self had beene
the Murderer of the *Duke*, then a fitt Guardyan for his posterity. These pearst muche into the myndes all redy inclyned
that way, in so muche, that moste parte of the Nobillity Confirmed *Tymantus* speeche and were redy to execute yt: When
Philanax came amongst them, and with a Constant but reverent
behavyour desyered them, they woolde not exercyse private
Judges in so Comon a necessity. Hee acknowledged hym self
a Man, and a faulty man, to the Clearing or satisfying of w^ch
hee woulde at all tymes submitt hymself: Synce his ende was
to bringe all thinges to an upright Judgement, yt shoulde evill
fitt hym to flee the Judgment. But (sayde hee) my Lordes lett
not *Tymantus* rayling speeche (who what soever hee fyndes evill
in his owne Sowle can withe ease lay upon an other) make mee
Loose youre good favour: Consider that all well doynge standes
so in the midle betuixt his twoo Contrary evells that yt ys a
redy matter to Cast a sclaunderus shade uppon the moste approoved vertues. Who hathe an evill Toungue can calle severity
Crewelty and faythfull diligence, diligent ambition, but my
ende ys not to excuse my self, nor accuse hym, for bothe those
hereafter will bee tyme ynoughe. There ys neyther of us whose
purging or punishing may somuche importe to *Arcadia*. Nowe
I request yow for youre owne Honors sake, and Requyer yo^w
by the Duty yo^w owe to this Estate, that yo^w doo presently
(acording to ye Lawes) take in hande the Chastizement of oure
Masters Murderers and laying order for the government? By
whome soever yt bee done, so yt bee done and justly done I
am satisfyed, my Laboure hathe beene to frame thinges so as
yo^w mighte determeyn: For my parte, I calle the heavens to
wittnes the Care of my harte standes to repay that wherein bothe
I and moste of yo^w were tyed to that Prince, wth whome all my
Love of worldly action ys Deade. As *Philanax* was speaking his
last wordes, there came one Ronning to hym with open mowthe
and fearefull eyes, telling hym, that, there were a greate nomber
of the People, that were bent to take the younge men owte of

Sympathus handes: And as yt shoulde seeme by theyre acclamations were like ynoughe to proclayme them *Princes*. Nay sayde, *Philanax* speaking alowde, and (looking wth a just anger, uppon the other Noble Men) yt ys now season to heare *Tymantus* evill sclaunders, while Straungers bee come oure Lordes & *Basilius* Murderers sitt in his Throane? But whosoever ys a true *Arcadian*, lett hym follow mee? with that hee went toward ye place hee hearde of, followed by those that had ever loved hym, and some of the Noble men: Some other remayning wth *Tymanthus*, who in the meane tyme was Conspiring by stronge hand to deliver *Gynecia*, of whome the weykest guarde was had. But *Philanax* where hee went founde them all in an uproare wch thus was fallen owte: The greatest Multitude of people whiche were come to the Deathe of *Basilius* were the *Mantineans*, as beeyng the nearest Citty to the Lodges. Among these the Cheef man bothe in authority and Love was *Kerxenus*, hee that had not longe before beene Hoste to the twoo Princes: whome thoughe hee knewe not somuche as by name, yet theyre Noble behavyoure had bredd muche Love in his harte towardes them, as bothe with teares hee parted from them when they lefte hym (under promyse to returne) and kept theyre Jewells and Apparell as the Reliques of twoo Demy goddes. Among others hee had entered theyre Prison and seene them, wch forthewith so invested his sowle, bothe with sorowe and desyer to help them (whome hee tendered as his Children) that, calling his Neighboures the *Mantineans* unto hym, hee toulde them all the prayses of ye twoo young men: Swearing, hee thoughte the goddes had provyded for them better then they them selves coulde have imagined. Hee willed them to Consider, that when all was done *Basilius* Children must enjoy the state: who synce they had Chosen so as all the worlde coulde not mend theyre Choyse, why shoulde they resist godds doyng and theyre Princes pleasure? This was the onely way to purchase quyetnes withowte blood, where otherwyse, they should at one instant Crowne *Pamela* with a Crowne of golde, and a dishonored Tytle, whiche whether shee woulde ever forgett hee thought yt fitt for them to weighe: Suche (sayde hee) Heroicall greatnes shynes in theyre eyes, suche an extraordenary Matie in all theyre actions, as surely Fortune by Parentage or Nature in Creation hathe made them *Princes*. And yet a State all redy wee have, wee neede but a Man, who since hee ys presented unto yow by the heavenly providence, embraced by youre undoubted Princes, worthy (for theyre youthe) of Compassyon, (for theyre bewty) of admiration, and for theyre excellent vertue to bee *Monarches* of the world, shall wee not bee Contented with oure owne blisse? Shall wee putt owte oure eyes bycause an other man can not see? or rather like some men when too muche happens unto them, they thincke them selves in a Dreame, and have not spirites to taste theyre owne good? No, No, my Frendes beleeve mee I am so unpartiall that I knowe not theyre Names, but so overcome I am wth theyre vertue, that I shall then thincke the Destinyes have ordayned a perpetuall florisshing to *Arcadia*, when they shall allott suche a governmet unto yt: This spoken by a Man bothe grave in yeares & knowne honest, prevayled still with all the *Mantineans*, that wth one voyce, they rañ to delyver the twoo Princes. But *Philanax* came in tyme to withstand them (bothe sydes yet standing in Armes) and rather wanting a Beginning then myndes to enter into a bloody Conflict: whiche *Philanax* foreseyng, thoughte best to remove the Prisoners secretly, and (yf neede were) withoute forme of Justice to kill them, then ageanst Justice (as hee thoughte) to have them usurp the State. But there ageane arase a newe truble, for *Sympathus* the Noble man that kepte them, was so stricken in Compassyon with theyre excellent presence that as hee woulde not fallsify his promyse to *Philanax* to give them Liberty, so yet, woulde hee not yeelde them to hym self, fearing hee woulde doo them vyolence. Thus Tumult uppon Tumult arysing, the Sunne (I thincke) aweary to see theyre Discordes had allredy gonñ downe to his western Lodging: But yet, to knowe what the pore Shepeheardes did (who were the first Discryers of these Matters) will not to some eares perchaunce bee a tedyous Digressyon.

The Ende of the Fourthe Booke.

HERE BEGIN THE FOURTHE EGLOGUES.

The Shepeheardes fynding no place for them in these garboyles to whiche theyre quyet hartes (whose hyest ambition was in keeping them selves up in goodnes) had at all no aptenes, retyered themselves from among the Clamorous multitude: And as Sorow desyers Company, went up together to the western syde of a hill whose prospect extended so farr, as they mighte well discerne many of *Arcadias* beutyes. And there looking uppon the Sunnes (as then) declyning race, the pore men sate pensive of theyre present miseryes, as yf they founde a werysomnes of theyre wofull wordes: Till, at last good oulde *Geron* (who, as hee had longest tasted ye benefittes of *Basilius* government, so seemed to have a speciall feeling of the present Losse) wyping his eyes and longe white bearde bedewed with greate Droppes of teares, began in this sorte to Complayne. Alas pore sheepe sayde hee wch hetherto have enjoyed youre fruitfull pasture in suche quyetnes, as youre wolle (amongst other thinges) hathe made this Contry famous? Youre best Dayes are now past, Now must yow become the victell of an Army, and perchaunce an Army of Forayne Enimyes, yo^w are now not onely to feare Home Wolves, but Alyen Lyons? Nowe I say, Nowe, the *Basilius* oure Right *Basilius* ys deceased: Alas sweete pastures, shall Souldyoures that knowe not howe to use yo^w possess yo^w? Shall they that can not speake *Arcadian* language bee Lordes over youre Shepehardes? For alas with good Cause may wee looke for any evell, synce *Basilius* oure onely strengthe ys taken from us: To that all the other Shepeheardes present uttered pittyfull voyces, especially the very borne *Arcadians*. For, as for the other, thoughe Humanity mooved them to pitty humane Cases (especially of a Prince under whome they had founde a Refuge for theyre miseryes and Justice equally administred) yet they coulde not so naturally feele the Lyvely touche of sorow: But rather used this occasyon to recorde theyre owne private sorowes, whiche they thoughte woulde have agreed wth a more Joyfull tyme. Amonge them, the Principalles were *Strephon*, *Klaius* and *Philisides*, *Strephon* and *Klaius*

306

woulde requyer a whole Booke, to recoumpt theyre sorowes, and the straunge Causes of theyre sorowes: An other place perchaunce will serve for the better Declaring of them, but in short, twoo gentlemen they were, bothe in Love with one Mayde in that Contry named *Urania* thought a Shepeherdes Daughter, but in deede of farr greater byrthe. For her sake they had bothe taken this trade of lyfe, eche knowyng others love, but yet of so highe a quality theyre Frendship was, that they never so muche as brake Company one from the other: But continewed theyre pursuite, like twoo trewe Ronners, bothe employing theyre best speede, but one not hindering the other. But after many merveylous adventures *Urania* never yeelding better then hate for theyre Love, uppon a straunge occasyon lefte the Contry; Giving withall streight Commaundement to these Twoo by wryting that they shoulde tarry in *Arcadia* untill they harde from her, and now some moneths were past that they had no newse of her. But yet, rather meaning to breake theyre hartes, then breake her Comaundement, they bare yt oute aswell as suche evill mighte bee: Untill nowe that the generall Complayntes of all men called in like questyon theyre particuler grieves, whiche Egloguewyse they specyfyed on this Duble Sestine.

Strephon.   Klaius.

Strephon. *Yee goteheard Gods that love the grassy Mounteynes?*
        Yee Nymphes *wch haunte the springes in pleasaunt valleys,*
        Yee Satyres *joyed with free and quyet Forestes,*
        Vouchesafe youre sylent eares to playing Musick,
           Whiche to my woes gives still an earely Morninge,
           And Drawes the Dolor on till weary Eevening.

Klaius.   *O* Mercury, *foregoer to the Eevening,*
        O heavenly Huntress of the Savage Mountaynes,
        O Lovely Starr, *entytled of the Morning,*
        (While that my voyce dothe fill these wofull valleys)
           Vouchsafe youre silent eares to playing Musick,
           W^{ch} ofte hathe Echo *tyred in secrett Forestes.*

Strephon. *I that was once free Burgess of the Forestes*
        (Where shade from Sunñ and sporte I sought in Eevening)
        I that was once esteemd for pleasaunt Musick,
        And banisht now amongst the Monsterus Mountaynes,
        Of huge Dispayre and fowle afflictions valleyes,
        Am growne a Scriche Owle to my self eche morning.

Klaius.   *I that was once delighted every morning,*
Hunting the wylde Inhabiters of the Forestes,
I that was once the Musick of the valleyes,
So Darckened am, that all my day ys Eevening,
    Hart broken so, that Mole hilles seeme hye Mounteynes,
    And fill the valleyes wth Cryes in steade of Musick.

Strephon. *Longe synce, alas, my Deadly Swannish Musick,*
Hathe made yt self a Cryer of the Morning,
And hathe with wayling strengthe clymed hyest Mountaynes,
Longe synce my thoughtes more Dezert bee then Forestes,
    Longe synce I see my Joyes come to theyre Eevening,
    And State throwne downe to every trodden valleys.

Klaius.   *Longe synce the happy dwellers of these valleyes,*
Have prayde mee leave my straunge exclaming Musick,
Whiche trubles theyre dayes worcke and Joyes of Eevening,
Longe since I hate the Nighte, more hate the Morning,
    Longe synce my thoughtes chase mee like Beastes in Forestes
    And make mee wish my self layde under Mountaynes.

Strephon. *Mee seemes I see the hye and stately Mountaynes,*
Transforme them selves to Lowe dejected valleys,
Mee seemes I heare in these yll chaunged Forestes
The Nightingales do learne of Owles theyre Musick,
    Mee seemes I feele ye Comfort of the Morning,
    Turne to the Mortall Siren of an Eevening.

Klaius.   *Mee seemes I see a filthy Clowdy Eevening,*
Assoone as Suñ begyns to clyme the Mountaynes,
Mee seemes I feele a Noysome sent the Morninge,
When I do smell the Flowers of the valleyes,
    Mee seemes I heare (when I do heare sweete Musick)
    The Dreadfull Cryes of Murdered men in Forestes.

Strephon. *I wish to fyre the trees of all these Forestes,*
I give the Sunne a Last farewell eche eevening,
I Curse the fidling fynders oute of Musick,
With Envy I do hate the lofty Mountaynes,
    And with Despyte do spyte the humble valleyes.
    I Do detest Nighte, Eevening day and Morning.

Klaius.   *Curse to myself my Prayer ys the Morninge,*
             My fyer ys more then can bee made with Forestes,
             My estate more base, then ys the basest valleyes,
             I wish no Eevening, more, to see eche eevening.
                Shamed, I hate my self in sighte of Mountaynes,
                And stopp myne Eares lest I growe Madd wth Musik.

Strephon. *For shee whose partes meyntayne a perfect Musick,*
             Whose bewtyes shyne more then the blusshing morninge,
             Who muche did pass in state, the Stately Mountaynes,
             In streightnes past the Caedars *of the forrestes,*
                Hathe cast mee wretche into Eternall Eevening,
                By taking her twoo Sunnes from these darck valleyes.

Klaius.   *For shee with whome Comparde the* Alpes *are valleyes,*
             Shee whose Least worde bringes from the Spheares *theyre*
                Musick,
             At whose approche the Sunne rase in the Eevening,
             Who where shee went bare in her forehead Morning,
                Ys goñ ys goñ from these oure spoyled Forestes,
                Turning to Dezartes oure best pastured Mountaynes.

Strephon. *These Mountaynes witnes shall, so shall these valleyes,*
Klaius.   *These Forestes eeke made wretched by oure Musick,*
             Oure Morning Hymne this ys and Songe at Eevening.

  But as though all this had bene but the taking of a taste to theyre waylinges, *Strephon* ageane began this *Dizaine*: Whiche was answered unto hym in that kynde of verse wch ys called ye Crowne.

Strephon. *I joy in greef and do detest all Joyes,*
              Despyse Delighte, and tyer with thoughtes of ease,
            I turne my mynde to all Formes of Annoyes,
              And with the Chaunge of them, my fancy please,
            I Study that wch moste may mee displease,
              And in Despite of that Displeasure mighte,
            Embrace, that moste that moste my Sowle destroyes,
              Blynded with Beames, fell Darcknes ys my sighte,
                Dwell in my Ruyns, fedd with sucking smarte,
                I thincke from mee, not from my woes to parte.

COUNTESS OF PEMBROOKES

Klaius. *I thincke from mee, not from my woes to parte,*
   And lo this tyme calde Lyfe may thinck that lyfe,
   Nature to mee, for Tormentes did imparte,
   Thinck my hard happes have blunted Deathes sharp knyfe,
   Not sparing mee in whome his worcke bee ryfe,
   And thincking this thincke Nature lyfe and deathe,
   Place, sorowes tryumphe, on my Conquerd hart,
   Whereto I yeelde, and seeke no other breathe,
    But from the sent of some infectious grave,
    Nor of my fortune, oughte but mischeef crave.

Strephon. *Nor of my Fortune oughte but myscheef Crave,*
   And seeke to nourish that wch now contaynes,
   All what I am, yf I my self will save,
   Then must I save what in mee cheefly raynes,
   Whiche ys the hatefull webb of sorowes paynes
   Sorow then Cherish mee for I am Sorowe,
   No beeyng now but Sorow I can have,
    Then deck mee as thyne owne, thy help I borowe,
    Synce thow Joy reckles arte, and that thow haste,
    Inoughe to make a fertyle mynde lye waste.

Klaius. *Inoughe to make a fertile mynde lye waste,*
   Ys that huge storme wch powers yt self on mee,
   Hayle stones of teares, of Sighes a Monsterus blast,
   Thunders of Cryes, Lightninges my wylde Lookes bee.
   The Darckened Heaven my Sowle wch nought can see,
   The Flying spirites wch Trees by Rootes up teares,
   Be those Dispayres wch have my hopes quite raste,
    The Difference ys all Folckes those stormes forbeare,
    But I can not, who then my self shoulde flee
    So close unto my self my wrackes do lye.

Strephon. *So close unto my self my wrackes do lye,*
   Bothe Cause, Effect beginning and the ende,
   All are in mee, what help then can I trye
   My Shipp my self whose Course to Love dothe bend,
   Sore beaten dothe her mast of Comfort spend
   Her Cable Reason, breakes from Ancker Hope,
   Fancy her Tackling, Torne away dothe flye,
    Rwyn the wynde hathe blowne mee from her scope,
    Brused with waves of Care, but broken ys
    On Rock Dispayre the Buryall of my Blisse.

Klaius. *On Rock Dispayre, the Buryall of my Blisse,*
 I longe do plowe with plowe of Depe Desyer,
The seede fast meanyng ys no truthe to misse,
 I harrowe yt with thoughtes wch all Conspyre,
Favoure to make my Cheef and onely hyer,
 But woe ys mee the yeare ys goñ aboute,
And now I fayne woulde reape, I reape but this,
 Hate fully growne, absence new spronge oute,
  So that I see allthoughe my sighte empayre,
  Vayne ys theyre payne, who Laboure in Dispayre.

Strephon. *Vayne ys theyre payne, who Laboure in Dispayre*
 For so did I when with myne Angle will,
I sought to catche the Fish Torpedo *fayre*
 Even then Dispayre did hope all redy kill,
Yet Fancy wolde perforce employ his skill,
 And this hathe gott the Catcher now hathe caught
Lamed with the Angle wch yt self did beare,
 And unto Deathe, quite Drownde in Doloures brought,
  To Deathe as then Disguysde in her fayre face,
  Thus, thus, alas I had my Losse in Chace.

Klaius. *Thus, thus alas, I had my·Losse in Chace,*
 When first that Crowned Basilik I knewe,
Whose Footsteppes I with kisses ofte did trace,
 Till (by suche happ, as I must ever Rue)
Myne eyes did lighte uppon her shyning Hue,
 And thus on mee astonisht with her sight,
Synce then my hart did Lose hys wonted place,
 Infected so with her sweete poÿsons mighte
  That Leaving mee for Deade to her yt went
  But ah her flight hathe my Dead Reliques spent.

Strephon. *But ah her flight hathe my Deade Reliques spent,*
 Her flight from mee, from mee, though Dead to mee,
Yet Living still in her while her beames lent,
 Suche vitall sparck, that her myne eyes might see,
But nowe these Living lightes absented bee,
 (Full Deade before) I nowe to dust should falle
But that eternall paynes my sowle have hent,
 And keepe yt still within this Body thralle.
  That thus I must while in this Deathe I dwell,
  In earthly fetters feele a Lasting hell.

Klaius.   *In earthely fetters feele a Lasting hell,*
      Alas, I doo, from wch to fynde release,
  I woulde the Earthe, I woulde the Heavens fell,
      But vayne yt ys, to thincke those paynes shoulde Cease,
  Wheare lyfe ys Deathe, and Deathe can not bringe peace,
      O fayre, O onely fayre from thee alas,
  These fowle moste fowle Desasters to my falle,
      Since thow from mee, (O mee) O Sunñ didst pass.
      Therefore esteeming all good blessinges Toyes,
      I joyed in greef and do Detest all Joyes.

Strephon. *I joy in greef and do Detest all Joyes,*
      But now an ende, O Klaius now an ende,
      For even the herbes oure hatefull Musick stroyes,
      And from oure burning Breath the Trees doo bend.

When they had ended (wth earnest intreaty) they obtayned of *Philisides*, that hee woulde imparte some parte of the Sorowe his Countenaunce well witnessed unto them : And hee who by no intreaty of the *Duke* woulde bee brought unto yt, in this Dolefull tyme was content thus to manifest hym self.

The name of *Samothea* ys so famous that (telling yow I am of that) I shall not neede to extend my self further in telling yo^w what that Contry ys : But there I was borne of suche Parentage as neyther lefte mee so greate that I was a Marck for envy, nor so base y^t I was subject to Contempt, brought up from my Cradell age with suche Care as Parentes are wont to bestow uppon theyre Children whome they meane to make the maynteyners of theyre Name. And assoone as my memory grewe stronge enough to receyve what might bee delyvered unto yt by my senses; they offered Learning unto mee, especially that kynde that teacheth what in truthe, and not in opinyon ys to bee embrased and what to bee eschewed. Neither was I barrd from seeyng the Naturall knowledg of thinges so farr as the narrowe sighte of man hathe pearsed into yt : And bycause the myndes Commaundement ys vayne withoute the body bee en-habled to obay yt, my strengthe was exercysed with Horsman-ship, weapons, and suche other qualityes, as besydes the practize carryed in them selves some servisable use, wherein, so I prof-fited that as I was not excellent, so was I accompagnable. After that by my yeares or perchaunce by sooner priviledg then yeares

comonly graunt, I was thought able to bee myne owne Master,
I was suffered to spende some tyme in travell, that, by the Comparyson of many thinges I might rypen my Judgment: Synce
greatnes, power, Riches, and suche like standing in Relation to
an other (who dothe knowe no thing but his owne) dothe not
knowe his owne. Then beeyng home returned and thought of
good hope (for the worlde rarely bestowes a better Tytle uppon
yowthe) I continewed to use the Benefites of a quyet mynde,
In truthe (I calle hym to witness that knoweth hartes) even in
the secrett of my Sowle bent to Honesty: Thus farr yow see,
as no pompous spectackle of an untrubled Tenor of a well guyded
lyfe. But alas what shoulde I make Patheticall exclamations to
a moste true event? So yt hapned that Love, (whiche what yt
ys, youre owne feeling can best tell yow) diverted this Course of
Tranquility, wch though I did with so muche covering hyde,
that I was thought voyde of yt, as any man: yet my wounde
wch smarted in my self brought mee in fyne to this Chaunge,
muche in state, but more in mynde. But how Love first tooke
mee, I did once (using the Liberty of versifying) sett downe in
a Songe, in a Dreame in deede yt was: And thus did I Poeti-
cally describe my Dreame.

Now was oure **Heavenly** *vaulte deprived of the Lighte*
  With Sunnes **Departe**, *and nowe the Darcknes of the Nighte,*
Did light those Beamy starres wch greater light did Darcke,
  Nowe eche thinge wch enjoyed that fyery quickning sparcke,
Whiche lyfe ys calde were mooved theyre Spirites to repose,
  And wanting use of eyes, theyre eyes began to Close,
And silence sweete eche where with one Consent embraste,
  (A Musick sweete to one in Carefull Musick plaste)
And Mother Earthe now cladd in Morning weedes did breathe,
  A Dull desyer to kisse the Image of oure Deathe.
When I Disgraced wretche, not wretched then did give,
  My sences suche Release, as they wch quyett live,
Whose braynes boyle not in woes, nor brestes wth beatinges ake,
  With Natures prayse are wonte in safty home to take.
Farr from my thoughtes was oughte whereto theyre myndes aspire,
  Who under Courtly pompes do hatche a base desyer.
Free all my powers were, from those Captiving snares,
  W^ch Heavenly purest giftes defyle in muddy Cares.

Ne coulde my sowle yt self accuse of suche a faulte,
   As tender Conscyence mighte wth furyous panges assault,
But like the feeble Flower (whose stalke can not sustayne,
   His weighty Topp) his Topp dothe downeward dropping leane.
Or as the silly Byrde in well acquaynted Nest
   Dothe hyde his heade wth Cares, but onely howe to Rest.
So I in simple Course, and unitangled mynde,
   Did suffer drowsy liddes myne eyes (then clere) to blynde.
And laying downe my heade, did natures Rule observe,
   Whiche sences up dothe shutt, the senses to preserve.
They first theyre use forgatt, then fancy lost theyre force,
   Till Deadly sleepe at lengthe possest my Living Corse.
A Living Corse I lay, but, ah my Wakefull mynde,
   (W^{ch} made of heavenly stuff, no mortall chaunge dothe bynde).
Flewe up with Freer winges, of Flesshly bondage free.
   And having plaste my thoughtes, my thoughtes thus placed mee,
Mee thoughte, nay, sure I was, I was in fayrest wood,
   Of Samothea Land, a Lande wch whilome stood,
An Honor to the Worlde, while Honor was theyre ende,
   And while theyre Lyne of yeares they did in vertue spend.
But there I was; and there my Callmy thoughtes I fedd,
   On Natures sweete repast, as helthfull sences ledd.
Her giftes my study was, her beutyes were my sporte,
   My worcke her worckes to knowe, her Dwelling my Resort.
Those Lampes of Heavenly fyer to fixed motion bounde,
   For ever turning Spheres the never mooving grounde.
What essence destny hathe yf fortune bee or no,
   Whence oure Immortall sowles, to mortall Earthe doo flowe.
What Lyfe yt ys, and howe that all these Lyves do gather,
   With owteward Makers force, or like an Inward Father.
Suche thoughtes (mee thought) I thought, and straynd my single mynde,
   Then voyde of nerer Cares, the Depthes of thinges to fynde.
Who, Loe, wth hugest Noyse, suche noyse as Tower makes,
   When yt (blowne up with myne) a falle of Rwyn takes.
Or suche a Noyse yt was, as hyest Thunders sende,
   Or Canons thunder like all shott together lend.
The Moone a sunder rent (O Gods) o pardon mee,
   That forste wth greef revayles what greeved eyes did see.
The Moone a sonder rent, whereat with sodeyn falle,
   (More swifte then Faulcons stoope, to feeding Falconers calle).

314

ARCADIA

There came a Charyott fayre by Doves and Sparowes guyded
  Whose stormelike Course stayde not, till hard by mee yt byded
I wretche astonisht was, and thought the Deathfull Doome,
  Of heaven of Earthe of hell of tyme and place was come.
But streight there issued forthe twoo Ladyes, (Ladyes sure,
  They seemde to mee) on whome did wayte a virgyn pure,
Straunge were the Ladyes Weedes, yet more unfitt then straunge,
  The first with Clothes tuckt up, as Nimphes in woodes do Range.
Tuckt upp even to the Knees, with Bowe and Arrowes prest,
  Her Right arme naked was, discovered was her brest.
But hevy was her pace, and suche a Maigre cheare,
  As litle hunting mynde (god knowes) did there appeare.
The other had with Arte (more then oure woemen knowe)
  As stuff ment for the sale sett oute to glaring showe,
A wanton womans face, and wth Curlde knottes had twynde,
  Her hayer wch by the help of Paynters Cunning shynde,
When I suche guests did see come oute of suche a howse,
  The Mountaynes great wth Chylde I thought brought forthe a mowse.
But walking forthe, the first, thus to the seconde sayde,
  Venus come on, (sayde shee) Diana yow are obayde,
Those Names abasht mee muche, when those great names I hearde,
  All thoughe theyre fame (mee seemd) from truth had greatly jarrd.
As I thus musing stoode, Diana calde to her,
  Her wayting Nymphe, a Nymphe, that did excell as farr,
All thinges that earst I sawe, as Oryent Perles exceede,
  That wch theyre Mother highte, or else theyre silly seede.
In Deede a perfect Hue, in deede a sweete Consent,
  Of all those graces giftes the Heavens have ever lent.
And so shee was attyrde, as one that did not pryze,
  So muche her pereles partes, nor yet coulde them despize.
But calde she came apace, a pace wherein did moove,
  The Band of Beutyes all the litle worlde of Love.
And bending humbled eyes (O eyes the Sunne of Lighte)
  Shee wayted Mistrys will, who thus disclosde her spright
Sweete Mira myne (quoth shee) the pleasures of my mynde,
  In whome of all my Rules the perfect proof I fynde,
To onely thee, (thow seest) wee graunt this speciall grace,
  Us to attend in this moste private tyme and place.
Bee silent therefore, nowe, and so bee silent still,
  Of what thow seest close up in secrett knott thy will.

315

Shee answerd was with looke and well performed behest,
  And Mira *I admirde, her shape, sancke in my brest.*
But thus with Irefull eyes, and face that shoke with spyte,
  Diana *did begyñ: What mooved mee to invite*
Youre presence, Sister Dere, first to my moovy spheare,
  And hether now vouchsafe to take with willing eare.
I knowe full well yow knowe, what discord long hathe raignd,
  Betwixt us twoo how muche that discord fowle hathe stainde,
Bothe oure estates while eache the other did deprave,
  Prooff speakes to muche to us, that feeling tryall have.
Oure names are quite forgott, oure Temples are Defaste
  Oure offeringes spoylde, oure Preestes from Preesthood are displaste?
Ys this the fruite of stryfe, those thowsand Churches hye,
  Those thowsand Alters fayre, now in the Dust to lye?
In mortall myndes oure myndes but Planetes names preserve,
  No knee once bowed forsoothe, for them they say wee serve,
Are wee theyre Servauntes growne? no Doubt a Noble stay,
  Celestiall powers to wormes Joves *Children serve to play,*
But suche they say wee bee, this prayse oure Discord bredd,
  While wee for mutuall stryfe, a stryving passyon fedd.
But let us wyser bee, and what fowle discorde brake,
  Somuche more stronge ageane let safest Concord make.
Oure yeares do yet requyer, yow see wee bothe doo feele,
  The weykning work of tymes for ever whirling wheele.
All thoughe wee bee Devyne, oure Graundsire Saturn *ys,*
  With ages force decayde, yet once the heveñ was his.
And now before wee seeke by wyse Appollos *skill,*
  Oure younge yeares to renewe (for so hee saithe hee will)
Lett us a perfect peace betuixt us twoo Resolve,
  Whiche lest the Ruynous want of government dissolve,
Let one the Princes *bee, to her the other yeelde,*
  (For vayne Equality ys but Contentions feelde)
And let her have the giftes that shoulde in bothe remayne,
  In her lett Beuty bothe and Chastenes fully raigne.
So as yf I prevayle, yow give youre giftes to mee,
  Yf yow, on yow I lay, what in my office bee.
Now resteth onely this, wch of us Twoo ys shee,
  To whome precedentes shall of bothe accorded bee.
For that (so that yow like) hereby dothe lye a youthe,
  (Shee beckened unto mee) as yet of spottless truthe.

Who may this Doubt discerne for better witt then Lott
  Becometh us, in us, Fortune determyns nott.
This Crowne of Amber *fayre, (an Amber Crowne shee helde)*
  To worthyest lett hym give, when bothe hee hathe beheld.
And bee yt as hee saythe, Venus *was glad to heare,*
  Suche proffer made wch shee well shewde wth smyling chere,
As thoughe shee were the same, as when by Paris *doome,*
  Shee had cheef Goddesses in beuty overcome.
And surely thus gan say, I never soughte debate,
  Diana *dere, my mynde to love and not to hate,*
Was ever apte, but yo^w my pastymes did despyse,
  I never spyted yow, but thought yo^w overwyse.
Nowe kyndenes proffered ys, none kynder ys then I,
  And so moste redy am, this meane of peace to try.
And lett hym bee oure Judge: The Ladd dothe please mee well,
  Thus bothe did come to mee and bothe began to tell.
(For bothe, together spake, eche lothe to bee behynde)
  That they by solempne oathe theyre Deityes wold bynde,
To stand unto my will, theyre will they made mee knowe,
  I that was first agast, when first I sawe theyre shawe
(Now boulder waxte) waxt prowde that I suche sway might beare,
  For, nere acquayntance dothe diminish reverent feare.
And having bounde them fast by Stix, *they shoulde obay,*
  To all what I decreed, did thus my verdict say.
How yll bothe yow can Rule, well hathe youre Discorde taughte,
  Ne yet, (for oughte I see) youre Beutyes merit oughte.
To yonder Nymphe *therefore, to* Mira, *I did poynt,*
  The Crowne above yo^w bothe, for ever I appoynt,
I woulde have spoken owte but oute they bothe did Crye,
  Fye, Fye what have wee done, ungodly Rebell fye,
But nowe wee must needes yeelde to what oure Oathes requyre,
  Yet thow shalt not goo free, (quoth Venus*) suche a fyer,*
Her Beuty kyndle shall within thy foolish mynde,
  That thow full ofte shalt wish thy Judging eyes were blynde,
*Nay, then (*Diana *sayde) thee Chastenes I will give,*
  In asshes of Dispayre, though burnt shall make thee live.
Nay, thow (sayde bothe) shalt see suche beames shyne in her face,
  That thow shalt never dare seeke help of wretched Case.
And with that Cursed Curse, away to heavens they fledd,
  First having all theyre giftes uppon fayre Mira *spredd.*

The Rest I can not tell, for therewithall I wakte,
  And founde with Deadly feare that all my synewes shakte.
Was yt a Dreame? O Dreame how haste thow wrought in mee?
  That I thinges earst unseene, shoulde first in Dreaming see.
And then (O Traytor sleepe) made for to bee oure Rest
  Howe haste thow framde the payne wherewith I am opprest.
O Cowarde Cupide thus doest thow thy honor keepe?
  Unarmde, alas unarmde to take a Man asleepe?

In suche or suche like sorte in a Dreame was offered unto
mee the sight of her in whose respect, all thinges afterward
seemed but blynde Darcknes unto mee: For, so in deede yt
fell oute that her I sawe, I say that sweete and incomparable
Mira, so like her (wch in that rather vision then Dreame of
myne I had seene) that I began to perswade my self in my
nativity I was allotted unto her. To her I say, whome even
Coredens had made the upshoote of all his despayring desyers, and
so alas from all other exercyses of my mynde bent my self onely
to the pursuite of her favour; But having spent some parte of
my youthe in followyng her, some tymes with some measure of
favoure sometymes with unkyride Interpretacyons of my moste
kynde thoughtes. In the ende havinge attempted all meanes to
establish my blisfull estate, & having bene not onely refused of
all Comfort, but new quarrells picked agenst mee, I did resolve
by perpetuall absence to choke my owne evill fortunes: Yet,
before I departed these followyng *Elegiackes* I sent unto her.

      – ◡ ◡ – – – – – – – – ◡ ◡ – –
      – – – ◡ ◡ – – ◡ ◡ – – ◡ ◡ –

Unto the Caytiff wretche whome long affliction holdeth;
And now fully beleeves help to bee quyte perisshed.
Graunt yet graunt yet a looke to the last monument of his anguish.
  O, yow (alas so I fynde) Cause of his onely Rewyn.
Dread not a whitt (o goodly crewell) that pitty may enter,
  Into thy hart by the sighte of this Epistle I sende.
And so refuse to beholde of these straunge woundes the Recitall,
  Least yt might thee allure home to thy self to returne,
(Unto thyself I do meane those graces dwell so within thee,
  Gratefullnes, sweetenes, Holylove, Harty regarde,)
Suche thinge can not I seeke, Dispayre hathe given mee my answer,
  Despayre, moste tragicall Clause to a Deadly Request.

318

Suche thinge can not hee hope that knowes thy determinate hardnes,
  Hard lyfe, a Riche Marble, hard, (but a fayre) Dyamond.
Can those eyes (that of eyes drownde in moste harty flowing teares,
  Teares and Teares of a man had no returne to remorse,)
Can those eyes now yeelde to the kynde Conceipt of a Sorowe?
  Whiche Inck onely Relates, but ne lamentes, ne Replyes,
Ah that I do not Conceyve, though that to mee Leefe were
  More then Nestors *yeares, more then a Kinges Dyadem.*
Ah that I do not conceyve to the Heaven when a Mowse clymes
  Then may I hope to atcheeve grace of a Heavenly Tygre.
But but alas like a Man Condempned dothe crave to bee heard speake,
  Not that hee hopes for amendes of the Disaster hee feeles.
But, fynding thapproche of Deathe with an Inly relenting,
  Gives an Adieu to the worlde, as to his onely delighte.
Right so my boyling harte enflamed wth fyre of a fayre eye,
  Bubbling oute dothe breathe signes of his huge doloures
Nowe that hee fyndes to what ende his lyfe and love bee reserved
  And that hee hence must parte, where, to Live, onely I lived,
O fayre, O fayrest, are suche the Tryumphes to thy fayrenes?
  Can Deathe Bewty become? must I bee suche Monument?
Must I bee onely the Marck shall proove that Vertue *ys angry?*
  Shall prove the fiercenes can with a white Dove abyde?
Shall to the worlde appeare, that faythe and Love bee Rewarded?
  With mortall disdayne bent to unendly Revenge?
Unto Revenge, O sweete, on a wretch wilt thow bee Revenged,
  As the offence ys done? and goo beyonde, yf hee can,
All my offence was Love, with Love then must I bee chastened,
  And with more by the Lawes that to revenge do belonge.
Yf that Love bee a faulte, more faulte in yo^w to bee Lovely,
  Love never had mee opprest, but that I sawe to bee Loved,
Yow bee the Cause that I love, what reason blameth a shadowe?
  That with a Body yt goes, synce by a Body yt ys?
Yf the Love hate yo^w did, yo^w shoulde youre Beuty have hidden,
  Yow shoulde those fayre eyes have wth a vayle covered.
But, Foole, Foole that I am, those eyes wolde shyne from a dark Cave?
  What vailes then do prevayle, but to a more Mirackle?
Or those golden Lockes (those Lockes wch lock mee to bondage,
  Torne), yow shoulde disperse unto the blastes of a wynde,
But, Foole, Foole that I am, tho I had but a hayer of her hed founde,
  Eeven as I am, so I shoulde, unto that hayer bee a thrall,

Or with a fayre handes nayles (Oh hande wch nayles mee to deathe)
   Yo^w shoulde have youre face (synce Love ys evell) blemysshed.
O, wretche, what did I say, shoulde that fayre face bee defaced?
   Shoulde my too muche sight cause so true a Sunñ to bee lost?
First let Cymmerian *Darcknes bee my only habitation,*
   First bee myne Eyes pulde oute, first bee my brayne perished
Ere I shoulde consent to doo suche excessive a Damage,
   Unto the Earthe by the hurt of this her heavenly evell.
Oh, not. But suche Love yo^w say yow coulde have afforded,
   As mighte learne Temperance voyde of outragius eventes
O sweete Simplicity, from whence shoulde Love bee so learned?
   Unto Cupide *that Boy shoulde a pendaunt bee founde?*
Well, but faulty I was reason to my passyon yeelded,
   Passyon unto my Rage, Rage to a hasty Revenge?
But, whatts this for a fault? for wch such faithe bee abolished?
   Suche faythe so stayneless Inviolate, violent.
Shall I not Oh may I not thus yet refresh the Remembrance?
   What sweete Joyes I had once, and what a place I did holde?
Shall I not once object that, yo^w, yo^w graunted a favoure?
   Unto the Man *whome now suche myseryes yo^w awarde?*
Bende youre thoughtes to the Dere sweete wordes wch then to mee
   given were.
   Thincke what a worlde ys now, thinck who hathe altered her hart.
What? was I then worthy of suche good? now worthy somuche evell?
   Now fledd, then cherished, then so nye, now so remote?
Did not a Rosed Breathe from Lippes more Rosy proceeding,
   Say, that I well shoulde fynde in what a Care I was hadd?
With muche more: Now, what do I fynde, but Care to abhorr mee?
   Care, that I sinck in greef, Care, that I live banisshed.
And banisshed, doo I live? nor nowe wee seeke a Recovery,
   Synce so shee will whose will ys to mee more then a Lawe,
Yf then a Man in moste evell Case may give yo^w a farewell,
   Farewell, longe Farewell all my wooe all my Delighte.

Philisides woulde have gon on in telling the rest of his unhappy adventures, and by what desperate worck of Fortune,
hee was become a Shepehearde; But the Shepehearde *Dicus* desyered hym hee woulde for that tyme leave particuler passyon,
and joyne in bewailing this generall Losse of that.Contry w^{ch}
had beene a Nurse to Straungers aswell as a Mother to *Arcadians*:

And so having purchased silence, hee rather cryed oute then sange this followinge Lamentation.

Since that to deathe ys goñ the Shepeheara hye,
   Who moste the silly Shepeheards pype did pryze,
Youre Dolefull Tunes sweete Muses *now applye,*
   And yow (O Trees) yf any lyfe there lyes
      In Trees, nowe throughe youre proved parckes receyve
     The straunge Resounde of these my Cawsefull Cryes.
And lett my Breath uppon youre Braunches cleave,
   (My Breath distinguisht into wordes of woe)
That so I may signes of my sorowes Leave,
   But yf among your selves some one Tree growe
That aptest ys to figure misery,
   Lett yt (embraced) beare youre greeves to showe.

The weeping Mirhe I thincke will not denye,
   Her help to this, this justest Cause of playnte,
Youre Dolefull Tunes sweete Muses *now apply,*
   And thow pore Earthe whome fortune dothe attaynt,
In natures name to suffer suche a harme,
   As for to loose thy gemm, or earthly Sainte,
Uppon thy face, let Cooly Ravens swarme,
   Lett all the sea thy teares accoumpted bee,
Thy Bowells with all killing Mettalls arme.

Let golde now Rust lett Dyamondes waste in thee,
   Let Perles bee wanñ with woe theyre Dañ dothe beare,
Thy self henceforthe the Light do never see,
   And yow (O Flowers) wch sometymes Princes were,
(Till these Straunge Alteringes yo^w did happ to trye,)
Of Princes Losse youre selves Foretokens reare,
Lilly in Morning black, thy whitenes dye,
   Ó Hyacinth *lett* ai *bee on thee still,*
Youre Dolefull tuñes sweete muses now apply
   O Echo *all these woodes with Roaring fill.*

And do not onely marcke the accentes Last,
   But all, for all, reache not my wailefull will,
One Echo, *to an other* Echo *cast,*
   Sounde of my greeves: and lett yt never ende,

Till that yt hathe all woodes and waters past,
  Nay, to the Heavens youre just Complayninges send,
And stay the Starres unconstant Constant race,
  Till that they do unto oure Doloures bend,

And aske the Reason of that speciall grace,
  That they wch have no Lyves shoulde live so longe,
And vertuous sowles shoulde so soone leave theyre place,
  Aske yf in great Men, good men so do thronge,
That hee (for want of Ellbowe roome must Dye,
  Or yf that they bee scant) yf this bee wronge,
  Did wisdome this oure wretched tyme espy?

In one true Chest, to Robbe all vertuous treasure,
  Youre Dolefull Tunes sweete Muses *now apply,*
And yf that any counseile yo^w to measure,
  Youre Dolefull Tunes, to them still playing say,
To well felt greef, playnt ys the onely pleasure,
  O Lighte of Sunne, whiche ys entitled Day,
O well thow doest, that thow no longer buydest,
  For mourning Night, her black weedes may display,
O Phebus *with good Cause thy face thow hydest,*
  Rather then have thy all beholding eye,
Fowlde with this sighte while thow the Charyott guydest
  And well meethinckes becomes this vaulty skye,
A stately Tombe to cover hym deceassed,
  Youre Dolefull Tunes sweete Muses *now apply.*
O Philomela *with thy Brest oppressed,*
  By shame and greef, help, help, mee to Lament
Suche Cursed harmes as can not bee redressed,
  Or yf thy mourning Notes bee fully spent,
Then give a quyett eare unto my playning,
  For I to teache the worlde Complaynt am bent,
Yee Dimmy Clowdes whiche well employ youre stayning,
  This Cherefull Ayer with youre obscured cheare,
Witnes youre wofull teares with dayly rayning,
And yf o Sunne, thow ever didst apeare,
  In shape wch by mans eye mighte bee perceyved,
Vertue ys Deade, now sett thy Tryumphe here,
  Now sett thy Tryumphe in this Worlde bereaved,

Of what was good, wheare now no good dothe lye,
  And by the Pompe " or " Losse will bee conceyved,
All notes of myne, youre selves together tye,
  With too muche greef mee thinckes yo^w are dissolved,
Youre Dollefull tunes sweete Muses now apply,
  Tyme ever oulde and younge ys still revollved,
  Within yt self and never taketh ende,
But Mankynde ys for ay to noughte resolved,
  The filthy snake her aged Cote can mend,
And getting yowthe, in yowth ageane can florish.
  But unto Man Age ever deathe dothe sende,
The very Trees with grafting wee can Cherish,
  So that wee can longe tyme produce theyre tyme,
But Man wch helpeth them must helples perish,
  Thus thus the Myndes wch over all do clyme,
When they by yeares experience gett best graces,
  Must finish then by Deathes detested Cryme,
Wee last short while, and buylde long lasting places,
  Ah lett us all ageanst fowle Nature Crye,
Wee Natures worckes do help, shee us defaces,
For howe can Nature unto this apply?
  That shee her Chylde I say her best Childe killeth,
Youre Dolefull Tunes, sweete Muses now apply,
  Alas mee thinckes my weykened voyce but spilleth,
The vehement Course of this just Lamentation,
  Mee thinckes my sounde no place wth sorrow filleth.
I knowe not I, but once in Detestation,
  I have my self and all what lyfe conteyneth,
  Synce Deathe on vertues forte hathe made invasyon,
One worde of woe, an other after trayneth,
  Ne doo I Care howe Rude bee my Invention,
So yt bee seene what sorowe in mee rayneth
O Elementes by whose (they say) Contention,
  Owre Bodyes bee in living power meyntayned
Was this Mans Deathe the fruite of youre Dissention,
  O Phisickes powre whiche (some say) hathe restrayned
Approche of Deathe; alas thow helpest meigerly,
  Whenn once one ys for Atropos *distrayned,*
Greate bee Phisicions bragges, but ayde ys beggerly,
  When Rooted moysture fayles or groweth dry,

They leave of all and say Deathe comes too aegerly,
  They are but wordes therefore wch men do bwye,
Of any synce Esculapius *ceassed,*
  Youre Dolefull tunes, sweete Muses now apply,
Justice, Justice, ys now (alas) oppressed,
  Bountyfullnes hathe made his last Conclusyon,
Goodnes for best attyre in Dust ys dressed,
  Shepeheardes bewayle youre uttermoste Confusion,
And see by this Picture to yow presented,
  Deathe ys oure Home, Lyfe ys but a Delusion.
For, see, (alas) who ys from yow absented,
  Absented, Nay, I say, for ever banisshed,
From suche as were to dye for hym, contented,
  Oute of oure sight in turne of hand ys vanished
Shepeheard of Shepeheardes whose well settled order,
  Private with wealthe, Publique with quyet garnisshed,
While hee did Live, farr, farr was all Disorder,
  Example more prevayling then Direction.
Farr was Home stryfe, and farr was fooe from border,
  His Lyfe a Lawe, his Looke a full Correction,
As in his healthe wee healthfull were preserved,
  So in his sicknes grewe oure sure infection.
His Deathe our Deathe, but ah my Muse hathe swerved,
  Frome suche deepe playnte, as shoulde oure woes discrye,
Whiche hee of us for ever hathe deserved,
  The style of heavy harte can never Flye,
So hye as shoulde make suche a fame notoryous,
  Cease Muse *therefore, thy Dart O Deathe apply?*
And Farewell Prince *whome goodnes hathe made gloryous.*

Agelastus, when *Dicus* had ended his Songe thus meyntayned the Lamentation in this Rhyming Sestine: Having ye Dolefull tune of the other Shepeheardes pypes joyned unto hym.

  Farewell O Sunne, Arcadias *clearest Lighte,*
    Farewell O Perle the Pore mans plenteous treasure,
  Farewell O golden staff the Weyke mans mighte,
    Farewell O Joy the Woofulles onely pleasure,
      Wisdome, Farewell, the skilles mans direction,
      Farewell with thee, Farewell all oure affection.

For what place now ys lefte for oure affection,
   Now that of purest Lampe ys queynte the Lighte
Whiche to oure Darckned myndes was best Direction,
   Nowe, that the Mynde ys Lost of all oure Treasure,
      Now Deathe hathe swallowed up oure worldly pleasure,
      Wee Orphantes lefte voyde of all publique mighte,

Orphantes in deede deprived of Fathers mighte,
   For hee oure Father was in all affection,
In oure well dooynge placing all his pleasure,
   Still studdying howe to us to bee a Lighte,
      As well in peace hee was a safest treasure,
      In warr his witt and worde was oure direction.

Whence, whence, alas shall wee seeke oure Direction?
   When that wee feare oure hatefull Neighboures mighte
Who longe have gapte to gett Arcadian *treasure,*
   Shall wee now fynde a Guyde of suche affection,
      Who for oure sakes will thincke oure travell lighte,
      And make his payne [to keepe us safe his] pleasure.

No; no, for ever goñ ys all oure Pleasure,
For ever wandering from all good direction,
For ever blynded of oure Clearest sighte,
For ever lamed, of oure surest mighte.
      For ever banisht from well plaste Affection
      For ever robbed of oure Royall Treasure.

Lett Teares for hym, therefore bee all oure Treasure
   And in oure wailefull naming hym, oure pleasure,
Lett Hating of oure selves bee oure affection,
   And unto deathe bend still oure thoughtes direction.
Lett us ageanst oure selves employ oure Might,
   And putting oute of eyes seeke wee oure Lighte.
      Farewell oure Lighte, Farewell oure spoyled treasure,
      Farewell oure Mighte, Farewell oure Daynted pleasure,
      Farewell Direction, Farewell all affection.

The Nighte begun to cast her dark Canapy over them and they
(even wearyed with theyre woes) bended homewardes, hoping
by a Sleepe forgetting them selves, to ease theyre present

Doloures: when they were mett with a Troupe of Twenty horsemen: The Cheef of whiche asking them for the *Duke*, and understanding ye hard newes did there uppon stay among them and sende away with speede to *Philanax*: But since the Night ys. an ease of all thinges, yt shall at this present ease my Memory tyered wth these trublesome matters.

Here ende the Fourthe Eglogues,
and the Fourthe Booke or Acte.

The Fifte and Last Booke
or Acte.

THE daungerus Devision of Mens myndes, the Ruynous renting of all estates had now broughte *Arcadia* to feele the pangues of uttermoste perill (suche Convulsions never Coming but that the lyfe of that government drawes nere his necessary peryod) when to ye honest and wyse *Philanax* equally distracted betwixt Desyer of Revenge and Care of the States establishment there came unlooked for a *Macedonian* gentleman: who in shorte but pithy maner delyverd unto hym that the renoumed *Evarchus* Kinge of *Macedon* having made a longe and tedyous journey, to vizitt his oulde Frende & Confederate the *Duke Basilius*, was nowe come within half a myle of the Lodges. Where having understood by certeyn Shepeheardes the sodeyn deathe of theyre Prince, had sent unto him, (of whose authority and faythe hee had good knowledg) Desyering hym to advertize hym in what security hee might rest there for that Nighte: Where, willing hee woulde (yf safely hee mighte) helpe to celebrate the funeralles of his auncyent Companyon and Alie: Adding, hee neede not Doubt, since hee had broughte but Twenty in his Company, hee woulde bee so unwyse as to enter into any forceable attempt wth so smalle force. *Philanax*, having intertayned the Gentleman aswell as in the mydst of so many tumultes hee coulde, pawsing a while wth hym self, and considering howe yt shoulde not onely bee unjust and ageanst the Lawes of Nations, not well to receyve a Prince, whome good will had broughte among them: But in respect of the greatnes of his mighte, very daungerus to give hym any Cause of due offence. Remembring w^th- all the excellent trialls of his equity wch made hym more famous then his victoryes, hee thoughte hee mighte bee the fittest instrument to redress the Ruyns they were in, since his goodnes putt hym withoute suspicyon and his greatnes beyond envy: yet weighing how hardd many heades were to bee brydeled and that in this monsterus Confusion suche mischeef mighte bee attempted of wch late Repentance shoulde after bee but a simple

Remedy hee judged best first to knowe howe the Peoples myndes
woulde sway to this Determenacyon. Therefore desyering the
Gentleman to returne to the Kinge his Master and beseech hym
(thoughe with his paynes) to stay for an hower or twoo where
hee was, till hee had sett thinges in better order to receyve hym:
Hee hymself went first to ye Noble Men, then to *Kerkxenus* and
the Principall *Mantineans,* who were most opposite unto him,
Desyering them, that as the Nighte had moste blessedly stayed
them from entering into Civill bloode, so they woulde bee contented in the Night to assemble the people together to heare
some Newes wch hee was to deliver them. There ys no thinge
more desyerus of noveltyes then a Man that feares his present
fortune, therefore, they whome mutuall Diffidence made doubtfull of theyre utter destruction were quickly perswaded to heare
of any newe matter wch mighte alter at least yf not help the
nature of theyre feare: Namely the Cheefest men who as they
had moste to lose, so were moste jelous of theyre owne Case,
and weare allredy growen to bee as weary to bee followers of
Tymantus ambition, as before they were envyers of *Philanax*
worthynes. As for *Kerkxenus* and *Sympathus,* as in the one a
vertuous Frendship had made hym seeke to advaunce, & in the
other a naturall Commiseration had made hym willing to protect the Twoo excellent (thoughe unfortunate) Prisoners, so
were they not ageanst this Convocation: For having no thing
but just Desyers in them, they did not mistrust the justifying
of them. Onely *Tymantus* laboured to have withdrawne them
from this assembly, saying yt was tyme to stopp theyre eares
from the ambicyous charmes of *Philanax*: Lett them first deliver *Gynecia* and her Daughters (sayde hee) wch were fitt persons
to heare, and then they might begyn to speake. That this was
but *Philanax* Cunning, to lincke Broyle uppon Broyle, bycause
hee might avoyde ye answering of his Trespasses, whiche as
hee had long intended, so had hee prepared coloured speeches
to disguyse them: But, as his wordes expressed rather a vyolence
of Rancoure, then any Just grounde of accusation, so pearsed
they no further, then some parciall eares, the multitude yeelding good attention to that *Philanax* woulde propose unto them.
Who like a Man whose best buylding was a well framed Conscyence, neyther wth fawning wordes nor fawning Countenaunce,
but even with the grave behavyour of a wyse Father (whome

no thinge but Love makes to chyde) hee thus sayde unto them:
I have (saide hee) a greate matter to delyver unto yo^w and there
oute am I to demaunde a greate Demaunde of yo^w. But truely
suche hathe this late proceeding bene of youres, that I knowe
not what ys not to be Demaunded of yo^w: Mee thinckes I
may have Reason to requyer of yo^w (as men are wonte among
Pyrates) that ye lyfe of hym that never hurte may bee safe.
Mee thinckes I am not withoute appearance of Cause, (as yf yo^w
were *Cyclopes* or Canyballes) to Desyer that oure *Princes* body
(which hathe xxx^ti yeares meyntayned us in a Flourishing peace)
bee not torne in peeces or devowered among yo^w. But may bee
suffered to yeelde yt self (wch never was defyled with any of
youre blood) to the naturall Rest of the earthe. Mee thinckes,
(not as to *Arcadians* renowmed for youre faythe to Prince and
love of Contry, but as sworne Enimyes to this sweete soyle)
I am to desyer yow, that at least (yf yo^w will have Straungers
to youre Princes) yet, yow will not Deliver the Seigniory of
this goodly Dukedome, to youre noble *Dukes* murderers? Lastly
I have reason (as yf I had to speake to madd meñ), to desyer
yow to bee good to youre selves. For, before God what eyther
barbarous vyolence or unnaturall folly hathe not this day had
his seate in youre myndes and lefte his footestepps in youre
actions? But in trothe I Love yo^w too well, to stand long dis-
playing youre faultes, I woulde yow youre selves did forgett
them, so yow did not falle ageane into them, for my parte I had
rather bee an Orator of youre prayses. But, now yf yow will
suffer attentive Judgment and not forejudging passyon to bee
the wayer of my wordes, I will deliver unto yow, what a
blessed meane the Heavens have sent unto yow, yf yow list to
embrace yt: I thincke there ys none among yo^w eyther so younge
in yeares or understanding, but hathe hearde the true fame of
that just Prince *Evarchus* Kinge of *Macedon*, a Prince with
whome oure late Master did ever holde moste perfect alyaunce.
Hee, even hee ys this day cõme havinge but xx^ti horse with
hym within twoo myles of this place hopinge to have founde
the vertuous *Basilius* alyve, but now willing to doo honor unto
his deathe: Surely surely the heavenly powers have in so full a
tyme bestowed hym uppon us, to unite oure Disunyons. For my
parte therefore I wish that (since amonge oure selves wee can not
agree in so manifolde parcialityes) wee doo putt the ordering of

all these thinges into his handes: Aswell tuchinge the obsequyes of the *Duke*, the Punishment of his Deathe, as ye Mariage and Crowning of oure *Princess*. Hee ys bothe by experience and wysdome toughte howe to direct his greatnes, suche as no man can disdayne to obay hym, his equity suche as no man neede to feare hym. Lastly as hee hathe all these qualityes to helpp, so hathe hee (thoughe hee woulde) no force to hurt: yf therefore, yow so thincke good, (since our Lawes beare,) that oure Princes murder bee chastezed before his murdered body bee buryed wee may invite hym to sitt to morowe in the Judgment seate, (after wch done) yow may proceede to the Buryall. When *Philanax* first named *Evarchus* landing there was a muttering murmure among the people as thoughe in the evill ordered weykenes of theyres hee had come to conquer theyre Contry: But when they understood hee had so smalle a Retinew (whispering one with an other, and looking whoo shoulde begin to confirme *Philanax* proposition) at lengthe *Sympathus* was the first that allowed yt then, the Rest of the Noble men. Neyther did *Kerkxenus* stryve, hoping so excellent a Prince coulde not but deale gracyously with suche Twoo younge men: (whose authority joyned to *Philanax*) all the populer sorte followed. *Tymanthus* still blynded wth his owne ambicyous haste, (not remembring factions are no longer to bee trusted, then the factious may bee perswaded yt ys for theyre owne good) woulde needes stryve ageanst the streame: Explaying ageanst *Philanax* that nowe hee shewed who yt was yt wolde betray his Contry to Straungers. But well hee founde that who ys to buysy in the foundacyon of a howse may well pull the buylding aboute his eares. For the people (tyered allredy with theyre Divisions, of wch his Complayning had beene principall Nurse) and beginning now to espy a haven of Rest, hated any thing that shoulde hynder them from yt, asked one an other, whether this were not hee whose evill toungue no man coulde escape? Whether yt were *Tymanthus* that made the first mutinous oration to strengthen the trobles? Whither *Tymanthus* withoute theyre Consent had not goñ aboute to deliver *Gynecia*? And thus enflaming one an other ageanst hym they threwe hym oute of the assembly and after pursued hym with stones and staves, so that with loss of one of his eyes (sore wounded and beaten) hee was fayne to flee to *Philanax* feete, for the succoure of his Lyfe, giving a true Lesson that vyce yt self ys forced to seeke the sanctuary of vertue: For *Philanax*, who hated his evill, but not his person, and knewe that a just punishm^t mighte by the maner bee unjustly done, Remembring wth all (that (allthoughe herein the peoples Rage might have hitt right ynough) yet yf yt were nourished in this) no man knewe to what extremityes yt mighte extend yt self, with earnest dealling, and employing the uttermoste of his authority, hee did protect ye trembling *Tymanthus*. And having taken a general Oathe, that they shoulde (in ye Nonage of the Princess, or till these thinges were settled) yeelde full obaydyence to *Evarchus*, so farr, as were not prejudiciall to the Lawes, Customes and Libertyes of *Arcadia*: And having taken a particuler oathe of *Sympathus* that the Prisoners should bee kept Close withoute Conference to any man, hee hym self Honorably accompanyed wth a great nomber of Torches went to the Kinge *Evarchus*. Whome hee founde taking his Rest under a Tree, with no more affected pompes, then as a Man that knewe (howe so ever hee was exalted) the beginning & ende of his Body was earthe. But first yt were fitt to bee knowne what Cause mooved this puisant Prince in this sorte to come to *Arcadia*: *Evarchus* did not further exceede his meanest Subject with the greatnes of his fortune, then hee did surmount the greatnes of his fortune, wth ye greatnes of his mynde. In somuche that those thinges wch often tymes the best sorte thinck rewardes of Vertue, hee helde them not at so hye a pryce, but esteemed them Servauntes to well dooyng: The Reward of vertue beeyng in yt self, on wch his Inward love was so fixed, that never was yt dissolved into other desyers, but keeping his thoughtes true to them selves, was neither beguyled with the paynted glasse of pleasure, nor dazeled with ye false lighte of Ambition. This made the Lyne of his actions streighte, and allwayes like yt self, no worldly thing beeynge able to shake the Constancy of yt; whiche among many other tymes yeelded some proof of yt self. When *Basilius* the Mightyest Prince of *Greece* next to *Evarchus* did sodenly withoute the advyse or allowance of his Subjectes (withoute eyther good showe of reasonable Cause, or good provision for likely accidentes in the sighte of the worlde) putt hym self from ye worlde: As a Man that not onely unarmed hym self but woulde make his nakednes manifest. This measured by the

myndes of moste Princes, even those whome great actes have
entitled wth the holy name of vertue, woulde have beene thought
a sufficyent Cause (where suche oportunity did offer so great
pray to theyre handes) to have soughte the enlarging of theyre
Dominions: wherein they falsely putt the more or less felicity
of an estate. But *Evarchus* that had conceyved what ys evill in
yt self no respect can make good, (and never forgatt his office)
was to meyntayne the *Macedonians* in the exercyse of goodnes
and happy enjoying theyre naturall lyves: Never used warr
(whiche ys meyntayned wth the Cost and blood of the Subject)
but when yt was to defend theyre Righte, whereon theyre well
beeyng depended: For this Reconing hee made, howe farr so
ever hee extended hym self, Neighboure hee must have: And
therefore as hee kept in peace tyme continuall Discipline of
warre, and at no tyme woulde suffer injury, so hee did rather
stand uppon a just moderacyon of keeping his owne in good and
happy Case, then multiplying desyer uppon desyer (seeking one
enemy after an other) putt bothe his honor and peoples safty
in the continuall dyce of Fortune. So that having this advauntage of *Basilius* contrey layde open unto hym, in steade of laying
an unjust grype uppon yt (wch yet mighte have bene beutyfyed
wth the noble name of Conquest) hee streighte Considered the
universal Case of *Greece* deprived by this meanes of a princely
piller, he wayed and pityed the pityfull Case of the *Arcadian*
people: Who were in worse Case then yf deathe had taken
away theyre Prince, for so yet theyre necessity woulde have
placed some one to the helme. Nowe a Prince beeyng, and
not doyng like a Prince keeping and not exercysing the place,
they were in so muche more evill Case, as they coulde not
provyde for theyre evell: Hee sawe the *Asiatickes* of ye one syde
the *Latines* of the other gaping for any occasyon to devoure
Greece, wch was no way to bee prevented but by theyre united
strength and strengthe moste to bee meyntayned by meynteyning theyre Principall Instrumentes. These Rightly wyse and
temperate Consideracyons mooved *Evarchus*, to take his Laboursome Journey to see whether by his authority hee might drawe
Basilius from this burying him self alyve, and to returne ageane
to employ his oulde yeares in doyng good, the onely happy
action of mans lyfe: Neyther was hee withoute a Consideracyon in hym self to provyde the Mariage of *Basilius* twoo

Daughters, for his Sonne and Nephewe ageanst theyre returne.
The tedyus expectation of wch joyned with the feare of theyre
miscarrying (having beene long withoute hearing any newes from
them) made hym the willinger to ease that parte of Melancholy
with chaunging ye objectes of his wearyed sences, and visiting
his oulde and well approoved acquayntance in every perfect state :
And having throwlye settled his late Conquestes (taking with
him a good nomber of *Galleys* to wafte hym in safty to the
Arcadian shore) hee sailed wth a prosperus wynde to a porte
not farr from *Mantinea.* Where Landing no more with hym,
but the smalle Company yo^w have hearde of, and goyng toward
the Dezart, hee understood to his great greef the newes of the
Princes deathe, and wayted in this sorte for his safe Conduct,
till *Philanax* came : Who assoone as hee was in sighte of hym,
(Lighting from his horse) presented hym self unto hym, in all
those humble behavyoures, wch not onely the great Reverence
of the party, but the Conceypt of ones owne misery ys wonte
to frame. *Evarchus* rase up unto hym, with so gracyous a
Countenaunce, as the goodnes of his mynde had longe exercysed
hym self unto, carefull so muche more to discend in all Curtesyes as hee sawe hym beare a Lowe representacyon of his
afflicted state : But, to *Philanax* as soone as by nere looking on
hym hee might perfectly beholde hym, (the gravity of his
Countenance and yeares, not muche unlike to his late deceased
but ever beloved Master) brought hys forme so lyvely into his
Memory, and revived so all the thoughtes of his wonted Joyes
wth hym, that in steade of speaking to *Evarchus,* hee stoode a
while like a Man gon a farr journey from hym self. Calling as
yt were with his mynde an accoumpte of his Losses, imagening,
that this payne needed not beene violently stopped of her owne
Course : And casting more Lovinge then wyse Conceyptes what
a worlde this woulde have beene, yf this sodayne accident had
not interrupted yt : And so farr strayed hee into this raving
melancholy that his eyes nymbler then his toungue, lett falle a
flood of Teares, his voyce beeyng stopped with extremity of
sobbing, somuche had his frendship carryed hym to *Basilius,* that
hee thoughte no age was tymely to his Deathe. But at lengthe,
taking the occasion of his owne weeping he thus did speake
to *Evarchus*; Lett not my Teares Moste worthy Renowmed
Prince make my presence unplesant nor my speeche unmarcked

of yo^w, for the justnes of the Cause takes away any blame of weykenes in mee, and the affinity that ye same beareth to youre greatnes, seemes even lawfully to clayme pitty in yo^w: A Prince of a Princes falle, a Lover of Justice, of a moste unjust vyolence. And give mee leave Excellent *Evarchus* so to say yt, I am but the Representer of all the late flourishing *Arcadia*, wch now with myne eyes doo weepe, with my toungue dothe Complayne, with my knees dothe lay yt selfe at youre feete, wch never have bene unredy to carry yo^w to the vertuous protecting of Innocentes: Imagyn, vouchesafe to Imagyn moste wyse and good Kinge y^t here ys before youre eyes, the pityfull Spectackle of a moste Dolerusly ending tragedy. Wherein, I doo but play the parte of all this now miserable Province, wch beeyng spoyled of her guyde dothe lye lyke a shippe withoute a Pylott, tumbling up and downe, in the uncerteyne waves, till yt eyther ronne uppon the Rock of self Division, or bee overthrowne by the stormy wynde of foreyne force: *Arcadia* fynding her self in these desolate Termes dothe speake, and I speake for her to thee, not vaynely, puisant Prince? That since now shee ys not onely robbed of the naturall support of her Lorde, but, so sodenly robbed, that shee hathe not breathing tyme, to stande for her savety. So unfortunately that yt dothe appall theyre myndes, thoughe they had leysure, and so mischevusly that yt dothe exceede bothe the sodennes & unfortunatenes of yt. Thow wilt lende thyne Arme unto her and as a Man take Compassion of Mankynde, as a vertuous man chastize moste abhominable vyce, and as a Prince protect a People, whiche all have wth one voyce called for thy goodnes: Thinckking that as thow arte onely able, so thow arte fully able to redress theyre Iminent Rwyns. They doo therefore with asmuche Confidence as necessity, flee unto yo^w for succoure. They lay them selves open to yo^w. To yow (I meane youre self) suche as yow have ever beene: That ys to say, one that hathe allwayes had his determynacyons bounded with equity, they onely reserve the Righte to *Basilius* blood, the manner to the auncyent prescribing of theyre Lawes. For, the Rest withoute exception they yeelde over unto yow as to the Elected Protector of this Dukedome: Whiche name and Office they beseeche yo^w (till yow have layde a sufficyent foundacyon of Tranquility) to take uppon yow; The perticularityes bothe of theyre Statutes and Demaundes yo^w shall presently after understand. Nowe onely I am to say unto yo^w, that this Contry falles to bee a fayre Feelde, to proove whether the goodly Tree of youre vertue will live in all soyles? Here, (I say) will bee seene, whether eyther feare can make yo^w shorte, or the Licorusnes of Dominyon make yo^w beyond Justice. And I can for Conclusion say no more but this, yo^w must thinck upon my wordes, and on youre answer dependes not onely the quyett, but the Lives of so many thowsandes, whiche for theyre auncyent Confederacy in this theyre extreme necessity, desyer neyther the expense of youre Treasure nor hazard of youre Subjectes: But onely the benefit of youre wisdome, whose bothe glory and encrease standes in the exercysing of yt. The Suſñe of this Request was utterly unlooked for of *Evarchus*, whiche made hym the more diligent in marcking his speeche, and after his speeche take the greater pawse for a perfect Resolucyon: For as of the one syde, hee thoughte Nature requyred no thing more of hym, then that hee shoulde bee a help to them of like Creation, and had his harte no way commaunded with feare, thincking his lyfe well passed, having satisfyed the tyrrany of tyme with the Course of many yeares, the expectation of ye worlde with more then expected honor, Lastly the tribute due to his owne mynde with the daily offering of moste vertuous actions: So, of the other hee wayed the just reproche y^t followed those, who easely entred into others folckes buysynes, with the opinion mighte bee conceyved Love of Seigniory (rather then of Justice) had made hym embarck hym self thus into a Matter nothing aperteyninge unto hym. But, in the ende, wysdome beeyng an essentiall and not an opinious thinge made hym rather bende to what was in yt self good, then what by evill myndes mighte bee judged not good: And therein did see, that, thoughe that people did not belong unto hym, yet dooyng good, (whiche ys enclosed within no Termes of people or place) did belonge unto hym. To this the secrett assurance of his owne worthynes (whiche allthough yt bee never so well clothed in modesty yet allwayes lives in the worthiest myndes) did muche pussh hym foreward: Saying unto hym self, the treasure of those Inward giftes hee had were bestowed by the goddes uppon hym to bee beneficiall, and not Idle. On whiche Determinacyon resting, and yet willing (before hee waded any further), to examen well the Depthe of the others proffer, hee thus with that well appeased

335

gesture wch unpassionate nature bestoweth uppon mankynde, made answer to *Philanax* moste urgent petition. Allthoughe longe experience hathe made mee knowe all men, and so Princes (wch bee Men) to bee subject to infinite Casualtyes, the very Constitution of oure Lyves remayning in continuall chaunge: yet the affares of this Contry, or at least my meeting so jumply wth them, makes mee even abasshed with the straungenes of yt. With muche payne I am come hether to see my longe approoved Frende, and now I fynde yf I will see hym, I must see hym deade. After for myne owne security, I seeke to bee warraunted myne owne lyfe: And here am I appoynted sodenly, to bee a Judge of other mens lyves, thoughe a Frende to hym, yet am I a Straunger to the Contry, and nowe of a Straunger yow woulde sodenly make mee a Director. I mighte object to youre Desyer my weykenes, wch age perhaps hathe wroughte bothe in body and mynde, and justly I may pretende the necessity of myne owne Contry, to whiche as I am by all true Rules nerely tyed, so can yt not longe beare the delay of my absence: But thoo I woulde and coulde Dispence wth these Difficultyes, what assurance can I have of ye Peoples will, wch having so many Circles of Imaginacyons, can hardly bee inclosed in one poynte? Who knowes a people that knowes not a sodayne opinion makes them hope, wch hope, yf yt bee not answered, they falle to hate, chosing and refusing, erecting and overthrowyng, according as the presentnes of any fancyes carryes them: Eeven this theyre hasty drawyng to mee makes mee thincke they may bee as hastely withdrawne from mee, for yt ys but one grounde of inconstancy, soone to take, or soone to Leave. It may bee they have hearde of *Evarchus* more then Cause, theyre owne eyes will bee perhaps Curyous Judges. Oute of heare say, they may have buylded many Conceiptes wch I can not perchaunce will not performe: Then will undeserved repentance bee a greater shame and injury unto mee then theyre undeserved proffer ys Honor: And to Conclude I must bee fully enformed howe the Pacyent ys mynded, before I can promyse to undertake the Cure. *Philanax* was not of the moderne myndes, who make Suiters Magistrates but did ever thincke the unwilling worthy man more fitt then the undeserving desyerer: Therefore, the more *Evarchus* drewe back, the more hee founde in hym that the Conningst Pylot dothe muche dreade a Rock, the more earnestly hee pursewed his publique Requestes unto hym. Hee desyered hym not to make any weyke excuses of his weykenes, since so many examples had well prooved his mynde was stronge to overpass the greatest trubles and his body stronge ynoughe to obay his mynde : And that so longe as they were joyned together, hee knewe *Evarchus* woulde thinck yt no wearysome exercyse to make them vessells of vertuous actions. The Duety to his Contry, hee knowledged wch as hee had so settled, as yt was not to feare any sodeyn alteration, so since yt did want hym, aswell yt might endure a fruitfull as an Idle absence: As for the Doubt hee conceyved of the Peoples constancy in this theyre election, hee sayde yt was a Doubte, as all humane actions are subject unto, yet asmuche as in politike matters (wch receyve not Geometricall certentyes) a man may assure himself there was evident Likelyoodes to bee Conceyved of the Continuance bothe in theyre unanimity and his worthynes: wherof the one was apte to bee helde and the other to holde joyned to the present necessity, the firmest bande of mortall myndes. In Sume hee alledged so many Reasons to *Evarchus* his mynde (allredy enclyned to enter into any vertuous action) that hee yeelded to take upon hym self the Judgment of the present Cause: So as hee mighte fynde in deede that suche was the peoples desyer oute of judgmet and not factions. Therefore mounting on theyre horses they hasted to the Lodges where they founde (though late in the Nighte) the People wakefully watching for the issue of *Philanax* embassade: No man thincking the matter woulde bee well done withoute hee had his voyce in yt, and eche deeming his owne eyes the best Guardyans of his throate in that unaccustomed tumult. But when they sawe *Philanax* returne having on his Right hand the Kinge *Evarchus,* on whome now they had placed the greatest burden of theyre Feares, with joyfull showtes and applauding acclamacõns they made hym and the worlde quickly knowe, that one Mans sufficyency ys more avaylable, then Tenñ thowsandes multitude: So evill ballaunced bee the extremityes of populer myndes, and so muche naturall imperiousnes, there restes in a well framed spirite. For as yf *Evarchus* had beene borne of the Princely bloode of *Arcadia,* or that longe and well acquaynted prooffe had ingrafted hym in theyre Community. So flocked they aboute this Straunger, moste of them all redy from dejected feares rysing to ambicyous Consideracyons, who shoulde catche the first holde of his favour: And then from those cryinge wellcomes, to babling one with an other, some praysing *Philanax* for his well succeeding paynes, others liking *Evarchus* aspect and as they judged his age by his face, so judging his wisdome by his age. *Evarchus* passed thorow them like a Man that did neyther disdayne a People, nor yet was any thinge tickled with theyre flatteryes, but holding allwayes his owne a Man mighte reade a Constant determinacyon in his eyes: And in that sorte dismounting amonge them, hee forthewith demaunded the Convocation to bee made, wch accordingly was done wth asmuche order and silence. And as yt mighte appeare *Neptune* had not more force to appease the Rebellious wyndes then the admiration of an extraordinary vertue hathe to temper a disordered Multitude: Hee beeyng raysed up uppon a place more hye then the Rest where hee mighte bee best understood, in this sorte spake unto them. I understand (saithe hee) Faythfull *Arcadians* by my Lord *Philanax*, that yow have with one Consent chosen mee to bee the Judge of the late evills happened, Orderer of the present Disorders and finally Protector of this Contry, till therein yt bee seene what the Customes of *Arcadia* requyre: Hee coulde say no further beeyng stopped with a generall Crye, that, so yt was, giving him all the Honorable tytles and happy wisshes they coulde imagyn. Hee beckened unto them for sylence, and thus ageane proceeded, Well (sayde hee) how good choyse yow have made, the attending must bee in yo^w, the proofe in mee: But, bycause yt many tymes falles oute wee are muche deceyved in others, wee beeyng the first to deceyve oure selves I am to requyre yo^w, not to have any overshooting expectation of mee, the moste crewell adversary of all honorable Doynges, nor promyse youre selves wonders oute of a sodeyne liking. But Remember that I am a Man, that ys to say a Creature, whose reason ys often darkened with error; secondly that yo^w will lay youre hartes voyde of foretaken opinyons, else what soever I doo or say will bee measured by a wronge Rule, like them that have the yealow Jaunders every thing seeming yealow unto them. Thirdly whatsoever Debates have risen among yo^w may bee utterly extinguisshed, Knowyng that even among the best men are diversityes of opinyons wch are no more in true Reason to breede hatred, then one that loves Black, shoulde bee angry with hym y^t ys Clothed in white. For, thoughtes and Conceyptes are the very apparell of the mynde. Lastly, that yo^w doo not easely judge of youre Judge, but since yo^w will have mee to Comaunde, thincke yt ys youre parte to obay: And in Rewarde of this I will promyse and protest unto yo^w that to the uttermoste of my skill, bothe in the generall Lawes of nature, speciall of *Greece*, and particuler of *Arcadia* (wherein I must Confess I am not unacquaynted) I will not onely see ye passed evills duely punished, and youre weale hereafter establisshed, but, for youre Desyer in yt yf neede shall requyer I will employ the forces and treasures of myne owne Contry. In the meane tyme, this shall bee the first order I will take, that no man under payne of greevous punishment name mee by any other Name, but Protector of *Arcadia*: For I will not leave any possible Coloure to any of my Naturall Successors to make Clayme to this wch by free election yow have bestowed uppon mee, and so I vowe unto yo^w to depose my self of yt, assoone as the Judgement ys passed, the *Duke* buryed, and his Lawfull Successor appoynted. For the first wherof (I meane the trying, whiche bee guilty of the *Dukes* deathe, and these other haynous trespasses) bycause youre Customes require suche haste, I will no longer delay yt, then till to morowe, assoone as ye Sunne shall give us fitt oportunity: Yow may therefore retyer youre selves to youre Rest, that yow may bee the Redyer to bee present at these so great important matters. With many allowing tokens was *Evarchus* speeche hearde, who now by *Philanax*, (that tooke the principall Care of doyng all due services unto hym) was offered a Lodging made redy for hym: The Rest of the people (aswell as the smalle Comodity of that place woulde suffer) yeelding theyre weary heades to sleepe, when, Lo, the night, thorowly spent in these mixed matters, was for that tyme banished the face of the earthe. And *Evarchus* seeyng the day begiñ to disclose his Comfortable Beutyes, desyering no thing more, then to joyne speede with justice, willed *Philanax* presently to make the Judgment place bee putt in order. And assoone as the People (who as yet were not fully dispersed) might bee broughte together, to bringe forthe the Prisoners and the *Dukes* body. Whiche the mañer was shoulde in suche Cases bee helde in sighte (thoughe covered with black vellvett) untill they that were accused to bee the Murtherers were quitted or condempned: whether the reason of the Lawe were to shewe the more gratefull Love to theyre Prince, or, by that spectacle the more to Remember ye Judge of his Duety, *Philanax*, (who now thought in hym self hee approched to the just revenge hee so muche desyered) went with all Care and diligence to performe his charge. But, first yt shall bee well to knowe, howe the pore and Princely prisoners passed this tedyous Nighte: There was never Tyrant exercysed his rage wth more greevous tormentes uppon any hee moste hated, then the afflicted *Gynecia* did crucify her owne sowle, after the guiltynes of her harte was surcharged with the suddennes of her Husbandes deathe. For, allthoo that effect came not from her mynde, yet her mynde beeyng evell and the effect evill, shee thought the Justice of God had for the beginning of her paynes coupled them together: This incessantly boyled in her brest, but moste of all when *Philanax* having closely imprisoned her, shee was lefte more freely to suffer the fyer brandes of her owne thoughtes. Especially when yt grewe darcke, and had no thing lefte by her, but a litle Lampe, whose smalle Lighte to a perplexed mynde mighte rather yeelde fearefull shadowes then any assured lighte: Then began the heapes of her miseryes to way downe the platforme of her Judgment, then began dispayre to lay his ougly Clawes uppon her, shee began then to feare the heavenly powers (shee was wonte to reverence) not like a Chylde, but like an enemy. Neyther kept shee her self from blaspheymous repyning ageanst her Creation: O Goddes? (woulde shee crye oute) why did yow make mee, to Distructyon? yf yo^w loved goodnes why did yow not give mee a good mynde? Or yf I can not have yt withoute youre guifte, why doo yo^w plaigue mee? Ys yt in mee to resist the mightynes of youre power? Then woulde shee imagyn shee sawe straunge sightes, and that shee hearde the Crye of Hellish ghostes: Then woulde shee skriche oute for succoure, but no man coming to her, shee woulde fayne have kilde her self but knewe not howe. At some tymes ageane the very hevynes of her imaginacyons woulde close up her sences, to a litle sleepe, but then did her Dreames become her Tormentors: One tyme yt woulde seeme unto her *Philanax* was haling her by the hayer of ye hedd, and having putt oute her eyes was redy to throwe her into a burning furnace. An other tyme shee woulde thincke shee sawe her husbande making the Complaynt of his deathe to *Pluto* and the Magistrates of that infernall region; contending in greate debate what eternall punishment they shoulde allott unto her. But, longe her Dreaming woulde not holde, but that yt woulde falle upon *Cleophila*, to whome shee woulde thincke shee was crying for mercy, and that hee did pass away by her in sylence, withoute any shewe or pitying her myscheef: Then waking oute of a broken sleepe, (and yet wisshing shee mighte ever have slept) newe formes but the same miseryes woulde seaze her mynde. She feared Deathe and yet Desyered deathe, shee had passed the uttermoste of shame and yet shame was one of her crewellest assaultes: Shee hated *Pyrocles* as the originall of her mortall overthrowe and yet the Love shee had conceyved to hym had still a hye authority in her passyons. O *Cleophila* woulde shee say, (not knowyng howe nere hym self was to as greate a Daunger) now shalte thow glutt thyne eyes wch the Dishonoured deathe of thyne enemy? Enemy? (alas Enemy) since so thow haste well shewed thow wilt have mee accoumpt thee: Couldest thow not aswell have given mee a determinate denyall as to disguyse thy first disguysing with a duble dissembling? Perchaunce yf I had not bene utterly hopeles the vertue was once in mee might have called together his forces and not have beene led Captive to this monsterus thraldome of punisshed wickednes? Then woulde her owne knowing of good, enflame a newe the rage of Dispayre, wch becomming an unresisted Lorde in her brest, shee had no Comfort but in deathe wch yet shee had in horror when shee thoughte of: But the wearysome detesting of her self made her longue for the dayes approche, at wch tyme shee determyned to continew her former Course, in acknowledging any thinge wch mighte hasten her ende. Wherein all thoo she did not hope for the ende of her tormentes, feeling allredy the beginning of hell agonyes, yet, according to the nature of payne, the present beeyng moste intollerable, shee desyered to chaunge that, and putt to adventure the ensewyng. And thus rested the Restles *Gynecia*. No less sorowfull, thoughe lesse Ragefull were ye myndes of the Princes *Pamela* and the Lady *Philoclea*, whose onely advauntages were that they had not Consented to somuche evill, and so were at greater peace with them selves: And that they were not lefte alone, but mighte mutually beare parte of eche others woes;

For when *Philanax* (not regarding *Pamelas* princely protestatyons) had, by force lefte her under guarde with her Syster, and that the twoo Sisters were matched aswell in the Disgraces of fortune, as they had beene in the best beutyes of nature: Those thinges that till then bashfullnes and mystrust had made them holde reserved one from the other, nowe feare the undermyner of all Determinacyons, and necessity the victoryous Rebell of all Lawes forced them interchaungeably to lay open. Theyre passions then so swelling in them, as they woulde have made Auditors of stones, rather then have swallowed up in sylence the Chokinge adventures were fallen unto them: Truly the hardest hartes wch have at any tyme thoughte woemens teares to bee a matter of sleighte Compassyon (imagening that fayre wether will quickly after followe) woulde have beene mollifyed, and beene compelled to Confess, that the fayrer a Dyamond ys the more pitty yt ys yt shoulde receyve a blemish: All thoughe no doubt theyre faces did rather beutify sorrowe, then sorrowe coulde darcken y^t whiche eeven in darcknes did shyne. But after they had (so longe as theyre other afflictions woulde suffer them) with dolorous Ceremonyes bemoned theyre Fathers deathe, they satt downe together apparelled as theyre. mysadventures had founde them: *Pamela* in her journeying weedes now converted to an other use, *Philoclea*, onely in her Nightgowne wch shee thoughte shoulde bee the Rayment bothe of her Mariage and funeralles. But when the excellent Creatures had after muche panting (with theyre Inward travell) gott somuche breathing power as to make a pityfull discourse unto the other what had befallen them, and that by the playne Comparing the Case they were in, they throwly founde that theyre greeves were not more like in regarde of them selves, then like in respect of the Subject (the twoo *Princes*, (as *Pamela* had learned of *Musidorus*) beeyng so mynded as they woulde ever make bothe theyre fortunes one) yt did more unite and so strengthen theyre Lamentation: Seeyng the one coulde not any way bee helped by the other, but rather the one coulde not bee miserable but that yt must necessarily make the other miserable allso. That therefore was the first matter theyre sweete mowthes delyvered, the declaring the passionat beginning, trublesome proceeding, and daungerus ending theyre never ending Loves had passed: And when at any tyme they entred into the prayses of the younge *Princes*, too

longe yt woulde have exercysed theyre toungues, but that theyre
memory forthewith warned them, the more prayseworthy they
were, the more at that tyme they were worthy of lamentatyon.
Then ageane to Crying, and wringing of handes, and then
anewe as unquyet greef soughte eche Corner to newe discourses,
from discourses to wisshes, from wisshes to prayers : Especially
the tender *Philoclea*, who as shee was in yeares younger, and
had never lifted up her mynde to any opinion of Soveraignty so
was shee apter to yeelde to her mysfortune having no stronger
debates in her mynde, then a Man may say a moste witty
Chyldehood ys wonte to nourish. As to imagin with her self,
why *Philanax* and the other noble Men shoulde dealle so cruelly
by her, that had never deserved evill of any of them ; And howe
they coulde fynde in theyre hartes to imprison suche a Personage as shee did figure *Pyrocles*, whome shee thought all the
worlde was bounde to love aswell as shee did. But *Pamela*,
allthoughe indewed wth a vertuous myldenes, yet the knowledg
of her self and what was due unto her made her hart full of
stronger disdayne ageanst her adversity : So that shee joyned
the vexacion for her Frend, with the spyte of her self (as shee
thought) rebellyously detayned, and mixed desyerus thoughtes
to help, with Revengefull thoughtes yf shee coulde not help.
And as in panges of death ye stronger hart feeles the greater
torment, bycause yt dothe ye more resist to his oppressor, so
her mynde the Nobler yt was sett and had allredy embraced the
higher thoughtes, somuche more yt did repyne : And the more
yt repyned, the more helples woundes yt gave yt self. But when
greate parte of the Nighte was passed over, the dolefull Musick
of the sweete Ladyes Complayntes, and that leysure (thoughe
with some stryfe) had broughte *Pamela* to knowe that an Eagle
when shee ys in a Cage must not thincke to doo like an Eagle :
Remembring with them selves, that yt was like ye next day the
Lordes woulde proceede ageanst those they had imprisoned, they
imployed the rest of the Night in wryting unto them with suche
earnestnes as the matter requyred, but in suche styles as the
state of theyre thoughtes was apte to fasshion.

In the meane tyme *Pyrocles* and *Musidorus* were Recomended
to so stronge a guarde as they mighte well see yt was mente
they sholde pay no less pryce then theyre lyves, for the getting
oute of that place ; Whiche they (like Men in deede) fortifying

corage wth the true Rampier of pacyence, did so endure, as they did rather appeare Governoures of necessity then Servauntes to fortune. The whole Suñe of theyre thoughtes resting uppon ye safety of theyre Ladyes, and theyre Care one for the other: wherein (yf at all) theyre hartes did seeme to receyve some softenes. For some tymes *Musidorus* woulde feele suche a Motion to his frende and his unworthy Case, that hee woulde falle into suche kynde of speeche: My *Pyrocles* (woulde hee say) how unhappy may I thinck *Thessalia*, that hathe beene as yt were the Midle way to this evell state of youres, for yf yo^w had not beene there brought up, the Sea shoulde not have had this power to sever yo^w thus from youre dere Father. I have therefore (yf Complayntes doo at any tyme become a Mans harte) moste Cause to complayne synce my Contrey wch receyved the honor of *Pyrocles* education shoulde bee a stepp to his overthrowe: Yf Humane chaunces can bee coumpted an overthrowe to hym that standes upon vertue. O excellent *Musidorus*, answered *Pyrocles*, how do yow teache mee rather to falle oute with my self and my fortune? synce by yow I have receyved all good; yo^w onely by mee this affliction: To yow and youre vertuous Mother, I in my tenderest yeares & Fathers greatest trubles was sent for succoure? There did I learne the sweete mysteries of *Philosophy*, There had I youre lyvely example to confirme that wch I learned, There lastly had I youre Frendship wch no unhappynes can ever make mee say but that hathe made mee happy, Nowe see how my destiny (the Goddes knowe) not my will hathe rewarded yow: My Father sendes for yow oute of youre Lande, whence, but for mee yo^w had not come, what after followed, yow know, yt was my Love not youres wch first stayed yo^w heare, and therefore yf ye heavens ever helde a just proportion It were I and not yo^w that shoulde feele the smarte. O blame not the heavens sweete *Pyrocles*, saide *Musidorus*, as theyre Course never alters, so ys there no thing done by the uncharitable Ruler of them but hathe an everlasting reason for yt: And to say the truthe of these thinges wee shoulde dealle ungratefully with *Nature* yf wee shoulde bee forgetfull Receyvers of her good giftes, & so diligent Auditors of ye Chaunces wee like not. Wee have lived and have lived to bee good to oureselves, and others, oure sowles wch are putt into the sturring earthe of oure bodyes have atcheved the causes of theyre hether comĩng, they have knowne and honoured with knowledg the cause of theyre Creation: And for many men (for in this tyme place and fortune yt ys lawfull for us to speake gloriusly) yt hathe beene behovefull that wee shoulde live. Synce then Eternity ys not to bee had in this conjunction, what ys to bee lost by the seperation, but tyme: whiche synce yt hathe his ende, when that ys once come all that ys past, ys nothing, and by the protracting, no thing gotten, but Laboure and Care. Doo not therefore that wrong to mee, (who something in yeares, but muche in all other Desertes am fitter to dye then yow) as to say, yow have broughte mee to any evell: Synce the Love of yow dothe overballance all bodily mischeefes, and those mischeefes bee but mischeefes to the baser myndes, too muche delighted wth the kennell of this lyfe. Neither will I any more yeelde to my passion of Lamenting yo^w, whiche howe soever yt might agree to my exceeding frendshipp, surely yt will no thing to youre exceeding vertue: Add this to youre Noble speeche my dere Cosen (saide *Pyrocles*) that yf wee complayne of this oure fortune, or seeme to oure selves faulty in having one hurt the other, wee shewe a repentance of the Love wee beare to these Matcheles Creatures, or at least a Doubt yt shoulde bee over dearly boughte. Whiche for my parte (and so dare I answer for yo^w) I calle all the goddes to witness, I am so farr from that, no shame, no torment nor deathe coulde make mee forgoo the least parte of the inwarde honor, essentiall pleasure and living lyfe I have enjoyed in ye presence of the faultles *Philoclea*. Take the preheminence in all thinges, but in true loving, answered *Musidorus* for, the Confession of that no deathe shall gett of mee: Of that, answered *Pyrocles* (soberly smyling) I perceyve wee shall have a debate in the other worlde yf at least there remayne any thinge of Remembrance in that place. I doo not thincke the Contrary saide *Musidorus*, allthoo yo^w knowe yt ys greatly helde that with the deathe of body and sences (wch are not onely the beginning but dwelling and nourisshinge of Passions, thoughtes and Imaginacyons) they falling, memory likewyse fayles, wch ryseth onely oute of them: And then ys there lefte nothing but the intellectuall parte or intelligence, wch voyde of all mortall vertues (wch stande in the meane of perturbations) dothe onely live in the Contemplative vertue, and power of the omnipotent good, the sowle of sowles and universall lyfe of this greate worcke, and therefore ys utterly voyde from the possibility of drawyng to yt self these sensible Consideracyons. Certeynly (answered *Pyrocles*) I easely yeelde, that wee shall not knowe one an other, and muche less these passed thinges with a sensible or passionate knowledg, for the Cawse beeyng taken away the effect followes. Neyther doo I thincke wee shall have suche a memory as now wee have, whiche ys but a relique of the sences, or rather a printe the senses have lefte of thinges passed in oure thoughtes. But yt shall bee a vitall power of that very intelligence, whiche as while yt was here, yt helde the cheef seate of oure lyfe, and was as yt were the last resorte, to wch of all oure knouledges the highest appealle came, and so by that meanes was never ignorant of oure actions (thoughe many tymes rebelliusly resisted, allwayes with this prison darckened): Somuche more beeyng free of that prison, and returning to the lyfe of all thinges where all Infinite knowledg ys, yt can not but bee a righte intelligence wch ys bothe his name and beeyng of thinges bothe present & passed, Thoughe voyde of imagening to yt self any thing, but even growne like to his Creator hathe all thinges wth a Spirituall knowledge before yt. The Difference of wch ys as harde for us to conceyve, as yt hathe beene for us when wee were in oure Mothers wombes to comprehend (yf any body coulde have toulde us) what kynde of lighte wee now in this worlde see; what kynde of knowledge wee now have: Yet, nowe wee doo not onely feele oure present beeyng, but wee Conceyve what wee were before wee were borne, thoughe Remembraunce make us not doo yt but knowledg. And thoughe wee are utterly withoute any remorse of any misery wee might then suffer. Even suche and muche more oddes shall there bee at that second delivery of us, when voyde of sensible memory or memorative passyon wee shall not see the Coloures but lyves of all thinges that have beene or can bee, And shall (as I hope) knowe oure Frendship, thoughe exempt from ye earthly Care of frendshipp having bothe united yt and oure selves in that hye and heavenly Love of the unquencheable Lighte: As hee had ended his speeche, *Musidorus* looking wth a heavenly joy uppon hym, sange this Songe unto hym, hee had made before Love turnde his Muse to another Subject.

ARCADIA

Since Natures *worckes bee good and* Deathe *dothe serve,*
  As Natures worckes, why shoulde wee feare to dye?
Synce Feare *ys vayne, but when yt may preserve?*
  Why shoulde wee feare that wᶜʰ wee can not flye?

Feare *ys more payne, then ys the* Payne *yt feares,*
  Disarming humane myndes of Native *mighte,*
While eache Conceipt, *an ugly* Figure *beares,*
  Whiche were not evill well wayed in Reasons *light.*

Oure Owly Eyes *wᶜʰ dymmd with passions bee,*
  And scarce discerne the Dawne of Coming Day,
Lett them bee Clearde, *and nowe begin to* See,
  Oure Lyfe *ys butt a* Stepp *in Dusty* Way.
    Then lett us holde the Bliss *of peacefull* Mynde,
    Since this wee feele, great Loss we can not Fynde.

Thus did they like quyett *Swannes* singe theyre owne obsequyes and vertuously enhable theyre myndes agenst all extremitys wᶜʰ they did thinck woulde falle uppon them: Especially resolving that the first Care they woulde have shoulde bee by takinge yᵉ faulte uppon them selves to Cleare the Twoo Ladyes, of whose Case (as of no thing else that had hapned) they had not any knowledg. Allthoo theyre Frendly hoste the honest gentleman *Kerkxenus* seeking all meanes how to help them, had endevoured to speake with them and to make them knowe who shoulde bee theyre Judge: But the heedefull Servant of *Philanax* forbadd hym the entrie uppon payne of Deathe, for so yt was agreed uppon that no Man should have any Conference with them, for feare of newe tumultes. In somuche that *Kerkxenus* was constrayned to retyre hym self having yet obtayned thus muche, that hee woulde delyver unto the Two Princes theyre Apparell and Jewells: wᶜʰ beeyng lefte with hym at *Mantinea* (wysely Considering that yᵉ disguysing weedes wᶜʰ were all as then they had, saving a certeyne meane Rayment *Philanax* had cast uppon *Pyrocles*, woulde make them more odyous in the sighte of the Judges) hee had that Nighte sent for, and now broughte unto them. They accepted theyre owne with great thanckfullnes knowyng from whence yt came and attyered them selves in yt ageanst the next day, wᶜʰ beeynge in deede Riche and Princely they accordingly determyned to meyntayn the names of *Palladius* and *Tymopherus* as before yt was mencioned: Then gave they them selves to Consider in what sorte they mighte defend theyre Causes, for they thought yt no lesse vayne, to wish Deathe, then Cowardly to feare yt: Till some thing before morninge, a smalle slomber taking them, they were by and by after calde up ageane to answer of no less then theyre lyves imported. But in this sorte was the Judgment ordered, (assoone as the Morning had taken a full possession of y*e* Element) *Evarchus* called unto hym *Philanax* and willed hym to drawe owte into the midste of the Greene, (before the Cheef Lodge) the Throane of Judgment seate, in w*ch* *Basilius* was wonte to sitt, and according to theyre Customes was ever carryed with theyre Prince: For *Evarchus* did wysely Consider y*e* people to bee naturally taken with exterior shewes, farr more then with inwarde Consideracyon of the Materiall poyntes. And therefore in this newe entrie into so entangled a Matter hee woulde leave no thinge w*ch* mighte bee eyther an Armoure, or Ornament unto hym: And in these pompous Ceremonyes hee well knewe, a Secrett of government muche to Consist. That was performed by the Diligent *Philanax*, and therein *Evarchus* did sitt hym self all Cloathed in Black, with the Noble men who coulde in that sodennes provyde them selves of suche mourning Raymentes: The whole People comaunded to keepe an Ordenary silence of eche side, whiche was duely observed of them, partely for the desyer they had to see a good Conclusion of the matters, and partely stricken w*th* admiration, aswell at the grave and Princely behavyour of *Evarchus*, as at y*e* greatnes of the Cause w*ch* was then to come in questyon. As for *Philanax*, *Evarchus* woulde have done hym the honoure, to have him sitt by hym, but hee excused hym self, Desyering to bee the Accuser of the Prisoners in his Masters behalf: And therefore since hee made hym self a party, yt was not Convenyent for hym to sitt in the Judiciall place. Then was yt a while deliberated whether the twoo younge Ladyes shoulde bee broughte forthe in open presence; But, that was stopped by *Philanax*, whose Love and faythe did descend from his Master to his Children. And onely desyered the smarte shoulde lighte upon the others whome hee thought guylty of his Deathe and Dishonor: Alledging for this, that neyther wisdome woulde they shoulde bee brought in presence of the presence of the people (w*ch* might thereuppon growe to newe uproares) nor Justice

requyred they shoulde bee drawne to any shame till some body
accused them. And as for *Pamela*, hee protested the Lawes of
Arcadia woulde not allowe any Judgment of her, alltho shee her
self were to determyn no thinge till age or Mariage inhabled her.

Then the *Dukes* body beeyng layde uppon a Table just before
Evarchus, and all covered over with black, the Prisoners namely
the *Duchess* and twoo younge *Princes* were sent for to appeare in
the Protectors name: whiche name was the Cause they came
not to knowledg howe nere a Kinseman was to judge of them,
but thought hym to bee some Noble Man chosen by the Contry
in this extremity. So extraordenary a Course had the order of
ye heavens produced at this tyme, that bothe *Nephew* and *Sonne*
were not onely Prisoners, but unknowne to theyre unckle &
Father, who of many yeares had not seene them: And *Pyrocles*
was to pleade for his lyfe before that Throane in wch Throane
lately before hee had saved the *Dukes* lyfe. But, first was *Gynecia*
ledd forthe in the same weedes, that the day and nighte before
shee had worne, saving in steade of *Cleophilas* garment (in w^ch
shee was founde) shee had cast on a longe Cloake wch reched
to the grounde of Russet Course Clothe with a pore felt hatt
wch allmoste covered all her face: Moste parte of her goodly
hayer (on wch her handes had layde many a spitefull holde) so
lying uppon her shoulders, as a Man mighte see had no artificiall Carelesnes: Her eyes downe on the grounde, of purpose
not to looke on *Pyrocles* face, wch shee did not so muche shunn
for the unkyndenes shee conceyved of her owne overthrowe, as
for the feare those Motions in this short tyme of her lyfe shoulde
bee revived wch shee had with the passions of infinite sorowes
mortifyed. Great was the Compassion the people felt to see
theyre Princes estate & beuty so deformed by fortune and her
owne desert, whome they had ever founde a Lady moste worthy
of all Honoures: But by and by the sighte of the other twoo
Prisoners, drewe moste of the eyes to that spectackle. *Pyrocles*
came oute ledd by *Sympathus* cloathed after the *Greek* maner, in
a longe Coate of white vellvett reaching to the smalle of his
Legg, with great Buttons of Dyamondes all a longe uppon yt:
His Neck withoute any Coller not so muche as hidden with a
Ruffe, did passe the whitenes of his garmentes, whiche was not
muche in fashion unlike to the Crymson Rayment of Knightes
of the Order, first putt on. On his feete hee had no thing but

Slippers, wch after the auncyent manner were tyed up by certeyne Laces, wch were fastened under his knee, havinge wrapped aboute (with many prety Laces) his naked legg: His fayre Awburne hayer (which hee ware in great lengthe, and gave at that tyme a delightfull shewe, wth beeyng stirred up & downe with the breathe of a gentle wynde) had nothing uppon yt, but a white Riband in those dayes used for a Dyadem: w^{ch} (rolled once or twyce aboute the uppermoste parte of his forehead) fell downe uppon his back, closde up at eche ende with the Richest Perle were to bee seene in the worlde. After hym followed an other noble Mañ guyding the Noble *Musidorus*, who had uppon hym a longe Cloake after the fashion of that wch wee call the *Apostles* Mantell made of purple Satten; Not that Purple whiche wee now have, and ys but a Counterfeit of that *Getidian* purple (wch yet was farr meaner in pryse and estimation) but of the Right *Tyrian* purple, wch was nearest to a Coloure betwixt oure Murrey and Scarlett: On his head, wch was black and Curled hee ware a *Persian Tiara*, all sett downe wth Rowes of suche riche Rubyes, as they were ynoughe to speake for hym, that they had to judge of no meane personage. In this sorte with erected Countenaunces did these unfortunate Princes suffer themselves to bee ledd, shewyng a righte by the Comparyson of them and *Gynecia* howe to dyvers persons, Compassion ys dyversly to bee ministred: For, as to *Gynecia* a Lady knowne of greate estate & greatly esteemed the more miserable Representation was made of her sodeyn Rwyn, the more Mens hartes were forced to bewayle suche an evident witnes of weyke humanity. So to these men not regarded bycause unknowne (but rather besydes the Detestation of theyre facte, hated as Straungers) the more they shoulde have fallen downe in an abject semblant, the more in steade of passion they shoulde have gotten contempt, but therefore were to use (as I may terme yt) the more vyolence of Magnanimity, and so to conquer the expectation of the Lookers wth an extra-ordenary vertue: And suche effect in deede yt wroughte in the whole assembly, theyre eyes yet standing as yt were in Ballaunce to whether of them they shoulde moste direct theyre sighte. *Musidorus* was in stature somuche hyer then *Pyrocles*, as comonly ys gotten by one yeares growthe, his face nowe beginning to have some tokens of a bearde, was composed to a kynde of Manlike beuty: His Coloure was of a well pleasing

Browñes, and the features of yt suche, as they carryed bothe delight and Majesty, his Countenance severe & promysing a mynde muche given to thincking. *Pyrocles* of a pure Complexion, and of suche a cherefull favoure, as mighte seeme eyther a womans face on a Boy, or an excellent Boyes face in a woman: His looke gentle & Basshfull wch bred the more admiration, having shewed suche notable proofes of Corage; Lastly thoughe bothe had bothe, yf there were any oddes *Musidorus* was the more goodly, and *Pyrocles* the more lovely.

But assoone as *Musidorus* sawe hym self so farr forthe ledd amonge the people, that hee knewe to a great nomber of them his voyce shoulde bee hearde, mysdowbting theire intention to the Princes *Pamela* (of wch hee was more Carefull then of his owne Lyfe) eeven as hee went (thoughe his Leader soughte to interrupt hym) hee thus wth a lowde voyce spake unto them: And ys yt possible O *Arcadians* (sayde hee) that yow can forgett youre naturall Duety yo^w owe to youre Princess *Pamela*? Hathe this soyle beene so litle beholding to her noble Auncestors? Hathe so longe a tyme rooted no Love in youre hartes that live? Where ys that faythe to youre Princes blood, whiche hathe not onely preserved yo^w from all daungers heretofore, but hathe spredd youre fame to all Natyons in the worlde? where ys that Justice the *Arcadians* were wonte to florish in, whose Nature ys to render to every one his owne? Will yow now keepe the Right from the Prince, who ys the onely giver of Judgment, the key of Justice and Lyfe of youre Lawes? Doo yo^w hope in a fewe yeares, to sett up an other Race, wch no thinge, but lengthe of tyme can establish? Will yo^w rewarde *Basilius* Children with ungratefullnes, the very poyson of Manhood? Will yo^w betray youre longe settled reputation with the fowle name of Traytors? ys this youre Mourning for youre *Duke* to encrease his Losse wth his Daughters misery? Imagyn youre Prince to looke oute of the heavens unto yo^w, what doo yo^w thincke hee coulde wish for more at youre handes, then that yo^w doo well by his Children? And what more honor I pray yo^w can yo^w doo to his obsequyes, then to satisfy his sowle with a Loving memory, as yo^w do his body wth an unfelt solempnity? what have yo^w done with the Princess *Pamela*? *Pamela* the just inheritrix of this Contry, *Pam*: whome this earthe may bee happy, that yt shoulde bee hereafter sayde shee was Borne in *Arcadia*: *Pamela* in her self youre ornament, in her education youre Foster Chylde and every way youre onely Princess? What accoumpt can yow^w render to youre selves of her. Truely I doo not thincke that yo^w all knowe what ys become of her, so soone may a Dyamonde bee lost, so soone may the fayrest light in the worlde be putt oute: But looke, Looke unto yt O *Arcadians*, bee not willfully robbed of youre greatest treasure, make not youre selves Ministers to private ambitions, who doo but use youre selves to putt on youre owne yokes; What soever yow determyn of us, yet lett not *Basilius* Daughters bee straungers unto yo^w; Lastly howsoever yo^w barr her from her publique Soveraignty, wch yf yow doo (litle may wee hope for equity when Rebellion raignes) yet deny not that Chyldes Right unto her, that shee may come and do ye last Duetyes to her fathers body. Deny not that happynes (yf in suche a Case there bee any happynes) to youre late *Duke*, that his body may have his last tuche of his dearest Chylde: with suche like broken maner of questyons & speeches was *Musidorus* desyerus (as muche as in passing by them hee coulde) to moove the people to tender *Pamelas* fortune. But at lengthe by that they came to the Judgment place bothe *Sympathus* and his guyder had greatly satisfyed hym with the assurance they gave hym, that this Assembly of people had neyther meaning nor power to doo any hurte to ye Princess whome they all acknowlledged as theyre Soveraigne Lady: But that ye Custome of *Arcadia* was suche (till shee had more yeares) the state of the Contry to bee guyded by a Protector, under whome hee and his fellowe were to receyve theyre judgment. That eased *Musidorus* harte of his moste vehement Care when hee founde his beloved Lady to bee oute of Danger: But *Pyrocles* assone as the *Duchess* of the one syde hee and *Musidorus* of the other, were stayed before the face of theyre Judge (having onely for theyre Barre the Table on wch the *Dukes* body lay) beeyng no thing less vexed wth the doubte of *Philoclea*, then *Musidorus* was for *Pamela*, in this sorte wth a lowely behaviour and onely then like a Supplyant, hee spake to the Protector. Pardon mee moste Honoured Judge (saide hee) that uncommaunded I begin my speeche unto yo^w, since bothe to yow and mee these wordes of myne shall bee moste necessary: To yow, having the sacred exercyse of Justice in youre hande, nothinge apertaynes more properly then Truthe

352

nakedly and freely sett downe. To mee (beeyng invironed
aboute wth daungerous Calamityes) what can bee more Convenyent & comfortablle then at least, to bee at peace within
my self, in having discharged my Conscyence in a moste be-
hoovefull verity : Understand therefore & truly understand that
the Lady *Philoclea* (to whose unstayned vertue yt hathe beene
my unspeakeable misery that my Name shoulde become a Blott)
yf shee bee accused, ys moste unjustly accused of any Dishonorable facte, whiche by my meanes shee mighte bee thoughte
to have yeelded unto, what soever hathe beene done, hathe bene
my vyolence. W^ch notwithstanding coulde not prevayle ageanst
her Chastity, but whatsoever hathe beene informed, was my
force, and I attest the heavens, (to blaspheyme wch I am not
now in fitt tyme) that somuche as my Coming into her Chamber
was wholly unwitting unto her. This youre wisdome may with
all Consider (, yf I woulde lye, I woulde lye for myne owne
behoof) I am not so oulde as to bee weary of my self : But the
very stinge of my Inward knowledg, joyned with the Consideracyon I must needes have, (what an infinite Losse yt
shoulde bee to all these, who Love goodnes in good folckes, yf
so pure a Chylde of vertue shoulde wrongefully bee destroyed)
compelles mee to use my Toungue ageanst my self and receyve
the Burden of what evell was uppon myne owne Dooyng.
Looke therefore with pityfull eyes uppon so fayre Beames, and
that mysfortune wch by mee hathe fallen unto her, help to
repayre yt wth youre publique Judgment : Since who so ever
dealles crewelly wth suche a Creature shewes hym self a hater
of Mankynde & an Envyer of the worldes blisse. And this
petition I make even in the name of Justice that before yo^w
proceede ageanst us, I may knowe howe yo^w conceyve of her
Noble thoughe unfortunate action, and what judgment yo^w will
make of yt : Hee had not spoken the last worde when all the
People bothe of great and lowe estate confirmed wth an united
murmure *Pyrocles* Demaund, longuing (for the Love generally
was borne *Philoclea*) to knowe what they mighte hope of her.

Evarchus thoughe neither regarding a Prisoners passionate
prayer nor bearing over plausible eares to a many headed motion
(, yet well ynoughe content to wynñ theyre liking wth thinges
in them selves indifferent) was content first to seeke asmuche as
mighte bee of *Philocleas* behavyour in this matter : wch beeyng

cleared by *Pyrocles*, and but weykely gaynesayed by *Philanax* (who had framed bothe his owne and *Dametas* evidence moste for her favour) yet fynding by his wisdome that shee was not alltogether faultles Hee pronounced that shee shoulde all her lyfe longe bee kept Prisoner amonge certeyne Woemen of Religion like the *Vestall* Nunnes, so to repay the touched honor of her howse with well observing a streighte profession of Chastity. Allthoughe this were a great prejudicating of *Pyrocles* Case, yet was hee exceedingly Joyous of yt beeyng assured of his Ladyes lyfe, and in the Depthe of his mynde not sory, that what ende soever hee had none shoulde obtayne the after enjoying that Jewell whereon hee had sett his Lyves happynes. After yt was by publique sentence delivered, what shoulde bee done with the sweete *Philoclea* (The Lawes of *Arcadia* bearing that what was appoynted by Magistrates in the Nonage of the *Prince* coulde not afterwarde bee repealed) *Evarchus* still using to him self no other name but Protector of *Arcadia* commaunded those that had to say ageanst the Duchess *Gynecia* to proceede: Bycause bothe her State requyred shee shoulde bee first hearde, and allso for that shee was taken to bee the Principall in ye greatest matter they were to judge of. *Philanax* incontinently stepped forthe, and shewyng in his greeved eyes, that hee did thirst for her blood, began a well thoughte on discourse of her (in his judgm{e}t) execrable wickednes: But *Gynecia* standing up before ye Judge casting abrode her Armes wth her eyes hidden under the bredthe of her unseemely hatt (laying open in all her gestures the despayrefull affliction to wch all the mighte of her Reason was converted) with suche like wordes stopped *Philanax*, as hee was entering into his invective oration. Stay, stay, *Philanax* (saide shee) do not defyle thy honest mouthe wth these Dishonorable speeches, thow arte aboute to utter ageanst a woman, now moste wretched lately thy Mistris: Lett eyther the Remembrance how greate shee was moove thy harte to some Reverence, or the seeyng how lowe shee ys, sturr in thee some pitty. It may bee, truthe dothe make thee deale untruly and love of Justice frames unjustice in thee, Do not therefore (neyther shalt thow neede) treade uppon my desolate Ruyns: Thow shalt have that thow seekest, and yet shalte not bee oppressor of her, who can not choose but love thee for thy singuler love to thy Master. I doo not speake this to procure

mercy, or to prolonge my lyfe, no no, I say unto yo^w I will not
Live, but I am onely loathe my Deathe shoulde bee engreeved
wth any wronge thow shouldest doo unto mee: I have beene
too paynefull a Judge over my self to desyer pardon in others
judgm^t, I have beene too crewell an executioner over myne
owne Sowle to desyer y^t execution of Justice shoulde bee stayed
for mee. Alas they that knowe howe sorrowe can rent the
spirites, they that knowe what fyery helles are conteyned in a
self condempning mynde neede not feare, that feare can keepe
suche a one, from desyering to bee seperated from that wch no
thing but deathe can seperate: I therefore say to thee, (O Just
Judge) that I and onely I was the worker of *Basilius* deathe
they were these handes that gave unto hym that poysonus potion
that hathe broughte deathe unto hym and Loss to *Arcadia*. It
was I, and none but I that hastened his aged yeares to an
unnaturall ende, and that have made all this people Orphanes
of theyre Royall Father. I am the Subject that have killed my
Prince, I am the Wyfe that have murdered my husband, I am a
degenerate woman, an undoer of this Contry, a shame of my
Children, what couldest thow have sayde more O *Philanax*;
And all this I graunte: There resteth then no thing else to say
but that I desyer yo^w will appoynte quickly some to ridd mee of
my lyfe, rather then these handes wch else are destenyed unto yt.
And that in deede yt may bee done wth suche speede as I may
not longe dye in this lyfe wch I have in so great horror: with
that shee crossed her armes and satt downe upon the grounde
attending in the judges answer. But a great while yt was before
any body coulde bee hearde speake, the whole people concurring
in a Lamentable Crye: Somuche had *Gynecias* wordes and behavyour stirred theyre hartes to a Dolefull Compassion. Neyther
in truthe coulde moste of them in theyre Judgmentes tell
whether they shoulde bee more sory for her faulte or her misery,
for the losse of her estate, or Losse of her vertue: But moste
were moste moved with that wch was under theyre eyes, the
sence moste subject to pitty. But at lengthe, the Reverent Awe
they stoode in of *Evarchus*, broughte them to a silent wayting
his determination, who having well Considered the abhominacyon
of the facte, attending more the manifest proof of so horrible a
trespas confessed by her self and prooved by others, then any
thing Relenting to those tragicall phrases of her (apter to sturr

a vulgar pitty, then his mynde, whiche hated evill, in what Coloure soever hee founde yt): Having conferred a while wth the Principall men of the Contry and demaunded theyre allowance hee indefinitively gave his Sentence. That whereas bothe in private & publique respectes this woman had moste haynously offended (in private) bycause Mariage beeyng the moste holy Conjunction that falles to Mankynde oute of whiche all famelyes & Consequ~etly all societyes do proceede, wch not onely by Community of goodes but Community of Children, as to knitt the myndes in a moste perfect union whiche who so breakes dissolves all humanity, No man living from the Daunger of so neare a Neighboure: Shee had not onely broken yt, but broken yt with deathe, and ye moste pretended Deathe that mighte bee. In publique Respect, y^{t}, the *Princes* person (beeyng in all *Monarchiall* governementes the very knott of the peoples wellfare and lighte of all theyre Doynges, to whiche they are not onely in Conscyence but in necessity bounde to bee Loyall) shee had traytoruslyimpoysoned hym, (neyther regarding the Contryes proffett, her owne Duty, nor the Rigor of the Lawes): That therefore aswell for the due satisfaction to Eternall Justice and accomplishment of y^{e} *Arcadian* Statutes, as for the everlasting Examples of all Wyves and Subjectes, shee shoulde bee presently conveyed to close prison, and there bee kept with suche foode as might serve to sustayne her alyve, untill the day of her husbandes buryall. At wch tyme shee shoulde bee buryed quick in the same Tombe with hym, that so his murder mighte bee a Murder to her self, and shee forced to keepe Company wth the body from wch shee had made so detestable a severance: And lastly deathe mighte redress theyre disjoyned Conjunction of Mariage. His Judgment was receyved of the whole assembly, as not with Dislyking so wth greate astonishment, the greatnes of the matter and person as yt were overpressing the mighte of theyre Conceyptes: But when they did sett yt to ye Beame wth the monsterusnes of her ugly misdeede, they coulde not but yeelde in theyre hartes there was no overballansing. As for *Gynecia* who had allredy setled her thoughtes not onely to looke but longue for this event having in this tyme of her vexation founde a sweetenes in the Rest shee hoped by deathe (with a Countenaunce witnessing shee had before passed throwe all the Degrees of sorowes, that shee had no newe looke to figure forthe

356

any more) rase upp and offered forthe her fayre handes to bee
bounde or ledd as they woulde: Beeyng in deede trubled with
no parte of this judgment, but that her Deathe was (as shee
thought) longe delayed. They that were appoynted for yt
conveyed her into ye place shee was in before, where the Guarde
was releved and ye number encreased to keepe her more sure,
for the tyme of her execution: None of them all that ledd her
(thoughe moste of them were suche, whose hartes had beene
longe hardened with the often exercysing suche offices) beeyng
able to barr teares from theyre eyes and other manifest tokens
of Compassionate sorowe; So goodly a vertue ys a Resolute
Constancy, that even in evell deservers yt seemes that party
mighte have bene notably well deserving. Thus the Excellent
Lady *Gynecia* having passed xxxv^ti yeares of her age, [even to
admiration of her beutyfull mynde and body, and having not in
her owne knowledge ever spotted her sowle with any willfull
vyce, but her inordinate love of *Cleophila*, was brought first by
the vyolence of that yll answered passyon, and then by the
dispayring Conceipte shee tooke of the Judgm^t of God in her
husbandes deathe and her owne fortune, purposely to overthrowe
her self: And confirme with a wronge Confession that
abhominable shame wch wth her wisdome joyned to the truthe
perhappes shee might have refelled. Then did *Evarchus* aske
Philanax whether yt were hee that woulde charge the twoo
younge Prisoners, or that some other shoulde do yt, and hee sitt,
according to his estate as an assistant in the Judgment: *Philanax*
tolde hym as before hee had done, that hee thoughte no man
coulde lay manifest the Naughtynes of those twoo younge men
with somuche eyther truthe or zeale as hym self. And therefore
hee desyerd hee might do this last service to his faythfully
beloved Master as to prosecute the Trayterus Causers of his
deathe and dishonor: whiche beeyng done, hee meante to give
up all deallinges in publique affares, synce that man was goñ
who had made hym love them. *Philanax* beeyng thus redy to
speake, the Twoo Princes were comaunded to tell theyre Names:
Who answered according to theyre agreement, that they were
Tymophirus Despata of *Licia* & *Palladius* Prince of *Caria*.
Whiche when they had sayde, they demaunded to knowe by
what authority they coulde judge of them, synce they were not
onely forreyners, and so not borne under theyre Lawes but

absolute Princes, and therefore not to bee tuched by Lawes: But answer was presently made them that *Arcadia* Lawes were to have theyre force uppon any were founde in *Arcadia*, since Straungeres have scope to knowe the Custome of a Contry before they putt them selves in yt, and when they once are entred they must knowe that what by many was made must not for one bee broken: And so muche lesse for a Straunger as hee ys to looke for no priviledge in that place, to wch in tyme of neede his service ys not to bee expected. As for theyre beeyng Princes, whether they were so or no, the belief stoode but in theyre owne wordes whiche they had so dyversly falsifyed, as they did not deserve beleef: But, what soever they were *Arcadia* was to knowledge them but as private Men, since they were by Magistracy nor allyaunce to the Princely blood to clayme any thinge in that Region. Therefore yf they had offended (whiche now by the Pleyntif and theyre Defence was to bee judged) ageanst the Lawes of Natyons, they were to bee chastized: yf ageanst the peculier ordenaunces of the Province, those peculier ordenaunces were to lay holde of them. The Princes stoode a while uppon that, demaunding leysure to give perfect knowledg of theyre greatnes: But when they were answered that in ye Case of a Princes deathe the Lawe of that Contry had ever bene that ymediat tryall shoulde bee had, they were forced to yeelde. Resolved that in those names they woulde (asmuche as they could) cover the shame of theyre Royall Parentage, and keepe as long as mighte bee (yf evell were determyned ageanst them) the evell newes from theyre carefull kinsfolk: Wherein the Cheef man (they considered) was *Evarchus*, whome the straunge and secrett working of Justice had broughte to bee Judge over them: In suche shadowe or rather pit of Darckenes the wormish mankynde lives that neyther they knowe howe to fore-see nor what to feare; and are but lyke Tennys balles tossed by the Rackett of the higher powers. Thus bothe sydes redy, yt was determeyned (bycause theyre Cases were seperate) first *Philanax* shoulde bee hearde ageanst *Pyrocles* whome they termed *Tymophirus*, and that hearde the other Cause shoulde folowe and so receyve together suche Judgment, as they shoulde bee found to have deserved: But *Philanax* that was even shorte breathed at the first with the extreme vehemency hee had to speake agenst them stroking once or twyce his foreheade, and wyping his eyes wch eyther wept, or hee woulde at that tyme have them seeme to weepe, looking first uppon *Pyrocles* as yf hee had proclaymed all hatefullnes ageanst hym humbly turning to *Evarchus* (who with quyet gravity shewed greate attention) hee thus began his Oration. That wch all men (who take uppon them to accuse an other) are wonte to desyer moste worthy Protector, to have many prooffes of many faultes in them they seeke to have condempned, that ys to mee in this present action my greatest Comber, and anoyaunce: For the Nomber ys so greate and the quality so monsterus of the Enormityes this wretched young man hathe committed, that neyther I my self can tell where to begin (my thoughtes beeyng confused with the horrible multitude of them) neyther do I thincke youre vertuous eares will bee able to endure the reporte of them. But will rather imagyn, yo^w heare some Tragedy invented of the extremity of wickednes, then a just recitall of a wickednes in deede committed: For suche ys the disposicion of ye moste synceare Judgmentes, that as they can beleeve meane faultes, and suche as Mans nature may easely slyde into, so when they passe to a certeyne degree, nay, when they pass all degrees of unspeakeable naughtynes then fynde they in them selves a hardnes to give Creditt, that humane Creatures can so from all humanity bee transformed. But in myself the strengthe of my Love to my deade Master will help the weyknes of my memory, in yo^w youre excellent Love of Justice will force yow to vouchsafe attention: And as for the matter yt ys so manifest, so pityfull evidences lye before youre eyes of yt, that I shall neede to bee but a breef recoumpter and no Retoricall Enlarger of this moste harmefull myscheef. I will therefore (in as fewe wordes as so huge a Trespas can bee conteyned) deliver unto yo^w the Some of t.iis miserable facte: Leaving oute a great nomber particuler tokens of his naughtynes, and onely tuching the essentiall poyntes of this dolefull Case. This Man whome (to begin w^thall I knowe not howe to name) synce beeyng come into this Contry unaccompanyed like a lost Pilgrim, from a Man grewe a woman from a woman a Ravissher of woemen, thence Prisoner & nowe a Prince: But this *Tymophirus*, this *Cleophila*, this what yo^w will (for any shape or Tytle hee can take uppon hym that hathe no restraynt of shame) having understood the Solitary lyfe my late Master lived, and considering how open hee had layde hym ~lf to any Trayterus attempt, for the first Maske of his falshoode disguysed hym self like a woman. Whiche beeyng the more simple and hurtles sex mighte easyer hyde his subtill harmefullnes and presenting hym self to my Master the moste Courteous Prince y^t lyved, was receyved of hym wth so great gratyousnes, that mighte have bounde not onely a gratefull mynde, but might have mollifyed any Enimyes rancor: But this venymous Serpent admitted into his bosome, as Contagion will fynde a fitt body for yt, so had hee quickly falne into so nere acquayntance with this naughty woman (whome even now yo^w moste justly condempned) that this was her Right hand, shee sawe with no eyes but his, nor seemed to have any lyfe but in hym. So glad shee was to fynde one more coñing then her self in covering wickednes with a modest vaile. What ys to bee thoughte passed betwixt twoo suche vertuous Creatures (wherof the one hathe confessed murder and the other Rape) I leave to youre wyse Consideration: For my harte hastens to the miserable poynte of *Basilius* murder. For the executing wherof with more facility, this young Nymphe of *Dianas* bringing up, fayned certeyne Rytes shee had to performe: So furyous an Impiety had carryed hym from all Remembrance of goodnes, that hee did not onely not feare the goddes as the beholders and punisshers of so ungodly a villany, but did blaspheymusly use theyre sacred holy name as a Minister unto yt. And forsoothe, a Cave hereby was chosen for the Temple of his Devotions a Cave of suche Darcknes as did prognosticate hee went to please the Infernall powers: For there this accursed Caytif uppon the Aulter of falshood sacrifyed the lyfe of the vertuous *Basilius*, by what meanes hee trayned hym thether, alas I knowe not, for yf I mighte have knowne yt eyther my lyfe had accompanyed my Master or this fellowes deathe had preserved hym. But this may suffise that in the mowthe of the Cave, where this fellow had his Lodging and Chappell (when allredy Master Shepeherd his Companyon had conveyed away the undoubted Inheritrix of this Contry) was *Gynecia* founde by the deade Corps of her husband (newly impoysoned,) apparelled in the garmentes of the younge Lady: And redy (no questyon) to have fledd to some place according to theyre Comforte, but that shee was by certeyne honest Sheepeheardes arrested. While in the meane tyme (bycause there shoulde bee lefte no Revenger of this bloody myscheef) this Noble *Amazon* was vyolently gotten into the Chamber of the Lady *Philoclea*: where by the mingling of her shame with his mysdeede hee might enforce her to bee accessary to her Fathers death, and under the Countenaunce of her and her sister (ageanst whome they knewe wee woulde not Rebell) seaze as yt were withoute grype into theyre Trecherus handes the Regiment of this mighty Province. But the Allmighty eye prevented hym of the ende of his myscheef by using a villayne *Dametas* hande to inclose hym in there, where with asmuche fortefication as in a howse coulde bee made hee thought hym self in moste security. Thus see yo^w (moste Just Judge) a short and simple story of ye infamus misery, falne to this Contry, in deede infamus, synce by an effeminate Man wee shoulde suffer a greater overthrowe then oure mightiest enimyes have ever bene able to lay uppon us: And that all this wch I have sayde ys moste manifest aswell of the murdering of *Basilius* as the Ravishing of *Philoclea* (for those twoo partes I establish of my accusation) who ys of so incredulus a mynde or rather who will so stopp his eyes from seeying a thinge clearer then the lighte, as not to holde for assured so pallpable a matter, for to begin wth his moste crewell mysdeede, yt ys to bee imagined that *Gynecia* (a woman thowghe wicked yet witty) wou.de have attempted and atchieved an enterpryse no less hazardus then horrible without having some Counsellours in the beginning and some Comforter in the performing: Had shee who shewed her thoughtes were so over Ruled with some straunge desyer, as in despite of good nature and Womanhood to execute that in deedes whiche in wordes wee can not heare withoute trembling, Had shee I say, no practize to leade her unto yt? Or had shee a practize withoute Conspiracy? Or coulde shee Conspire withoute some body to Conspire with? And yf one were, who so likely as this, to whome shee comunicated (I am sure) her mynde (the worlde thinkes) her body. Neither lett her wordes (taking the whole faulte uppon her self) bee herein any thinge avaylable, for to those persons, who have vomited oute of theyre sowles all remnauntes of goodnes there restes a certeyne pryde in evill; And having else no shadow of glory lefte them, they glory to bee Constant in Iniquity: And that (God knowes) bee helde oute to ye last gaspe withoute reveyling theyre accomplishes as thinckinge great Corage ys declared in beeyng neyther affrayed

361

of ye goddes nor asshamed of the worlde. But let *Gynecias* action dye wth her self what can all the Earthe answer for his coming hether? whye alone, yf hee bee a Prince? Howe so Richely Jewelled yf hee bee not a Prince? why, then a woman, yf now a Man, why nowe *Tymophirus* yf then *Cleophila*? Was all this play for no thinge? or yf yt had an ende, what ende? but the ende of my dere Master? Shall wee doubt so many secrett Conferences with *Gynecia*? suche fayned favoure to the oversoone beguyled *Basilius*? A Cave made a Lodging, and the same made a Temple of his Religion? Lastly suche chaunges and traverses, as a quiett Poett coulde scarce fill a poem wth all were directed to any less scope then to this monsterus Murder? O snaky ambition wch can wynde thy self into so many figures to slyde thether thow desyerest to come? O Corrupted Reason of Mankynde, that can yeelde to deforme thy self with so filthy desyers? And full graceles bee those Myndes whome so unnaturall desyers doo not with theyre owne uglynes sufficyently terrify? But yet even of favoure let us graunt hym thus muche more, as to fancy that in these foretoulde thinges Fortune mighte bee a greate Actor perchaunce to an evell ende? yet, to a lesse evell ende all these intangled devises were intended? But I beseeche youre Ladyship my Lady *Tymophirus* tell mee what excuse yo^w can fynde for the Chaunging youre garmētes with the *Duchess* that very instant shee was to finish her execrable practize? Howe can yo^w Cloake the lending of youre Cloake unto her? was all that but by chaunce too? Had the starres sent suche an influence unto yo^w as yow shoulde bee just weary of youre Lodging and garmentes when oure *Prince* was destyned to this slaughter? What say yo^w to this O shamefull and shameles Creature? Fitt in deede to bee the Dishonor of bothe sexes. But alas, alas, I spende too many wordes in so manifest and so miserable a Matter? They must bee fowre wylde horses w^{ch} (according to oure Lawes are the executioners of Men wch murder oure prince) wch must decyde this questyon with yo^w. Yett see, so farre had my zeale to my beloved Prince transported mee, that I had allmoste forgotten my second parte and the seconde abhominacyon, I meane his vyolence offered, I hope, but offered to the Lady *Philoclea*: wherewith (as yt had well become his Womanhoode) hee came raving to the Judgment seate. In deede oure Lawes appoynt not so crewell a deathe (alltho Deathe too) for this facte as for the other: But who-soever well wayes yt shall fynde yt sprounge oute of the same fountayne of myschevous naughtynes. The killing of the Father, Dishonouring the Mother & Ravishing the Chylde: Alas coulde not so many benefites receyved of my Prince, the Justice of *Nature*, the Righte of hospitallity bee a brydle for thy Lust, yf not to thy Crewelty? Or yf thow hadst as surely thow haste, a harte recompensing goodnes wth hatred coulde not his deathe (wch ys the last of Revenges) satisfy thy mallys? But thow must heape uppon yt the shame of his Daughter? were thy eyes so stony, thy Brestes so Tygrish as the sweete and beutyfull shewes of *Philocleas* vertue did not astonish thee? O wofull *Arcadia*, To whome the name of this Mankynde Courtizen shall ever bee remembred, as a Procurer of thy greatest Losse. But, too farr I fynde my passion, yet honest passion hathe guyded mee. The Case ys every way too muche unmesurable. It resteth in yo^w O excellent Protector to pronounce Judgment, whiche yf there bee hope that suche a younge man may proove proffitable to the worlde who in the first exercyse of his owne determeynacyons farr passed the Arrauntest Strumpett in luxuriusnes, the Coningst Forger in falshood, A Player in disguysing, a Tygre in Crewelty a Dragon in ungratefullnes, let hym bee preserved like a Jewell to doo greater myscheef? yf his yowthe bee not more defyled with trechery then the Eldest mans age, lett I say his yowth bee some Cause of Compassyon: yf hee have not every way sought the overthrowe of Humane society, yf hee have done any thinge like a Prince, let his naming hym self a Prince breede a Reverence to his base wickednes. Yf hee have not broken all Lawes of hospitality and broken them in the moste detestable degree y^t can bee, let his beeyng a Guest bee a sacred protection of his more then savage doynges: Or yf his whorish beuty have not beene as the highe way of his wickednes let the picture drawn uppon so poysonus a wood bee reserved to shewe howe greatly coloures can please us. But yf yt ys (as yt ys) what shoulde I say more? a very spirit of Hellish naughtynes, yf his acte bee to bee punished and his defyled person not to bee pittyed, then restore unto us oure Prince by duly punisshing his murderers. For then shall wee thincke hym and his name to live when wee shall see his killers to dye, Restore to ye excellent *Philoclea* the honor by taking oute of the worlde her dishonour:

And thincke that at this day in this matter are the eyes of ye worlde uppon yo^w, whether any thinge can sway youre mynde from a true administration of Justice. Alas, thoughe I have muche more to say, I can say no more, for my Teares & Sighes interrupt my speeche, and force mee to give my self over to private sadnes. Thus when *Philanax* had utterd the uttermoste of his mallice, hee made sorowe the Cause of his Conclusion. But while *Philanax* was in the Course of his speeche, and did with suche bitter reproches defame the Princely *Pyrocles*, yt was well to bee seene his harte was unused to beare suche injuryes, and his thoughtes suche as coulde arme them selves better ageanst any thinge then shame : For, sometymes blusshing his bloode wth dyvers motions coming and goyng, sometyme cloasing his eyes & laying his handes over them : Sometymes ageane giving suche a Looke to *Philanax* as mighte shewe hee assured hym self hee durst not so have spoken yf they had beene in indifferent place, with some impacyence hee bare the lengthe of his Oration. W^ch beeyng ended, with as muche modest humblenes to the Judge as dispightfull scorne to the Accuser with wordes to this purpose hee defended his honor : My accusers tale may well beare witnes wth mee moste Rightfull Judge in how harde a Case and invironed wth how many trubles I may esteeme myself. For yf hee who shewes his toungue ys not unacquaynted with rayling was in an Agony in the beginning of his speeche with the multitude of his matters hee had to lay unto mee, wherein not withstanding the moste evill coulde falle unto hym, was that hee shoulde not do so muche evill as hee woulde : How combred do yo^w thincke I may acknoledge my self, who in thinges no less importing then my lyfe must bee myne owne advocate withoute leysure to answer or foreknowledg what shoulde bee objected. In thinges I say promoted with so cunning a Confusion, as having mingled truthes with falshoodes, surmyses wth certeyntyes Causes of no moment with matters capitall scolding wth complayning I can absolutely neyther graunt nor deny. Neither can I tell whether I come hether to bee judged, or before judgment to bee punisshed, beeyng compelled to beare suche unworthy wordes farr more greevous then any deathe to mee : But since ye forme of this governement allowes suche Toungue liberty unto hym, I will picke aswell as I can oute of his Invective those fewe poyntes wch may seeme

364

of some purpose in ye touching of mee. Hoping that as by youre easy hearing of mee yo^w will shewe that allthoughe yo^w hate evill yet yo^w wish men may proove them selves not evill, so in that hee hathe sayde, yo^w will not waye somuche, what hee hathe sayde, as what hee hathe prooved: Remembring that Truthe ys simple and naked, and that yf hee had guyded hym self under that Banner, hee needed not oute of the way have soughte so vyle and false disgracinges of mee, ynoughe to have made the untruest accusation beleeved. I will therefore using truthe as my best eloquence repeate unto yow asmuche as I knowe in this matter, and then by the onely clearenes of this Discourse, youre wisdome (I knowe) will fynde the Difference betuixt Caveling supposicion and direct declaration: This Prince *Palladius* and I beeyng inflamed with love (a passion farr more easily reprehended then refrayned) to the Twoo pereles Daughters of *Basilius*, and understanding howe hee had secluded himself from ye worlde that (Lyke princes) there was no access unto hym, wee disguysed oure selves in suche formes as might soonest bringe us to ye revealing of oure affections. The Prince *Palladius* had suche event of his dooynges, that, with *Pamelas* consent, hee was to convey her oute of the thraldome shee lived in to receyve the subjection of a greater people then her owne, untill her Fathers Consent might bee obtayned. My fortune was more hard, for I bare no more [love] to the Chaste *Philoclea*, then *Basilius* deceyved in my sexe shewed unto mee: Insomuche that by his importunacy I coulde have no tyme to assayle the Constant Rock of the pure *Philocleas* mynde till this pollicy I founde. Taking (under coloure of some Devotions) my Lodging to drawe *Basilius* thether wth hope to enjoy mee wch lykewyse I revealed to the *Duchess* that shee might keepe my place, and so make her husband see his error: while I in the meane tyme (beeyng delivered of them bothe) and having so lockt the dores as I hoped the Imaculate *Philoclea* shoulde bee succourles, my attempt was suche, as even now I confessed, and I made prisoner there, I knowe not by what meanes, when beeyng repelled by her devyne vertue I woulde faynest have escaped. Here have yo^w the Thridde to guyde yow in Labyrinth this man with his toungue had made so monsterus: Here see yow the true discourse wch hee (mountbanck facyon) dothe make so wyde a mouthe over: Here may yo^w conceyve the Reason why the

Duchess had my garment, bycause by her goyinge to the Cave in the Mooneshyne Nighte shee mighte bee taken for mee. Whiche hee useth as ye knott of all his wyse assertions, so, that as this Duble mynded fellowes accusation was duble, Duble lykewyse myne Answer must needes bee to the murder of *Basilius* and vyolence to the Inviolate *Philoclea*: For the first, O heavenly goddes, who woulde have thought any mowthe coulde have beene founde so immodest, as to have opened so sleighte prooffes of so horrible matters. This first argumēt ys a question, who woulde imagyn, that *Gynecia* woulde accomplish suche an acte withoute some accessaryes, and yf any? who but I? Truly I am so farr from imagining any thinge, that till I sawe these mourning tokens, and hearde *Gynecias* confession I never imagined the *Duke* was deade: And for my parte so vehemently and more like the maner of passionate then guylty folckes, I see the *Duchess* persecute her self, That I thincke Condempnacyon may goo too hastily over her, considering the unlikelyood (yf not impossibility) her wisdome and vertue so longe nourisshed, shoulde in one moment throwe downe yt self to the uttermoste ende of wickednes. But, whatsoever shee hathe done (wch as I say I never beleeved) yet howe unjustly shoulde that aggrevate my faulte? shee founde abrode, I within dores: For (as for the wearing of my garment I have toulde the Cause) shee seeking (as yo^w say) to escape, I locking my self in a howse, withoute perchaunce the Conspiracy of one pore Straunger mighte enable her attempt? or the fortification of the Lodge (as the trim man alledged) might make mee hope to resist all *Arcadia*? And see how injuryously hee seekes to drawe from mee my cheefest Clearing by preventing the Credit of her wordes wherewith shee hathe wholly taken the faulte uppon her self: An honest and unparciall Examiner, her wordes may condempne her, but may not absolve mee? Thus voyde of all probable allegacyon the Craven crowes uppon my affliction, not leaving oute any evell that ever hee hathe felte in his owne sowle to charge my youthe withall: But who can looke for a sweeter breathe oute of suche a stomack or for hony from so filthy a spyder? What shoulde I say more? yf in so inhumane a matter wch hee hymself confesseth syncerest Judgmentes are lothest to beleeve, and in the severest Lawes, proofes clearer then the sunne are requyred, his Reasons are onely the skōe of a base mallice, my answers

moste manifest shyning in theyre owne Truthe. Yf there
remayne any doubt of yt (bycause yt standes betuixt his affirming
and my Denyall) I offer, nay I desyer, and humbly desyer, I
may bee graunted the Tryall by Combatt : By Combatt, wherein
let hym bee armed, and mee bee in my shyrt, I doubt not
Justice will bee my shielde, and his harte will shewe yt self as
fainte as yt ys false. Nowe come I to the second parte of my
offence towardes ye younge Lady, whiche I confess, and for her
sake hartely lament: But in fyne I offered force to her (Love
offered more force to mee) lett her Beuty bee compared to my
yeares, and suche effectes will bee made no myrackles. But
synce yt ys thus as yt ys, (and that Justice teacheth us not to
love punishment, but to flee yt for necessity) the salve of her
Honor, I meane, as the worlde will take yt (for else in truthe yt
ys moste untouched) must bee my Mariage, and not my deathe :
Synce the one stoppes all mouthes the other becomes a doubtfull
fable. This matter Requyers no more wordes, and youre
experience (I hope) in these Cases shall neede no more; For
my self, mee thinckes I have shewed allredy too muche love of
my lyfe, to bestowe so many. But certeynly yt hathe beene love
of truthe wch coulde not beare so unworthy falshood, and love
of Justice that will brooke no wronge to my self nor other : And
makes mee now even in that respect to desyer yo^w to bee
mooved rather wth pitty at a Just Cause of teares, then with the
bloody teares this Crocodile spendes, who weepes to procure
deathe & not to lament Deathe. Yt will bee no honor to
Basilius Tombe to have guiltless bloode sprinckled uppon yt?
And muche more may a Judge overweigh hym self in Cruelty,
then in Clemency. Yt ys hard, but yt ys excellent, where yt
ys founde, a Right knowledge when Correction ys necessary,
when grace dothe more avayle: For myne owne Respect, yf I
thought in wysdome, I had deserved deathe I woulde not desyer
lyfe, for, I knowe nature will condempne mee to dye, thowgh
yo^w doo nott. And longer I woulde not wish to drawe this
Breathe, then I can kepe myself unspotted of any horrible
Cryme: Onely I can not nor ever will deny the Love of
Philoclea, whose vyolence wrought vyolent effectes in mee.
With that hee finisshed his speeche casting up his eyes to the
Judge, crossing his handes wch hee helde on theyre lengthe before
hym, declaring a resolute pacyence in whatsoever shoulde bee

done with him. *Philanax* like a watchfull adversary curyusly marcked all that hee sayde, saving that in ye beeginning hee was interrupted by twoo Lr̃es were broughte hym the *Princess Pamela*, and the Lady *Philoclea*: who having all the Night considered and bewayled theyre estate, carefull of theyre Mother likewyse, of whome they woulde never thincke somuche evell. But considering with them selves that shee assuredly shoulde have so due tryall by the Lawes, as eyther shoulde not neede theyre help or shoulde bee past theyre help. They looked to that wch nearestly touched them and eche wrate in this sorte for hym, in whome theyre lyves Joye consisted.

The Humble Harted *Philoclea*,
wrate muche after this manner.

My Lordes what yow will determeyne of mee, ys to mee uncerteyne: But what I have determyned of myself, I am moste certeyne, whiche ys, no longer to enjoy my lyfe, then I may enjoy hym for my husband, whome the Goddes for my highest glory have bestowed uppon mee. Those that judge hym lett them execute mee, lett my throate satisfy the hungre of murder, for alas, what hathe hee done that had not his Originall in mee? Looke uppon hym (I beseeche yow) with indifferency whether that face coulde hyde a Murder? take leysure to knowe hym, and then youre selves will say, yt hathe beene an Inhumanity to suspect suche excellency. Are the Goddes, thinck yo^w deceyved in theyre Worckmanship? Artificers will not use Marble, but to noble uses, shoulde those powers bee so overshott as to frame so precyous an Image of theyre owne but to honorable purposes. O speake with hym, O heare hym, O knowe hym, and become not the putters oute of the worldes lighte. Hope yow to joy my Fathers sowle with hurting hym hee loved above all the worlde? Shall a wrong suspicion make yo^w forgett the certeyne knowledge of those benefites this howse hathe receyved by hym? Alas, alas, lett not *Arcadia*, for his losse bee accursed of the whole earthe and of all posterity? Hee ys a greate Prince, I speake unto yo^w that wch I knowe, for I have seene moste evident Testimonyes: Why shoulde yo^w hinder my advauncement? Who, yf I have past my Chyldehood hurtles to any of yo^w, yf I have refused no body to doo what good I coulde? yf I have often mitigated my Fathers anger, ever soughte to meynteyne his favour towardes yo^w, Nay, yf I have helde yow all as Fathers and Brothers unto mee, Robbe mee not of more then my lyfe comes unto, Teare not that wch ys unseparable to my self. But yf hee rest mysliked of yo^w (wch O God, howe can yt bee) yet give hym to mee, let mee have hym, yow knowe, I pretend no Right to youre State, therefore yt ys but a private petition I make unto yo^w: Or yf yo^w bee hardly harted bent to appoynte otherwyse (whiche, O sooner lett mee dye then knowe) Then, to ende as I began, lett mee by yow bee ordered to the same ende, withoute, for more Crewelty, yow meane to force *Philoclea* to use her owne hande to kill one of youre *Dukes* Children.

> *Pamelas* Letter wch shee ment to sende to the generall Assembly of the *Arcadian Nobility* (for so closely they were kept as they were utterly ignorant of the newe taken orders) was thus framed.

In suche a State (my Lordes) yo^w have placed mee, as I can neither wryte, nor bee silent: For howe can I bee silent, synce yow have lefte mee nothing but my solitary wordes to testify my misery? And howe shoulde I wryte, for as for speeche I have none (but my Jaylor) that can heare mee, who neither can resolve what to wryte, nor, to whome to wryte: what, to wryte ys as harde for mee to say, as, what I may not wryte, so litle hope have I of any success, and so muche hathe no injury bene lefte undone to mee wardes. To whome to wryte, where may I learne, synce yet, I wott not howe to entitle yo^w: Shall I calle yo^w my Soveraignes? Sett downe youre Lawes, that I may doo homage? Shall I falle downe lower, and name yo^w my fellowes, shewe mee I beseche yow the Lorde and Master over us? But shall *Basilius* heyre name her self youre Princes? Alas I am youre Prisoner.

But whatsoever I bee, or whatsoever yo^w bee, all yo^w beholders of these dolefull lynes, this do I signify unto yo^w, and signify yt wth a harte that shall remayne in that opinyon: The good or evill yow doo the excellent Prince was taken with mee, and after by force from mee I will ever impute yt, as every way done to my owne person. Hee ys a Prince, and worthy to bee my Husband, and so ys hee my husband by mee worthely chosen: Beeleeve yt, beleeve yt, eyther yow shall bee Traytors fo murdering of mee, Or yf yo^w lett mee live, the Murderers of hym shall smarte as Traytors.

For, what doo yo^w thincke I can thincke, am I so Chyldish as not to see, wherein yow tuche hym, yo^w do condempne mee? Can his shame bee withoute my Reproche? No, nor shall bee since no thing hee hathe done, that I will not avowe. Ys this the Comfort yo^w bringe mee in my Fathers deathe? to make mee fuller of shame then sorrowes? Neede yo^w doo this, yf yt were not with full intention to prevent my power with slaughter? And so do, I pray yow. Yt ys hye tyme for mee to bee weary of my lyfe so longe ledd, since yow are weary of mee before yo^w have mee: I say ageane, I say infinitly unto yo^w, I will not live withoute hym, yf y^t bee not to revenge hym, eyther doo justly in saving bothe, or wyse in killing bothe. Yf I bee youre Prince, I commaunde his preservation, yf but a private person, then are wee bothe to suffer, I take all truthe to witness hee hathe done no faulte, but, in gooynge with mee: Therefore to conclude, in judging hym yo^w judge mee, Neyther conceyve wth youre selves the matter yo^w treate of, ys the lyfe of a Straunger, Thoughe even, in that name hee deserved pitty, nor of a Shepeherd, to whiche estate, Love of mee made suche a Prince to descend, But determeyne moste assuredly the lyfe that ys in questyon ys of *Pamela*, *Basilius* Daughter.

Many blottes had the Teares of these sweete Ladyes made in theyre Letters, wch many tymes they had altered, many tymes torne, and written a newe; Ever thincking some thing either wanted, or were too muche, or woulde offend, or wch was worst, woulde breede denyall. But, at last, the day warned them to dispatche, whiche they accordingly did, and calling one of theyre Guarde (for no body else was suffered to come neare them) with great intreaty they requested hym, that hee woulde present them to ye Principall Noble men and Gentlemen together: For they had more Confidence in the Nombers favoure, then in any One upon whome they woulde not lay the [lives] they helde so precyous. But, the fellow trusty to *Philanax* (who had placed hym there) delyvered them bothe to hym (what tyme *Pyrocles* began to speake) wch hee sodenly opened: And seeyng, to what they tended, by the first wordes, was so farr from publisshing them (whereby hee feared in *Evarchus* just mynde eyther the

ARCADIA

Princesses mighte bee endaungered, or the Prisoners preserved, of
wch choyse hee knewe not wch to thinck the worste) that hee
woulde not hym self reade them over, doubting his owne harte
mighte bee mollifyed, so bent upon Revenge. Therefore utterly
suppressing them, hee lent a spitefull eare, to *Pyrocles* and
assoone as hee had ended, with a very willing harte desyered
Evarchus hee might accept the Combatt, allthoughe yt woulde
have framed but evell with hym: *Pyrocles* never having founde
any Matche nere hym, besydes *Musidorus*. But *Evarchus* made
an answer, Synce bodely strengthe ys but a Servaunt to the
mynde, yt were very barbarus and preposterus, that force shoulde
bee made Judge over Reason: Then woulde hee allso have
replyed in wordes unto hym. But *Evarchus* (who knewe what
they coulde say, was allredy sayde) taking theyre Argumentes
into his mynde, commaunded hym to proceede ageanst the other
Prisoner; And that then hee woulde sentence them bothe
together. *Philanax* nothing the mylder for *Pyrocles* purging
hym self, (but rather according to the nature of arguinge,
especially when yt ys bitter) so muche ye more vehement,
entered thus into his speeche ageanst *Musidorus*: Beeing so
overgõn with rage, that hee forgatt in his oration his precyse
Methode of Oratory. Beholde moste noble Protector, to what
estate *Arcadia* ys come, since suche Men may Challenge in
Combatt ye faythfullest of Nobility, and having merited the
shamefullest of all deathes dare name in Mariage the *Princesses*
of this Contry. Certeỹly my Masters I must say yow were
muche oute of Taste, yf yow had not rather enjoy suche Ladyes,
then bee hanged; But, the one yo^w have asmuche deserved, as
yo^w have dishonored ye other. But now my speeche must bee
directed to yow good Master *Dorus*, who with *Pallas* help pardy
are lately growne *Palladius*. Too muche, too muche this sacred
seate of Justice grauntes unto suche a Fugitive bondslave, who
in stede of these examinacyons shoulde bee made confess with
a whipp that wch a halter should punish: Are not yow hee Sir,
whose sheepehooke was prepared to bee oure Scepter, in whome
lay the knott of all this Tragedy? Or else perchaunce they that
shoulde gayne litle by yt were dealers in the Murder: yow,
onely that had provyded the fruites for youre self knewe no
thing of yt, knewe no thinge? hathe thy Companyons here
infected thee wth suche impudency, as even in the face of all the

worlde to deny that wch all the worlde perceyveth? The other pleades ignorance and yo^w I doubt not will alledg absence: But, hee was ignorāt when hee was harde by, and yow had framed youre absence just ageanst the tyme the acte shoulde bee committed. So fitt a Lievetenaunt hee knewe hee had lefte of his wickednes, that for hym self his safest meane was to convey away the Lady of us all: Who (once oute of the Contrye) hee knewe, wee woulde come with Ollive braunches of intercession unto her, and falle at his feete to beseeche hym, to leave keeping of sheepe and vouchsafe the tyrannising over us. For to thincke that they are *Princes*, (as they say, allthoughe in oure Lawes yt behooves them nothing) I see at all no reason: These Jewells certeynly with theyre disguysing sleightes they have pilfered in theyre vagabonding Race: And thincke yo^w suche *Princes* shoulde bee so longe withoute some followers after them? Truly yf they bee Princes, yt manifestly shewes theyre vertues suche as all theyre Subjectes are glad to bee ridd of them. But bee they as they are, for wee are to consider, the Matter and not the men: *Basilius* murder hathe beene the Cause of theyre coming, *Basilius* murder they have moste trecherusly brought to passe, yet that I doubt not yo^w will deny, aswell as youre fellowe. But howe will yow deny the stealing away the *Princess* of this Province, wch ys no less then Treason? So notably have the justice of the goddes provyded for the punishing of these Malefactors, as yf yt were possible men woulde not beleeve the certeyne evidences of theyre Principall myscheef, yet have they discovered them selves sufficiently for theyre moste just over-throwe: I say therefore (to omitt my cheef Matter of the *Dukes* Deathe) this wollvish shepehearde, this Counterfet Prince hathe Trayterusly contrary to his allegiance (having made hym self a Servant and a Subject) attempted the depriving this Contry of oure naturall *Princess*, and therefore by all Righte must receyve the punishm^t of Treytors. This matter ys so assured as hee hym self will not deny yt beeyng taken and brought back in the facte, this Matter ys so odyous in nature, so shamefull to the worlde, so contrary to all Lawes, so hurtfull to us, so false to hym: As yf I shoulde stande further in declaring or defacing yt I shoulde eyther shewe greate Doubtes in youre wisdome, or in youre Justice. Therefore I will transferr my Care uppon yo^w and attend to my learning and Comfort the eternall example yo^w will leave to all Mankynde of Disguysers, falsifyers, adulterers Ravishers Murderers and Traytors. *Musidorus*, (while *Philanax* was speaking ageanst his Coszen and hym) had looked rounde aboute hym, to see whether by any meanes hee might come to have caught hym in his Armes and have killed hym: Somuche had his disgracing wordes filled his Brest wth rage. But perceyving hym self so guarded, as hee shoulde rather shewe a passionat acte, then performe his Revenge, his hande trembling with desyer to stryke, and all the vaynes in his face swelling (Casting his eyes over the Judgment seate) O Goddes (saide hee) and have yow spared my lyfe to beare these injuryes of suche a Drivell? Is this the Justice of this place, to have suche men as wee are submitted not onely to apparant falshood, but moste shamefull Revyling? But marcke I pray yow the ungratefullnes of the Wretche, howe utterly hee hathe forgotten the Benefites bothe hee and all his Contry hathe receyved of us: For, yf men ever may Remember theyre owne noble Deedes, yt ys then when theyre just defence, and others unjust unkyndenes dothe requyte yt. Were not wee the men y^t killed the wylde Beastes, whiche otherwyse had killed the *Princesses*, yf wee had not succoured them? Consider I pray yo^w yf yt please yo^w, where had beene *Tymophirus* rape or my treason, yf the sweete beutyes of the earthe had then beene devowred? eyther thincke them now deade, or remember they live by us. And yet this Telltale full often can acknowledg the loss they shoulde have by theyre taking away, while maliciusly hee overpasseth who were theyre preservers. Neither let this bee spoken by mee, as yf I meant to Ballance this evill with that good, for I must Confess, that the saving suche Creatures was rewarded in the acte yt self: But onely to manifest the parciall jangling of this vyle Pickthanck. But yf wee bee the Traytors where was youre fidelity, O onely tounge valyant gentleman, when not onely the younge *Princesses*, but the *Duke* hym self was defended from uttermoste perill, partly by mee, but principally by this excellent younge Mans bothe wisdome and valeure: Were wee (that made oure selves ageanst hundreds of armed men openly the shieldes of his lyfe) like, secretly, to bee his poysoners? Did wee then shewe his lyfe to bee dearer to us then oure owne, bycause wee mighte after robb hym of his lyfe to dye shamefully? Truly, truly, Master Orator, whoso-ever hathe hyered yo^w to bee so buysy in theyre matters, (who

keepe honester Servauntes then youre self) hee shoulde have bid
yo^w in so many Raylinges bringe some excuse for hym self, why
in the greatest neede of youre Prince (to whome yo^w pretend
miraculus good will) yow were not then as Forwarde to doo like
a Man youre self, or at least to accuse them that were slack in
that service? But comonly they use theyre feete for theyre
Defence whose toungue ys theyre weapon; Certeynly a very
simple subtilty yt had beene for us, to repose oure lyves in y^e
Daughters when wee had killed the father? But as this Gentleman
thinkes to wynñ the reputation of a gallant speaker (by leaving
nothing unsayde wch a filthy mowthe can imagyn) so thincke I
(or ellse all wordes are vayne) that to wyse mens judgment oure
Clearenes in y^e *Dukes* deathe ys sufficyently notoryous. But at
length, when the Merchaunt hathe sett oute his gylded bagage,
lastly hee comes to some stuff of importance, and saythe I
conveyde away the *Princess* of this Contry? And ys shee in deede
youre *Princess*? I pray yow then, whome shoulde I wayte of else,
but her that was my Mistris by my professed vowe? and Princess
over mee while I lived in this soyle? Aske her, whye shee went aske
not mee why I served her, synce (accountpting mee as a *Prince*)
yo^w have not to doo with mee, taking mee her Servaunt, then
take withall that I must obay her. But yo^w will say I perswaded
her to flee away, certeynly I will for no deathe deny yt,
knowyng to what Honoure I shoulde bring her, from the
thraldome by suche fellowes Counsell as yo^w shee lived in:
Shall perswasion to a *Prince*, growe treason ageanst a *Prince*? yt
mighte bee error in mee, but falshood yt coulde not bee, since I
made my self partaker of what soever I wisshed her unto: who
will ever Counsell his kinge yf his Counseyll bee judged by the
event? and yf yt bee not founde wyse shall yt bee thoughte to
bee wicked? But yf I bee a Traytor I hope yow will graunte
mee a Correlative to whome I shall bee a Traytor: For the
Princess (ageanst whome the treasons are considered) I am sure
will avowe my faythfullnes, withoute that yow will say, I am a
Traytor to her bycause I lefte the Contry, and a Traytor to the
Contry, bycause I went with her? Here do I leave oute my
just excuses of Loves force, whiche as the narrow hart hathe
never had Noble rowme ynoughe in yt to receyve so yet, to those
Manlike Corages, that by experience knowe how subject the
vertuous myndes are to love a moste vertuus Creature (witnessed

to bee suche by the moste excellent giftes of Nature) will
deeme yt a veniall trespass to seeke the satisfaction of honorable
desyers: Honorable, even in the curyousest poyntes of honor,
whereoute there can no disgrace nor disparagemēt come unto
her. Therefore (O Judge) wch I hope doste know what yt ys
to bee a Judge, that youre ende ys to preserve & not to destroy
mankynde, that Lawes are not made like Lymetwigges or nettes
to catche every thinge that tucheth them: But rather lyke sea
Marckes to avoyde the Shippwrackes of ignorant passingers synce
that oure doynge (in the extreymest interpretation) ys but a
humane error. And that of yt yo^w may make a profitable event
(wee beeyng of suche estate as theyre Parentes woulde not have
misliked theyre affinity) yo^w will not I trust at the perswasion
of this Brabler, burne youre howse to make yt cleane: But, like
a wyse Father, turne even the faulte of youre Children to any
good, that may come of yt, synce that ys the fruite & ende of
all Judgmentes. While this matter was thus handling a silent
and as yt were astonished attention possest all the people, a
kyndely Compassyon mooved the noble Gentleman *Sympathus*:
But as for *Kerkxenus* eyvery thinge was spoken eyther by or of
his dere guestes mooved an effect in hym, some teares, sometymes
hopefull Lookes, sometymes whispering perswasions in theyre
eares that stoode by hym to seeke the saving of the twoo younge
Princes. But the generall multitude wayted the judgment of
Evarchus, who shewyng in his face no motions eyther at the ones
or others speeche, lettinge pass the flowers of Rethorique, and
onely marckyng whether theyre reasons tended, having made
the questyon to bee asked of *Gynecia*, who continewed to take
the whole fault upon her self and having caused *Dametas* with
Miso and *Mopsa* (who by *Philanax* order had beene helde in
crewell prison) to make a full declaration howe muche they
knewe of these passed matters: And then gathering as assured
satisfaction to his owne mynde, as in that case hee coulde, (not
neading to take leysure for that, wherof a long practize had
bredd a well grounded habite in hym) wth a voyce and gesture
directed to the universall assembly in this forme pronounced
sentence. This weighty matter wherof presently wee are to
determeyn, dothe at the first Consideracyon yeelde twoo
important Doubtes. The firste

Whether these men bee to bee judged. The seconde
Howe they are to bee judged.   375

The first Doubt aryseth bycause they give them selves oute for *Princes* absolute, a Sacred name, and to wch any vyolence seemes an Impiety: For how can any Lawes wch are ye bondes of all humane society bee observed, yf the Lawe givers & Lawe Rulers bee not helde in an untouched admiration? But hereto all thoughe all redy, they have bene sufficyently answered yet, thus muche ageane I will repeate unto yo^w. That whatsoever they bee or bee not, here they bee no *Princes* synce betuixt *Prince* and *Subject*, there ys as necessary a Relation, as betweene father and sonne. And as there ys no Man a Father but to his Chylde, so ys not a Prince a Prince, but to his owne Subjectes, therefore ys not this place to acknowledge in them any principallity, withoute yt shoulde at ye same tyme by a secrett Consent, confess subjection: yet hereto may bee objected, that the universall Civility, the Lawe of Nations (all mankynde beeyng as yt were Coinhabiters or worlde Citizens together) hathe ever requyred publique persons shoulde bee (of all partyes) especially regarded: Since not onely in peace but in warres, not onely *Princes*, but Herauldes and Trompettes are wth greate reasons exempted from injuryes. This poynt ys true, but, yet so true, as they that will receyve the benefites of a Custome must not bee the first to breake yt, for then can they not Complayne, yf they bee not helpt by that, wch they themselves hurt: Yf a *Prince* do actes of hostility withoute denouncing warre, yf hee breake his oathe of Amity, or innumerable suche other thinges contrary to the Lawe of Armes, hee must take heede howe hee falleth into theyre handes whom hee so wrongeth, for then ys Curtesy the best custome hee can clayme: Muche more these men, who have not onely lefte to doo like *Princes*, but, to bee like *Princes*, not onely entered into *Arcadia*, and so into the *Arcadian* Orders, but into Domesticall services, and so by making them selves private, deprived them selffes of respect due to theyre publique Calling. For no proportion yt were in Justice, that a Man might make hym selfe no *Prince* when hee will do evell, and mighte a newe create hym self *Prince* when hee will not suffer evell: Thus therefore by all Lawes of Nature and Nations, and specially by theyre owne putting them selves oute of the Sanctuary of them, these younge Men can not in justice avoyde the judgment but like private men must have theyre Doynges eyther cleared excused or condempned. There resteth then the second poynte, Howe to Judge well: And that must undoubtedly bee done, not by a free Discourse of Reason and skill of philosophy, but must bee tyed to the Lawes of *Greece* and municipall statutes of this Kingdome. For allthough oute of them these came and to them must in deede referr theyre Ofspringe, yet bycause Philosophicall discourses stande in the generall Consideration of thinges, they leave to every man a scope of his owne interpretacyon. Where the Lawes (applying them selves to the necessary use) foulde us within the Boundes assured, wch once broken, mans nature infenitely raungeth: Judged therefore they must bee, and by youre Lawes Judged. Nowe the action offereth yt self to due Ballance betwixt the accusers twoo foulde accusation, and theyre answer accordingly applyed: The questyons beeynge, the one of a fact simply, the other of the quality of a facte. To the first they use direct Denyall, to the second, qualification and excuse: They deny the Murder of the *Duke*, and ageanst mighty presumptions bringe forthe some probable answers, whiche they do principally fortify with the *Duchess* acknouledging her self onely culpable. Certeynly as in equallity of Conjectures wee are not to take holde of the worste, but rather to bee glad wee may fynde any hope, that Mankynde ys not growne Monsterus (beeyng less evell undoubtedly, a guilty man shoulde escape, then a guiltless parrish) so yf in the rest they bee spottless, then ys yt no furder to bee remembred: But yf they have aggrevated these suspicions with newe evills, then are those suspicions so farr to shewe them selves, as to cause the other poyntes to bee thorowly examyned and with less favoure weighed, since this no man can denye, they have beene accedentall yf not Principall Causes of the *Dukes* death.

Nowe then wee are to determeyn of the other matters wch are layde to them, wherein they doo not deny the facte, but deny or at least dimenish the faulte: But first I may Remember (thoughe yt were not first alledged by them) the services they had before done, truly honorable and worthy of great Reward, but, not worthy to counterveyle with a followyng wickednes: Rewarde ys proper to well doynge, ponishment to evell doynge, wch must not bee confounded, no more then good & evill are to bee mingled. Therefore yt hathe beene determeyned in all wysdomes, that no man bycause hee hathe done well before, shoulde have his present evilles spared, but rather, so muche the more punished: As having shewed hee knewe howe to doo good, woulde ageanst his knouledge bee naughte. The facte then ys nakedly withoute passion, or parciality, to bee viewed, wherein hee that termes hym self to bee *Tymophirus*, denyes not hee offered vyolence to the Lady *Philoclea*: An acte punished by all the *Grecian* Lawes, with beeyng throwne downe from a hye Tower to the earthe, a Deathe wch dothe noo way exceede the proportion of the Trespas. For, nothing can bee ymagined more unnaturall, then by force to take that, wch beeynge holyly used, ys the Roote of humanity, the beginning & meynteyning of Living Creatures, wherof the Confusion must needes bee a generall Rwyn: And synce the wickednes of Lust ys by oure Decrees punished by deathe, (thoughe bothe so consent) muche more ys hee whose wickednes so overflowes, as hee will compell an other to bee wicked. The other younge Man hee confesseth, hee perswaded the Princess *Pamela* to flee her Contrey, and accompanyed her in yt, withoute all questyon, a Ravishment no less, then the other: For, allthoughe hee ravisshed her not from her self yet hee ravisshed her from hym y^t owed her wch was her Father. This kynde ys chastized by the loss of the heade, as a moste execrable thefte, for yf they must dye, who steale from us oure goodes howe muche more they who steale from us that, for whiche wee gather oure goodes: And yf oure Lawes have yt so in ye private persons muche more forcible are they to bee in *Princes* Children? Wheare one steales as yt were the whole state, and well beeyng of that People, tyed by the secrett of a longe use to bee governed by none but the next of the blood. Neyther lett any man merveile oure Auncesters have bene so severe in these Cases, since the example of the *Phenecian Europa*, but especially the *Gretian Helen* hathe taughte them, what destroyng fyers have growne of suche sparckles: And allthoughe *Helene* was a wyfe, and this but a Chylde, that booteth not, since the Principall Cause of marying wyves ys that wee may have Children of oure owne. But lett us see howe these younge meñ (truely for theyre persons worthy of pity yf they have pityed them selves) doo goo aboute to mitigate ye vehemency of theyre Errors: Some of theyre excuses are comon to bothe, some peculier, onely to hym that was the Shepeheard bothe Remember the force of Love, and as yt were the mending up the matter by theyre Mariage. Yf that unbrydeled Desyer wch ys intituled

378

Love mighte purge suche a sicknes as this, surely wee shoulde
have many Loving excuses of hatefull myscheefes: Nay, rather
no myscheef shoulde bee committed that shoulde not bee vailed
under the name of Love. For aswell hee that steales mighte
alledg the Love of money hee that murders the Love of Revenge,
hee that rebells the Love of greatnes as the Adulterer y^e
Love of a woman: since in all speeche they do affirme they
Love that wch an yll governed passyon makes them to follow.
But love may have no suche priviledge. That sweete and
heavenly uniting of the myndes, wch properly ys called Love,
hathe no other knott but vertue: And therefore, yf yt bee a
Right Love, yt can never slyde into any action y^t ys not vertuous.
The other and in deede more effectuall reason ys, that they may
bee marryed unto them, and so honorably redress the Dishonor
of them, whome this matter seemeth more to tuche: Surely, yf
the questyon were, what were convenyent for ye parties, and
not what ys just in the never chaunging Justice, there might
bee muche sayde in yt. But herein wee must consider that y^e
Lawes looke howe to prevent by due examples, that suche
thinges bee not done: For, yf the Governoures of Justice, shall
take suche a scope, as to measure the force of the Lawe by a
shewe of Convenyency, and measure that Convenyency not by
the publique Society (but by y^t wch ys fittest for them to offend)
younge men, stronge men & riche men shall ever fynde private
Convenyences, how to cover suche committed disorders, as to
the publique shall not onely bee inconvenyent but pestilent.
This Mariage perchaunce might bee fitt for them, but very
unfitt for the state yt were to allowe a Paterne of suche
procurations of Mariage, and thus muche doo they bothe alledge:
Furder goes hee that went with the Princes *Pamela*, and
requireth ye benefitt of a Counsellor, who hathe place of free
perswasion & ye reasonable excuse of a Servaunt that did but
wayte of his Mistris. Withoute all question as Counseilors have
greate Cause to take heede how they advise any thinge directly
opposite to the forme of that present governem^t, especially when
they doo yt simply, withoute publique allowance; So yet ys this
Case muche more apparant, since neyther shee was an effectuall
Princess (her Father beeyng then alyve, and thoughe hee had
bene deade) shee not come to the yeares of authority, nor hee her
servant in such maner to obay her, but by his owne preferment,

379

first belonging to *Dametas* and then to the *Duke*. And therefore
yf not by *Arcadian* Lawes yet by howsholde orders bounde to
have done nothing withoute his agreem^t. Thus therefore, since
the Deedes accomplisshed by these Twoo are bothe abhominable,
and inexcusable, I doo in the behalf of Justice, and by ye force
of *Arcadian* Lawes pronounce: That *Tymophirus* shall bee
throwne of, from a hye Tower, to receyve his deathe by his
Falle, *Palladius* shall bee beheaded, the tyme before the Sunne
sett, the place in *Mantinea*, the executioner *Dametas* wch office
hee shalle execute all the dayes of his lyfe, for his beastly
forgetting the carefull Duty owed to his Charge: This sayde
hee turned hym self to *Philanax* and twoo other of the Noble
men comaunding them to see the Judgment presently performed.

Philanax more greedy then any hunter of his pray, went
streighte to lay holde of the excellent Prisoners: who casting a
Farewell looke one uppon the other represented in theyre faces as
muche unapalled Constancy as the moste excellent Corage can
delyver in owteward graces: Yet yf at all there were any shewe
of Chaunge in them, yt was that *Pyrocles* was some thinge
nearer to Bashfullnes, and *Musidorus* to anger, bothe over Ruled
by reason and resolutyon. But, as with great nomber of armed
men *Philanax* was descending unto them, and that *Musidorus*
was beginning to say some thing in *Pyrocles* behalf. Beholde
Kerkxenus that with Armes caste abroade and open mowthe
came crying to *Evarchus*, holding a Straunger in his hande that
cryed muche more then hee, desyering they mighte bee
hearde speake before ye Prisoners were remooved. Eeven the
Noble gentleman *Sympathus* ayded them in yt (and taking suche
as hee coulde comaund) stopped *Philanax* betwixt intreaty, and
force from carrying away the *Princes*: untill yt were hearde
what newe Matters those men did bringe. So ageane mounting
to the Tribunall they hearckened to the Straungers vehement
speeche or rather a passionate exclaminge: But, first, yow will
bee content to knowe, what hee was, and what Cause and
meane brought hym thether. It ys not forgotten (I hope) howe
in the first begining of *Musidorus* love, when (in despyte of his
best grounded determinacyons, hee became a slave to affection)
howe leaving the place of his eye infection hee mett with the
Shepehearde *Menalcas*; By the help of whose rayment hee
advaunced hym self to y^t estate, whiche hee accompted moste

highe in his mynde. And howe at least by his presence his purpose mighte bee reveiled, hee hyered hym to goo into *Thessalia*, wryting by hym to a trusty servant of his, that hee shoulde arrest hym untill hee knewe his furder pleasure : *Menalcas* faythfully performed his errant and was as faythfully imprisoned by *Kalodulus*, for suche was the Gentlemans name to whome *Musidorus* directed hym. But, as *Kalodulus* perfurmed the first parte of his Duety in doyng the Comaundement of his *Prince* : So was hee wth abundance of sincere Loyalty extremely perplexed when hee understood of *Menalcas* the straunge disguysing of his Beloved Master. For as the actes hee and his Coszen *Pyrocles* had done in *Asia* & *Egipt*, had filled all the eares of the *Thessalians* & *Macedonians* with no less joy then admiration : So was the feare of theyre Losse no less greevus unto them, when by the noyse of Reporte they understood of theyre lonely committing them selves to ye sea, the issue of wch they had no way learned. But, now that [by] *Menalcas* hee perceyving where hee was guessing the like of *Pyrocles*, comparing the unusednes of this acte wth the unrypenes of theyre age, seeyng in generall Conjecture they coulde do yt for no thinge that mighte not falle oute daungerus : Hee was some while trubled with hym self what to doo betuixt doubte of theyre hurte and doubte of theyre Displeasure. Lastly hee resolved his safest and honestest way was to reveyle yt to the Kinge *Evarchus*, that bothe his authority might prevent any domage, and under his winges hee hym self might remayn safe : Thetherwarde therefore hee went. But beeyng come to the City of *Pella*, where hee had hearde the Kinge lay, hee founde hym not longe before parted towarde *Arcadia* : This made hym with all the speede hee coulde followe *Evarchus* aswell to advertize hym yf neede were, as to doo his *Prince* service in his unckles thether coming. And so yt hapned that beeyng even this day come to *Mantinea* and as warely as hee coulde enquyring after *Evarchus* hee streight receyved a straunge Rumor of these thinges, but so uncerteynly as Popular Reportes carry so rare accidentes. But this by all men hee was willed to seeke owte *Kerkxenus* a great gentleman of that Contry who woulde soonest satisfy hym of all these occurrentes : Thus instructed hee came aboute the midst of *Evarchus* judgment to the Dezart, where seeyng great Multitudes & hearing unknowne names of *Palladius* and *Tymophirus*, &

not able to press to the place where *Evarchus* satt, hee enquyred for *Kerkxenus*, and was soone brought unto hym. Partely bycause hee was generally knowne unto all men & partly bycause hee had withdrawne hymself from the prease when hee perceyved by *Evarchus* wordes whether they tended, not beeyng able to endure his Guestes Condempnation: Hee enquyred forthe with of *Kerkxenus* the Cause of the assembly and whether hee had hearde of *Evarchus*. Who with many teares made a dolefull recitall unto hym bothe of yᵉ *Amazon* and Shepeheard, setting forthe theyre naturall graces & Lamenting theyre pityfull undoynge. But his Description made *Kalodulus* ymediatly knowe the Shepehearde was his *Duke* and so judging the other to bee *Pyrocles* & speedely communicating [it] to *Kerkxenus* (who hee sawe did favoure theyre Case,) they brake the presse with astonisshing every man wᵗʰ theyre Cryes: And beeyng come to *Evarchus*, *Kalodulus* fell at his feete telling hym, those hee had judged were his owne Sonne & Nephewe the one the Comfort of *Macedon*, the other the stay of *Thessalia* with many suche like wordes. But as from a Man yᵗ assured hym self in that matter hee shoulde neede smalle speeche, while *Kerkxenus* made yt knowne to all men what the Prisoners were: To whome hee cryed, they shoulde salute theyre Father, & joye in the good happ the Goddes had sent them; who were no less glad, then all the people amazed at the straunge event of these matters. Even *Philanax* revengefull hart was mollifyed, when hee sawe how from dyvers partes of the worlde so nere kinsemen shoulde meete in suche a necessity: And withall the fame of *Pyrocles* and *Musidorus* greatly drewe hym to a compassionate Conceypte, and had all redy uncloathed his face of all shewe of mallice. But *Evarchus* stayed a good while uppon hym self, like a valyaunt Man that shoulde receyve a notable encounter, beeyng vehemently stricken with the Fatherly love of so excellent Children, and studying wᵗʰ his best reason what his office requyred: At lengthe with suche a kynde of gravity as was nere to sorowe hee thus uttered his mynde. I take witnes of yᵉ immortall goddes (sayde hee) O *Arcadians*, that what this day I have sayde, hathe bene oute of my assured perswasion, what Justice yt self, and youre just Lawes requyer: Thoughe Straungers then to mee, I had no desyer to hurte them, but leaving assyde all Consideracions of the partyes I weyghed the

Matter wch yow committed into my handes wth my moste unparciall and furdest reche of reason; and thereoute have condempned them to loose theyre Lyves, contaminated wth so many fowle breaches of hospitality, Civility and vertue. Nowe contrary to all expectation I fynde them to bee my onely Sonne and Nephewe suche uppon whome yo^w see what giftes nature hathe bestowed, suche who have to the wonder of the worlde so behaved them selves as might give just Cause to the greatest hopes, that in an excellent yowthe may bee conceyved: Lastly in fewe wordes, suche in whome I placed all my mortall Joyes, and thoughte my self now nere my grave, to recover a newe lyfe. But alas shall Justice haulte, or shall shee wincke in ones Cause wch had *Lynxes* eyes in an other, or rather shall all private respectes give place to that holy name? Bee yt so, bee yt so, lett my gray hayers bee layde in the Dust wth sorowe, lett the smalle Remnant of my lyfe bee to mee an inward & owteward desolation, and to the worlde a gasing stock of wretched misery. But, never, never let sacred Rightfullnes falle, yt ys Immortall and Immortall oughte to bee preserved: yf Rightly I have judged, then rightly I have judged myne owne Children, unless the name of a Chylde shoulde have force to chaunge the never chaunging Justice. No, no, *Pyrocles* and *Musidorus*, I preferr yo^w muche before myne owne lyfe, but I preferr Justice as farr before yow: When yow did lyke youre selves my body shoulde willingly have beene youre sheelde, but I can not keepe yo^w from the effectes of youre owne doynge. Nay I can not in this Case acknowledg yo^w for myne, for never had I Shepeheard to my Nephewe, nor never had woeman to my sonne, youre vyces have degraded yow from beeyng *Princes* & have disanulde youre Birtheright: Therefore, yf there bee any thing lefte in yo^w of Princely vertue, shewe yt in constant suffering, that youre unprincely deallinge hathe purchaste unto yow. For my parte I must tell yo^w, yo^w have forced a Father to robb hym self of his Children. Do yo^w therefore O *Philanax* and yo^w my other Lordes of this Contry, see the judgment bee rightly performed in tyme place and maner before appoynted: With that thoughe hee woulde have refrayned them, a mañ mighte perceyve the Teares dropp downe his longe white Bearde, wch mooved not onely *Kalodulus* & *Kerkxenus* to roaring lamentations, but all the Assembly dolefully to recorde y^t pitifull spectacle. *Philanax* hym self coulde not abstayne from greate shewes of pitying sorowe, and manifest with drawyng from performing ye Kinges Comandement: But, *Musidorus* having the hope of his safty and Recovering the Princes *Pamela*, wch made hym moste desyer to lyve so, (sodeynly dasshed, but especially mooved for his dere *Pyrocles* for wch hee was ever resolved his last speeche shoulde bee) and styrred up wth the rage of unkyndenes hee thus spake. Enjoy thy bloody Conquest Tyrannicall *Evarchus* (sayde hee) For neyther ys convenyent the Tytle of a Kinge to a Murderer nor the Remembrance of Kynred, to a Destroyer of his Kynred: Go home and glory, that yt hathe beene in thy power shamefully to kill *Musidorus*. Lett thy flattering Orators dedicate Crownes of Lawrell unto thee, that the first of thy Race, thow haste overthrowne a Prince of *Thessalia*. But for mee I hope the *Thessalians* are not so degenerate from theyre Auncestors, but that they will revenge my Injury and theyre Losse upon thee: I hope my Deathe ys no more unjust to mee, then yt shall bee bitter unto thee, howsoever yt bee, my Deathe shall tryumphe over thy Cruelty, neyther as now woulde I live, to make my lyfe beholding unto thee. But yf thy Crewelty hathe not so blynded thyne eyes that tho^w canst not see thyne owne hurte, yf thyne harte bee not so develish as thow haste no power but to torment thy self, then looke uppon this younge *Pyrocles* with a Manlike eye, yf not wth a pitifull: Give not occasion to the whole earthe to say, See how ye goddes have made the Tyrant teare his owne Bowells? Examen the eyes and voyces of all this people, and what all men see, bee not blynde in thyne owne Case? Looke, I say, looke upon hym in whome the moste Curyous searcher ys able to fynde no faulte but that hee ys thy Sonne: Beleeve yt, thy owne Subjectes will detest thee, for Robbing them of suche a Prince? in whome they have Right aswell as thy self. Some more wordes to that purpose hee woulde have spoken, but *Pyrocles* who had ofte calde to hym, did now fully interrupt hym, Desyering hym not to doo hym the wronge to give his Father yll wordes before hym: Willing hym to Consider yt was theyre owne faulte and not his unjustice, and withall to Remember theyre Resolution of well suffering all accidentes whiche this Impacyence did vary from. And then kneeling downe with all humblenes hee tooke the speeche in this order, to *Evarchus*: Yf my dayly prayers to the goddes

384

Allmighty had so farr preveyled as to have graunted mee the
ende, whereto I have directed my actions, I shoulde rather have
bene now a Comfort to youre mynde, then an example of youre
Justice, rather a preserver of youre memory by my lyfe, then a
Monument of youre judgment by my deathe. But since yt
hathe pleased theyre unsearcheable wisdomes to overthrowe all
the Desyers I had to serve yow, and make mee become a shame
unto yow: Synce the last obeydyence I can shewe yow ys to
dye, vouchesafe yet O Father (yf my faulte have not made mee
alltogether so to terme yow) vouchesafe I say to lett the fewe
and last wordes youre Sonne shall ever speke not bee tedyous
unto yow. And yf the Remembrance of my vertuous Mother
who once was dere unto yow, may beare any sway with yow, yf
the name of *Pyrocles* have at any tyme beene pleasant, lett one
Request of myne wch shall not bee for myne owne lyfe bee
gracyusly accepted of yow, what yow owe to Justice ys performed
in my Deathe: A Father to have executed his onely Sonne will
leave a sufficyent example for a greater Cryme then this, my
blood will satisfy the highest poynte of equity, my blood will
satisfy the hardest hartes of this Contry. O save the lyfe of this
Prince, that ys the onely all I will with my last breathe demaund
of yow: with what face will yow looke uppon youre Sister when
in Rewarde of nourisshing mee in youre greatest neede, yow take
away, and in suche sorte yow take away that wch ys more deare
to her then all the worlde, and ys the onely Comforte wherewith
shee nourisheth her oulde age. O give not suche an occasion
to the noble *Thessalians* for ever to curse the Matche that theyre
Prince did make with the *Macedonians* bloode. By my Losse
there followes no publique losse, For yow are to holde the seate,
and to provyde youre self perchaunce a worthy Successor but
howe can yow or all the earthe recompence the Damage yt pore
Thessalia shall sustayne: Who sending oute (whome otherwyse
they woulde no more have spared then theyre owne eyes) theyre
Prince to yow, and yow requesting to have hym by yow, hee
shoulde thus dishonourably bee distinguisshed. Sett before yow
I beseche yow the face of that miserable people, when no sooner
shall the Newes come that yow have mett youre Nephewe, but
withall they shall heare, that yow have beheaded hym: How
many teares they shall spende, how many Complayntes they
shall make, so many Just execrations will lighte uppon yow. And

take heede O Father, (For since my deathe answers my faulte, while I live I will calle uppon that dere name) least, seeking too precyse a Course of Justice, yo^w bee not thoughte moste unjust: In weykening youre Neighboures mighty estate, by taking away theyre onely piller. In mee, in mee this matter began, in mee let yt receyve his ending, assure youre self, no man will doubte youre severe observing of the Lawes, when yt shall bee knowne *Evarchus* hathe killed *Pyrocles*: But the tyme of my ever Farewell approcheth yf yow do thincke my Deathe sufficyent for my faulte, and do not desyer to make my Deathe more myserable then deathe, Lett these dying wordes of hym that was once youre Sonne pearse youre eares? Lett *Musidorus* live, and *Pyrocles* shall live in hym, and yo^w shall not want a Chylde. A Chylde? (Cryed oute *Musidorus*) to hym that killes *Pyrocles*? with that ageane hee fell to intreat for *Pyrocles*, and *Pyrocles* as fast ageane for *Musidorus*, eche employing his witt howe to shewe hym self moste worthy to dye, to suche an admiration of all the Beholders, that moste of them examening the Matter by theyre owne passions, thoughte *Evarchus* (as often extraordenary excellences not beeyng rightly conceyved do rather offend then please) an obstinate harted Man, and suche a one who beeyng pittyles his Dominion must needes bee insupportable. But *Evarchus* that felt his owne misery more then they, and yet loved goodnes more then hym self, (with suche a sadd assured beehaviour as *Cato* kilde hym self withall) when hee had hearde ye uttermoste of that theyre speeche tended unto: Hee comaunded againe they shoulde bee carryed away, rysing up from the seate (wch hee woulde muche rather have wisshed shoulde have beene his grave) and looking who woulde take the Charge, whereto every one was exceeding backward. But as this pityfull matter was entering into, those that were next the *Dukes* body mighte here from under the vellvett wherewith hee was covered a great voyce of groaning: whereat every man astonished (and theyre spirittes appalled with these former miseryes, apte to take any straunge Conceypte, when they mighte perfectly perceyve the body sturr) then some began to feare Spirites, some to looke for a Mirackle, moste to imagyn they knewe not what. But *Philanax* and *Kerkxenus*, whose eyes honest love (thoughe to dyvers partyes) helde moste attentive, leapte to the Table; and putting of the vellvet Cover mighte playnely discerne, with asmuche wonder as gladnes, that yᵉ *Duke* lived: whiche howe yt fell oute shall in fewe wordes bee declared. So yt was, that the Drincke hee had receyved was neyther as *Gynecia* first imagined a Love potion, nor as yt was after thoughte a Deadly poyson, but a Drincke made by notable Arte, (and as yt was thought not withoute Naturall Magique) to procure for xxxᵗⁱ howers suche a Deadly sleepe as shoulde oppress all shewe of lyfe: The Cause of the making of this Drinck had first beene, that a Princess of *Cyprus* grandmother to *Gynecia* beeyng notably learned (and yet not able wᵗʰ all her Learninge to answer the objections of *Cupid*) did furiusly love a younge Noble man of her Fathers Courte, who fearing the Kinges Rage and not once daring eyther to attempt, or accept so hye a place shee made that sleeping drincke: And founde meanes by a trusty servaunt of hers (who of purpose invited hym to his Chamber) to procure hym that suspected not, suche thinge, to receyve yt. Whiche done, hee, no way able to resist, was secretly carryed by hym, into a pleasaunt Chamber in the midst of a gardeyn shee had of purpose provyded for this enterpryse. Where that space of tyme pleasing her self wᵗʰ seeyng and Cherisshing of hym when the tyme came of the Drinckes ende of worcking, and hee moste astonisshed, then, yf hee had fallen from the Clowdes shee bad hym choose, eyther then to marry her, and to promise to flee away with her in a Barck shee had made redy; Or else shee woulde presently crye oute, and shewe in what place hee was with oathe, hee was come thether to ravish her. The Noble man, in these streytes her beuty preveiled, hee marryed her and escaped the Realme wᵗʰ her, and after many straunge adventures were reconcyled to the Kinge her Father: But shee gratefully remembring the service the Drinck had done her, preserved in a Bottell (made by singuler arte longe to keepe yt withoute perishing) great quantity of yt with the foretolde inscription. Whiche, wronge interpreted by her Daughter in Lawe the Queene of *Cyprus*, was given by her to *Gynecia* at the tyme of her Mariage: And the Drincke fynding an oulde Body of *Basilius* had kept hym some howers longer in the Traunce, then yt woulde have done a younger. But a good while yt was before good *Basilius* coulde come ageane to hym self: In whiche tyme *Evarchus* (more glad then of the whole worldes Monarchy to bee ridd of his miserable Magistracy whiche even in Justice hee was now to surrender to ye Lawfull *Prince* of that Contry) came frome the Throane unto hym: And there wth muche a doo made hym understand how these intricate matters had falne owte, many garboyles passed thorow his fancy before hee coulde bee perswaded *Cleophila* was other then a woman. At lengthe, Remembring the Oracle, wch now indeede was accomplisshed (not as before hee had imagined) Considering all had falne oute by the highest providence: And withall weighing in all these matters (his owne faulte had bene the greatest) the first thinge hee did was wth all honorable pompe to sende for *Gynecia*. Who pore Lady, thought shee was leading forthe to her Living buryall, and (when shee came) to recoumpte before all the people the excellent vertue was in her, wch shee had not onely meyntayned all her lyfe moste unspotted, but, now was content so miserably to dye to followe her husbande: Hee toulde them howe shee had warned hym to take heede of that drincke: And so with all the exaltinges of her yt mighte bee, hee publiquely desyered her pardon, for those errors hee had Committed, and so kissing her lefte her to receyve ye moste honourable fame of any *Princess* throughe oute the worlde. All men thincking (saving onely *Pyrocles* and *Philoclea* who never bewrayed her) that shee was the perfect mirror of all wyvely Love: whiche (thoughe in that poynte undeserved) shee did in ye remnaunt of her lyfe duely purchase, with observing all duety & faythe to the Example and glory of *Greece*: So uncerteyne are mortall Judgmentes the same person moste infamus and moste famus and neyther justly. Then, with Princely interteynment to *Evarchus*, and many kynde wordes to *Pyrocles* whome still hee derely loved, (thoughe in a more vertuous kynde) the Mariage was concluded to the inestimable joy of *Evarchus* (towardes whome now *Musidorus* acknoulledged his faulte) betwixt those Pereles *Princes* and *Princesses*. *Philanax* for his singuler faythe ever helde dere of *Basilius* while hee lived, and no less of *Musidorus*: who was to inherite that Dukedome, and therein confirmed to hym and his the second place of that Province wth greate Increase of his Living to meyntayne yt, wch like proportion hee used to *Kalodulus* in *Thessalia*. *Sympathus Evarchus* tooke with hym into *Macedone*, and there highely advaunced hym: But as for *Kerkxenus*, *Pyrocles* (to whome his Father in his owne tyme gave the Kingdome of *Thrace*) helde

388

hym allwayes aboute hym, giving hym in pure gifte, the greate City of *Abdera*.

But the solempnityes of the Marriages wth the *Arcadian* pastoralles full of many *Comicall* adventures happening to those Rurall Lovers the straunge story of the fayre Queene *Artaxia* of *Persia* and *Erona* of *Lydia*, with the Prince *Plangus* wonderfull Chaunces whome the later had sent to *Pyrocles*, and the extreme affection *Amasis* kinge of *Egipt* bare unto the former: The Sheperdish Loves of *Menalcas* w^th *Kalodulus* Daughter, and the pore hopes of *Philisides* in the pursuite of his affections, the strange Countenance of *Claius* and *Strephons* desyer, Lastly the Sonne of *Pyrocles* and *Melidura* the fayre Daughter of *Pamela* by *Musidorus*: who even at theyre byrthe entred into admirable Fortunes may awake some other Spirite to exercyse his penñ in that, wherewith myne ys allredy dulled.

Here endeth the Fifte and last Booke
or Acte.
of the Countess of Pembrookes
ARCADIA.

A LIST OF ERRORS IN THE MS, WHICH HAVE BEEN CORRECTED

2. 3. no *omitted*
6. 4. prevailed   38. *Misio*
7. 4. *Misidorus*
10. 29. *Pyroles*
11. 18. *Misidorus*
14. 11. Thessalia
15. 19. see, will   mee, And   31. Cossen, and   37. him) with
16. 12. home, to
18. 12. sectes of whome
21. 28. greeevous
24. 29, 36. *Cleofila*
28. 5. simplicity, And
31. 29. Lovelynes
45. 7. *Genesia*
46. 21. *Genicia*
49. 7. The *Duke* toulde tolde with   8. after *Cleophila* with
51. 8. conning had
53. 9, 11. *Ginesia*   34. voyces. w^ch
55. 24. *where highe*
63. 37. no chaunged
64. 5. *Otones* [*see* Corrigenda]   29. *Baizanes*, Lorde of *Hiramia*
68. 7. *comma omitted after "smarte"*
70. 32. [*margin*] Geron. *omitted*
73. 33. dothe holde
74. 7. [*margin*] Geron. *omitted*
87. 12. *MS has a blank between* dezartes *and* full
89. 25. Jofull
91. 26. *Genecia*   36. *Cleofila*
95. 18. *"Mapema" instead of "Pamela"*
96. 30. say lifted   heighe
97. 16. Therefore, wth with an
98. 11. Souldyors   30. Contry. Longe
99. 9. have *omitted*
100. 29. mase of Lodging
102. 30. *Menachas*
104. 3. Lovely
105. 17. had adjoyned
109. 25. her wordes
112. 2. Lady *Philoclea*   23. *Ginesia*
116. 31. *blank in MS after* y^e
118. 12. ragefull, *Cleophila*
119. 4. sayle,   14. *comma omitted after "growes"*   20. *comma omitted after "prevayle"*
124. 17. *blank in MS before* meanes
131. 27. *owne bravely*
133. 12. *hunting reconde*
136. 2. *like berde*

A LIST OF ERRORS

139. 15. histor
140. 6. *some onely*
149. 20. loved *Thermuthis*
154. 39. *Anacirons*
155. 29. *Instead of this line MS has the following:* [*The Slippery Kisse, the Monasticall*
156. 24. *Phaleuciactes*
157. 21. Asclepiadictes
160. 38. well dothe
161. 4. have wonne mee
163. 12. worthynes. Hee
164. 26. *Genicia*
166. 23. Combynacyon, (having
169. 16. moste ease fall
170. 15. *Gohstes*
172. 6. Fellowes) shee   24. am deforced from
174. 39. umprovyded
175. 3. self, thoughte) thoughte   34. to bee wooe her
176. 38. secrett) and a
178. 23. leave gyrning
181. 21. come)
182. 11. with Joyes
183. 23. Dezert. (where   39. *Apollo*
186. 10. fatall *Paludina*   25. meytayning
188. 15. Castle of his hurt   33. *"to trye" omitted after "smalle force"*
        35. *Galle mee*
190. 32. *Pamela.* Whose
191. 2. awakes
192. 32. Man Nay;
194. 35. Lovely place
196. 11. *Thy litle great*
198. 20. overthrowe?: Coulde   29. wth with so
199. 2. contended   25. mynde (sayde
212. 14. Lust. And
215. 29. Resolving to hym
216. 35. *3 omitted above* "*Arme*"
217. 7. *3 omitted above* "*thoughte*"   8. *3 omitted above* "*refrayne*"
        15. motyons of of
219. 17. loved) had then Cause had then Cause enowghe
220. 40. Daungerus Coming
221. 12. spott or Fellowship, then
223. 1. Armes) hee   2. servisabe   4. undkynde
225. 28. *"mewes" omitted*
230. 1. *Heaven*
231. 10. Cupid, *fyer, to*
232. 37. example, through yt
233. 4. singe then well
239. 28. *That ys bothe*
240. 1. *foxe*   5. Ernon   8. *Beare*   13. Ape (*greate*
241. 9. *Beastes* (as
244. 10. [*margin*] Geron. omitted   37. them, But
245. 21. *not first fonde*   27. *note of interrogation omitted after* "*norishe*"
248. 14. Lovelynes

A LIST OF ERRORS

249. 37. *Pamelas*
250. 16. not *omitted*
251. 10. encorrging
255. 33. Dukes   36. to the *Spectator*
257. 15. cõming *instead of* conning   25. dothe onely   30. *Cleophila*) was
259. 39. hee whome
260. 28. her, amased
261. 13. of my evill
265. 13. an insterly meyntayned   21. *withouteward*   32. *ys my Blowe*   33. Arcadias *ginne*
270. 3. was) was
271. 13. so pore goodnes
272. 8. coulde no fynde no fitt   14. well preserved myne   24. hee to 34. good How
274. 5. deathe by youre
281. 32. bring her, to
289. 22. cruelty crewe for
290. 9. uppon then   33. judgedment
292. 40. *Tymomophorus*
294. 6. dyed (who
298. 21. wᶜʰ lett falle *repeated twice*
301. 2. yt : Of   26. was prevented
305. 15. the rañn
308. 29. *Musick,*
310. 27. *By those*
311. 23. Footeppes
314. 14. *stuff*) *no*
318. 36. *meane*) *those*
319. 7. *Conceyve* (*though*   35. *am*) *those*
321. 6. *there lyes*)
325. 18. *MS has a blank between* "*payne*" *and* "*pleasure*"
327. 16. knowled
330. 16. an other) and   34, 35. *Tymantus*
331. 8. *Timantus*
339. 10. establisshed But
340. 32. gohstes
346. 18. can not but but bee
349. 30. & beuty and beuty so
350. 8. forehead, fell   30. an object semblant
354. 30. saide shee do
355. 21. else to stay
356. 6. private, bycause
358. 30. rather pitty of Darckenes
362. 11. fill a peññ   18. let hus graunt
365. 15. refrayned) to to the Twoo   24. no more to the 33. succourles) my
366. 17. unlikelyood, yf
367. 4. Tryall by by Combatt : By
370. 34. *MS has a blank between* lay the *and* they
373. 2. *Musidors*   25. the less they   36. lyfe, like
377. 16. Duke
379. 22. measure That
381. 15. theyre lovely   17. that Menalcas

A LIST OF ERRORS

382. 13. communicating to
383. 31. in unconstant suffering
385. 9. yet (O Father
389. 11. *Cladius*

NOTES

All the corrections noted below are by the same hand, unless otherwise stated.

9. 26. litle *underlined*
12. 2. may *underlined*
14. 36. that *underlined and* and *written above*
18. 12. sectes *underlined and* Sexe *written above* [*see* List of Errors in the MS, which have been corrected]
23. 25. Patern *underlined and* Paragon *written above*
42. 21. pastymes *underlined and* Pastoralles *written above*
52. 4. woulde *underlined and* coulde *written above*
57. 26. "*can*" *underlined and* "*may*" *written above*
58. 10. "*sone*" *underlined and* "*sonne*" *written above*
63. 7. *after* understanding *the word* therof *has been crossed out*
64. 13. the *underlined and* that *written above*
81. 15. "*this smalle*" *underlined and* "*my minute*" *written above*
90. 29. sorrowe *underlined and* Succoure *written above*
105. 17. had *underlined* [*see* List of Errors in the MS, which have been corrected]
111. 28. safely *underlined and* softly *written above*
118. 38. *the end of* "*flowes*" *is blotted and nearly illegible*
126. 22. "*blood*" *underlined and* "*blade*" *written above*
129. 3. bringe *underlined and* begin *written above*
132. 15. "*gratify*" *underlined and* "*ratify*" *written above*
133. 12. "*reconde*" *underlined and* "*rounde*" *written above* [*see* List of Errors in the MS, which have been corrected]   37. "*his*" *underlined and* "*theyre*" *written above*
135. 24. "*founde*" *underlined and* "*mett*" *written above*
139. 24. "*whiche*" *underlined and* "*whilest*" *written above*   34. "*the*" *underlined and* "*to*" *written above*
141. 20. "*they*" *underlined and* "*that*" *written above*   21. "*His*" *underlined and* "*theyre*" *written above*   "*hym self*" *underlined and* "*themselves*" *written above*   22. "*receyve*" [? *for* "*wee*"] *underlined and* "*they*" *written above*   24. "*his*" *underlined and* "*theyre*" *written above*
142. 29. "*her*" [*before* "*hart*"] *underlined and* "*my*" *written above*
146. 29. yt *underlined and* hym *written above-*
147. 9. Justice *underlined and* Justes *written above*
155. 39. "*abject*" *altered to* "*object*"   40. "*My*" *altered to* "*Myne*" *by the scribe*
156. 7. "*to heare*" *underlined and* "*Lo here*" *written above*
158. 34. While *underlined and* Whiche *written above*
160. 37. confusion *underlined and* Infusion *written above*   38. well *underlined and* evell *written above* [*see* List of Errors in the MS, which have been corrected]
161. 4. wonne *underlined and* woven *written above* [*see* List of Errors in the MS, which have been corrected]
162. 10. tryed *underlined and* tyred *written above*
165. 8. content *crossed out after* mighte *and* please *written above by the scribe*   33. Domage *underlined and* happynes *written above*
167. 25. "*thy*" [*before* "*fyers*"] *underlined and* "*my*" *written above*
169. 16. fall *underlined and* full *written above* [*see* List of Errors in the MS, which have been corrected]

NOTES

175. 22. lyves *underlined*
180. 14. *"shrillnes" underlined and " Clearenes" written above*
183. 27. share *has been altered several times by the scribe and the original word is illegible. It is underlined and* cheyre *written above*
184. 33. For *underlined and* But *written above*
187. 25. *"Was" underlined and "Ys" written above*
189. 28. her *[before* fancyes] *underlined and* his *written above*
192. 19. faulte *underlined and* secrett *written above*
194. 11. suche *underlined and* so *written above*
196. 11. *"litle" underlined and " Title" written above* [*see* List of Errors in the MS, which have been corrected]
199. 14. *"the" underlined and " they" written above*
201. 27. hawty *underlined and* hardy *written above*
205. 22. were *underlined and* was *written above*
206. 19. use *underlined and* urge *written above*
212. 26. done *underlined and* lyen *written above*
215. 29. hym *[before* full] *underlined and* wyn *written above* [*see* List of Errors in the MS, which have been corrected]
219. 3. *"forthe" underlined and "up" written above*
220. 24. self *underlined and* lyffe *written above*
224. 1. *"dothe" underlined and "did" written above*
230. 10. *"effectes" underlined and "affectes" written above*
233. 27. *"this" [before " Table"] underlined and " his" written above*
238. 4. *"feared" underlined and "dreaded" written above*
242. 35. *"stryfe" underlined and "knyfe" written above*
243. 26. *"fremd" underlined and "foes" written above*
244. 25. *"Lyne" underlined and "Live" written above*
245. 21. *"first" underlined and "forste" written above* [*see* List of Errors in the MS, which have been corrected]
248. 33. fast *underlined and* hard *written above*
255. 36. the *underlined and* bee *written above* [*see* List of Errors in the MS, which have been corrected]
261. 13. my *underlined and* theire *written above* [*see* List of Errors in the MS, which have been corrected]
265. 12. his *underlined and* theyre *written above*   theyre *[before " Poetry"] interlined by the scribe*   13. insteerly *underlined* [*see* List of Errors in the MS, which have been corrected]   33. *"ginne" underlined and " Gemm" written above* [*see* List etc.]
266. 3. *"compost" underlined and "posde" written above the end of the word*
268. 1—3. And farr more...Frendes *underlined in different ink* [*same ink as* 26—28; 303. 23; 336. 36; 338. 40; 345. 34—346. 1; 358. 30; 361. 35]   26—28. yf hee now...Fortune *underlined in different ink* [*see above, note to* 1—3]
272. 14. preserved *underlined and* persevered *written above* [*see* List of Errors in the MS, which have been corrected]   27. to thee *corrected to* unto thee *by the scribe*
281. 32. her *underlined and* mee *written above* [*see* List of Errors in the MS, which have been corrected]
284. 5. harte *underlined and* zeale *written above*
285. 36. [*margin*] Musidorus *in Italian hand* [*see note to* 304. 16]
294. 21. the [*before* ende] *underlined and* yoᵣ *written above*
297. 11. pacyence *underlined and* passion *written above*

NOTES

303. 19. upon *underlined and* to *written above*   23, 24. Who hathe...
diligent ambition *underlined in different ink* [*see note to* 268. 1]
304. 16. [*margin*] Kerxenus *in Italian hand* [*apparently by the same hand as*
285. 36 *and the other marginal notes*]
307. 17. of *underlined and* from *written above*
313. 5. no thing *underlined and* none *written above*
319. 22. the *underlined and* that *written above*
324. 9. addressed *has been crossed out and* presented *substituted by the scribe*
325. 17. "oure" [*before* "travell"] *underlined and* "his" *written above*
327. 10. [*margin*] Evarchus *in Italian hand* [*see note to* 304. 16]
331. 31. Lyne *underlined and* Lyfe *written above*
335. 29. hym *has been crossed out after* in *and* yt *interlined above by the scribe*
336. 36—38. who make...desyerer *underlined in different ink* [*see note to* 268. 1]
338. 40—339. 2. then one...of the mynde *underlined in different ink* [*see note
to* 268. 1]
340. 10. [*margin*] Ginecia *in Italian hand* [*see note to* 304. 16]
341. 37. [*margin*] Pamela: Philoclea: *in Italian hand* [*see note to* 304. 16]
343. 37. [*margin*] Pyrocles and Musidorus: *in Italian hand* [*see note to* 304. 16]
344. 8. [*margin*] Musidorus *in Italian hand* [*see note to* 304. 16]
345. 8. that *underlined and* what *written above*   33. [*margin*] memory *in
Italian hand. This note and* 352. 35, 37; 359. 5 *are in a smaller hand
and darker ink than the other marginal notes* 33—346. 1. yt ys
greatly...power of the *underlined in different ink* [*see note to* 268. 1]
349. 28. revealed *crossed out after* bee *and* revived *interlined above by the scribe*
350. 23. ministred *underlined and* sturred *written above*
351. 25. the [*before* Prince] *underlined and* youre *written above*
352. 35. [*margin*] Pyrocles to Evarchus: *in Italian hand* [*see note to* 345. 33]
37. since *underlined and* but *written above* [*see note to* 345. 33]
353. 17. self *underlined and* lyfe *written above*   22. yeelde *has been crossed
out before* use   36. [*margin*] Evarchus *in Italian hand* [*see note
to* 304. 16]
354. 21. [*margin*] Philonax *in Italian hand* [*see note to* 304. 16]
24. [*margin*] Gynecia *in Italian hand* [*see note to* 304. 16]
355. 1. self *crossed out after* my   37. [*margin*] Evarchus sentense up on
Genesia *in Italian hand* [*see note to* 304. 16]
357. 23. [*margin*] Evarchus *in Italian hand* [*see note to* 304. 16]
26. [*margin*] Phlonax *in Italian hand* [*see note to* 304. 16]
358. 30—33. In suche...powers *underlined in different ink* [*see note to* 268. 1]
359. 5. [*margin*] Philanax agaynst Pirocles *in Italian hand* [*see note to* 345. 33]
361. 35—362. 1. for to those...of the worlde *underlined in different ink* [*see
note to* 268. 1]
364. 20. [*margin*] Pyrocle to Philonax *in Italian hand* [*see note to* 304. 16]
365. 4. remember *crossed out after* not *and* waye *interlined above by the scribe*
366. 5. needes *underlined and* perforce *written above*
371. 13. [*margin*] Evarchus *in Italian hand* [*see note to* 304. 16]
373. 10. [*margin*] Musidorus *in Italian hand* [*see note to* 304. 16]
375. 37. [*margin*] Evarchus *in Italian hand* [*see note to* 304. 16]
380. 6. [*margin*] sentense of Evarchus *in Italian hand*   24. [*margin*]
Kerkenius *in Italian hand*   39. [*margin*] Menalcas *in Italian hand*
[*see note to* 304. 16]
382. 30. [*margin*] Evarchus *in Italian hand* [*see note to* 304. 16]
384. 7. [*margin*] Musidorus *in Italian hand* [*see note to* 304. 16]
10. Kyndred [*after* of] *altered to* Kynred *by the scribe*   39. [*margin*]
Pirocles *in Italian hand* [*see note to* 304. 16]

A TABLE SHOWING THE RELATION BETWEEN THE "OLD ARCADIA" AND THE 1590—93 ARCADIA

The numbers in the left column refer to this volume; those in the right column refer to volumes I and II of the present edition.

OLD ARCADIA	1590—93 ARCADIA	OLD ARCADIA	1590—93 ARCADIA
1. 4—28	I. 19. 7 etc.	10. 4—10	I. 78. 25; 80. 8 etc.; 85. 40 etc.
33—2. 7	20. 4 etc.	11—11. 12	54. 25 etc.
2. 9—13	26. 16 etc.	11. 15, 16	55. 31 etc.
13—18	20. 26 etc.	17—12. 14	55. 39 etc.
21—24	327. 6 etc.	12. 14—23	56. 35 etc.
25—27	327. 13 etc.	23—14. 34	57. 3 etc.
36	327. 2	14. 39—15. 1	84. 32 etc.; 85. 1
37—3. 3	23. 26 etc.	15. 6—9	76. 33 etc.
3. 4—7	26. 22 etc.	14—30	86. 20 etc.
7—10	24. 1 etc.	32	77. 3
12—14	20. 33 etc.	35—17. 17	77. 4 etc.
14—18	21. 2 etc.; 29. 2 etc.	17. 17—39	78. 25 etc.
20	20. 37	39—18. 5	55. 33 etc.
21—35	23. 26 etc.; 26. 25 etc.	18. 5, 6	79. 10 etc.
39—4. 1—12	24. 6 etc.	8—19. 1	79. 13 etc.
4. 14—35	24. 18 etc.	19. 1—21. 9	80. 12 etc.
35—5. 6	25. 1 etc.	21. 11—38	82. 18 etc.
5. 6	25. 19	38—23. 4	83. 6 etc.
7—40	25. 21 etc.	23. 6—9	94. 40 etc.
6. 24—26	23. 26; 26. 25	12, 13	62. 21 etc.
31—40	20. 33 etc.; 21. 2 etc.; 26. 39	15	86. 31
7. 1—5	233. 27 etc.	20—24. 4	75. 17 etc.
5, 6	190. 16 etc.	24. 9	76. 2, 3
8—11	184. 31; 185. 12 etc.	25. 3	95. 2 etc.
11, 12	186. 36; 187. 1	5	86. 32 etc.
12—20	188. 33 etc.	9—17	94. 30 etc.
25—30	160. 22; 189. 20 etc.	25—38	76. 14 etc.
30, 31	190. 20 etc.	26. 13—29	87. 1 etc.
31—39	189. 29 etc.	29—31	88. 1 etc.
39—8. 13	160 etc.; 190 etc.; 261 etc.; 289 etc.	34—27. 29	21. 9 etc.
8. 18, 19	206. 7 etc.	27. 30—28. 16	22. 5 etc.
20—24	303. 21 etc.	28. 19—29. 27	87. 7 etc.
24	12. 15	31. 19—32. 5	88. 7 etc.
26—29	12. 17, 28; 14. 18; 48. 5	32. 5	89. 16
		11—37	88. 30 etc.
29—9. 4	18; 51. 28 etc.; 84. 33 etc.; 85. 2 etc.	33. 2—35. 14	89. 17 etc.
		35. 28—36. 19	112. 26 etc.
9. 5, 6	26. 33 etc.; 86. 22	36. 21	114. 24
7—10. 3	85. 4 etc.; 86. 24 etc.	29—37. 4	115. 3 etc.
		37. 11	151. 28
		14	114. 30

"OLD ARCADIA" AND 1590—93 ARCADIA

Old Arcadia	1590—93 Arcadia	Old Arcadia	1590—93 Arcadia
37. 16—31	I. 116	100. 2—101. 14	I. 160. 32 etc.
38—38. 38	113. 18 etc.	101. 18—36	177; 178; 180
39. 12—20	117. 14 etc.	36—102. 8	163. 31 etc.
24—30	117. 27 etc.	102. 10—26	180
30—36	117. 2 etc.	26—103. 12	164. 17 etc.
36—40	117. 31 etc.	103. 14—106. 33	168 etc.
40—40. 35	118. 1 etc.	106. 35—111. 24	251. 12 etc.
40. 36	118. 31	111. 25—112. 25	308. 22 etc.
41. 2	118. 31	112. 25—114. 35	256. 25 etc.
4	118. 36	114. 36—115. 11	259. 19 etc.
39—42. 34	118. 39 etc.	115. 12—116. 14	259. 40 etc.
42. 37—43. 37	119. 32 etc.	116. 14—23	261. 6 etc.
43. 39—44. 13	120. 22 etc.	116. 23—118. 25	309. 29 etc.
44. 25—45. 10	120. 35 etc.	119. 28—120. 10	311. 29 etc.
45. 27—30	93. 36 etc.	120. 11—18	313. 22 etc.
32—46. 7	121. 12 etc.	20—122. 23	321. 33 etc.
46. 9—50. 8	121. 27 etc.	122. 24—123. 3	313. 25 etc.
50. 19—51. 2	94; 171; 177	123. 3—7	314. 21 etc.
51. 4—7	124. 37 etc.	7—11	314. 28 etc.
52. 2—32	26. 39; 27. 38 etc.	12—124. 24	316. 7 etc.
34—53. 5	126. 2 etc.	124. 26—125. 17	317. 38 etc.
53. 5—21	93 etc.; 125; 177	125. 22—37	320. 34 etc.
21—59. 21	126. 10 etc.	38—126. 38	325. 14 etc.
59. 22—34	131. 21 etc. [notes]	38—127. 2	328. 14 etc.
35—60. 9	131. 33 etc.	127. 4—20	327. 27, 37 etc.
60. 9—15	565. 1 etc.	20—24	326. 15 etc.
15—19	340. 28 etc.	24—128. 11	328. 14 etc.
23—62. 24	238. 28 etc.	129. 1—130. 26	339. 1 etc.
63. 1—67. 33	226; 231 etc.; 329 etc.	130. 27	125. 2
67. 36—68. 4	565. 4 etc.	28—139. 2	340. 25 etc.
68. 5—69. 31	II. 228. 6 etc.	139. 7—10	348. 30 etc.
70—71	229. 37 etc.	14—18	348. 33 etc.
72. 5—18	I. 565. 14 etc.	25—144. 25	227. 1 etc.
19—75. 8	II. 231. 32 etc.	144. 32—35	351. 35 etc.
75. 9—13	I. 565. 28 etc.	145. 1—14	261. 19 etc.
13—19	563. 10 etc.	14—146. 10	204. 25 etc.; 206. 5; 300 etc.
22—76. 6	II. 208. 5 etc.	146. 13—36	204; 292. 2 etc.
76. 7—16	I. 563. 17 etc.	147. 8—10	283 etc.
21—77. 12	143. 15 etc.	12—35	278. 30 etc.
77. 13—22	563. 27 etc.	149. 3—150. 31	242. 30 etc.
23—86. 7	II. 208. 25 etc.	150. 31	288. 16
86. 8—19	I. 144. 9 etc.; 564. 1 etc.	151. 33—152. 12	132. 10 etc.; 352. 4 etc.; 565. 31 etc.
87. 2—92. 4	145. 8 etc.	152. 12—154. 30	352. 12 etc.
92. 4—36	150. 21 etc.	154. 31—39	137. 19 etc.; 353. 25; 565. 48 etc.; II. 78. 23 etc.
39—93. 8	151. 12 etc.	155. 1—156. 18	II. 234. 18 etc.
93. 10—25	168—171	156. 19—24	I. 144. 14 etc.; 566. 7 etc.
29—94. 29	153; 154; 177. 26 etc.		
94. 29—100. 2	155. 9 etc.		

"OLD ARCADIA" AND 1590—93 ARCADIA

Old Arcadia	1590—93 Arcadia	Old Arcadia	1590—93 Arcadia
156. 26—157. 16	II. 236. 1 etc.	266. 16—23	II. 100. 20 etc.
157. 17—20	I. 566. 14 etc.	24—267	I. 324. 34; 326. 21
22—158. 25	II. 237. 1 etc.		etc.
158. 25—35	I. 353. 25 etc.;	267. 4—269. 19	II. 100. 30 etc.
	566. 19 etc.	269. 19—27	103. 1 etc.
159. 11—26	II. 1. 11 etc.	28—30	103. 10 etc.
162. 22—163. 13	I. 152 etc.	270. 1—27	103. 11 etc.
163. 13—164. 18	II. 2. 1 etc.	28—272. 23	103. 39 etc.
164. 21—23	I. 26 etc.	272. 23—273. 12	105. 31 etc.
27—166. 31	3. 10 etc.	273. 13—279. 21	106. 18 etc.
166. 31—35	I. 329. 1 etc.	279. 22—27	112. 17 etc.
35—167. 37	II. 5. 12 etc.	279. 27—282. 38	112. 23 etc.
167. 37—169. 7	6. 15 etc.	282. 39—283. 29	115. 29 etc.
169. 7—173. 14	7. 27 etc.	283. 29—34	116. 20 etc.
173. 14—174. 30	11. 30 etc.	35—39	116. 26 etc.
174. 36—190. 13	13. 4 etc.	284. 1—8	116. 32 etc.
190. 27—204. 34	27. 32 etc.	8—27	117. 1 etc.
204. 34—205. 4	41. 17 etc.	28—285. 25	117. 22 etc.
205. 5	41. 28	285. 25—34	118. 20 etc.
7—209. 8	42. 3 etc.	286. 1—5	118. 29 etc.
209. 8—213. 17	45. 38 etc.	11—14	118. 33 etc.
213. 18—215. 29	49. 40 etc.	18—36	118. 35 etc.
215. 31—35	52. 9 etc.	37—287. 10	119. 15 etc.
36—216. 1	60. 35 etc.	287. 11—293. 27	119. 27 etc.
216. 1—4	52. 13 etc.	293. 28—38	61. 6 etc.
4—16	52. 16 etc.	38, 39	125. 30
17—219. 20	52. 34 etc.	39, 40	61. 18 etc.
219. 20—25	55. 30 etc.	294. 1—295. 30	125. 31 etc.
25—221. 3	55. 34 etc.	295. 30—298. 40	127. 19 etc.
221. 6	57. 13	298. 40—304. 18	130. 26 etc.
8—22	57. 15 etc.	304. 18—305. 14	136. 5 etc.
22—222. 30	57. 32 etc.	305. 14—306. 34	136. 39 etc.
222. 31	58. 40	306. 37—307. 19	I. 5 etc.; 15; 27;
40—223. 1	59. 4		140. 36 etc.;
223. 6—226. 28	I. 218. 32 etc.		II. 214. 17 etc.
228. 1—237. 12	II. 61. 21 etc.	307. 21—309. 22	I. 141. 2 etc.
237. 13—18	70. 20 etc.	309. 24—312. 14	349. 2 etc.
19	73. 39	312. 16, 17	352. 4, 5
22—242. 21	I. 132. 19 etc.;	313. 22—318. 8	394. 33 etc.
	II. 74. 1 etc.	318. 28—319. 25	357. 22 etc.
242. 21—245. 33	I. 137. 23 etc.;	319. 26—320. 33	358. 22 etc.
	II. 78. 27 etc.	320. 38, 39	II. 139. 19 etc.
245. 34—36	II. 81. 33 n.	321. 1—324. 29	I. 498. 31 etc.;
37—246. 10	81. 34 etc.		II. 139. 23 etc.
247. 2—4	119. 12 etc.	324. 30—326. 4	II. 143. 12 etc.
6—8	83. 10	327. 3—11	145. 4 etc.
10—254. 29	83. 11 etc.	12—331. 13	145. 12 etc.
254. 31	90. 15	331. 13—16	149. 9 etc.
36—255. 5	90. 16 etc.	16—19	153. 1 etc.
255. 5—264. 29	90. 25 etc.	20	149. 12
264. 29—265. 9	100. 1 etc.	21—34	I. 185
265. 11—266. 15	138. 11 etc.	34—333	II. 149; 150; 151; 152

Old Arcadia	1590—93 Arcadia	Old Arcadia	1590—93 Arcadia
333. 11—14	II. 152. 38 etc.	378. 5	II. 196. 31
14—335. 27	153. 4 etc.	16	196. 25 etc.
335. 27—33	155. 16 etc.	17—379. 20	196. 28 etc.
33—347. 32	155. 23 etc.	379. 20—380. 33	197. 32 etc.
347. 33—352. 10	167. 3 etc.	380. 36	199. 5
352. 10—353. 10	171. 15 etc.	39—381. 1	199. 7 etc.
353. 12—354. 3	172. 15 etc.	381. 2	I. 116. 20
354. 3—358. 17	173. 6 etc.	3	116. 27 etc.
358. 17—361. 3	177. 15 etc.	4	II. 199. 11
361. 3—362. 23	179. 38 etc.	7—26	199. 12 etc.
362. 24—37	181. 18 etc.	31—33	199. 37 etc.
40—365. 26	181. 33 etc.	33—382. 7	199. 40 etc.
365. 27—33	184. 18 etc.	382. 8—384. 38	200. 15 etc.
34—366. 6	184. 26 etc.	384. 38—387. 1	203. 1 etc.
366. 6—367. 8	184. 37 etc.	387. 2—29	205. 2 etc.
367. 8—368. 21	185. 39 etc.	29—388. 36	205. 29 etc.
368. 21—369. 3	187. 10 etc.	388. 38—389. 7	206. 37 etc.
369. 3—373. 18	187. 32 etc.	389. 8—15	207. 11
373. 19—378. 3	192. 2 etc.		

INDEX OF FIRST LINES OF POEMS

INDEX OF FIRST LINES OF POEMS